THE CHARLTON STANDARD CATALOGUE OF

ROYAL DOULTON JUGS

SECOND EDITION

By
Jean Dale

Introduction By
Louise Irvine

W.K. Cross
Publisher

The Charlton Press
Birmingham, Michigan • Toronto, Ontario

Printed in Canada in the Province of Quebec

The Charlton Press

Editorial Office
2010 Yonge Street
Toronto, Ontario. M4S 1Z9

EDITORIAL

Editor	Jean Dale
Design	Janet Cross
Layout	Frank van Lieshout

SPECIAL THANKS

The publishers would like to thank Louise Irvine for writing the introduction to the Second Edition of the Charlton Standard Catalogue of Royal Doulton Jugs. Louise Irvine is an independent writer and lecturer on Royal Doulton's history and products and is not connected with the pricing of this catalogue.

Also to Stephen M. Mullins of the American Jug Museum, Chicago, Illinois, for allowing us to document and photograph parts of his toby jug Collection.

CONTRIBUTORS

The following contributors graciously supplied photographs, price lists, data and other valuable information for the second edition for which we offer a profound Thank You:

DEALERS

Arnie and Judi Berger, Yesterday's South, Miami, Florida; **Laura Campbell,** Site of the Green, Dundas, Ontario; **Anthony Cross,** Anthony Cross and The Englishman, Blackburn, England; **David Harcourt,** Thornton Antiques and Fine China Ltd. Wellington, New Zealand; **Ronald Griffin,** Griffin Collectibles, Ypsilanti, Michigan; **Arnold and Margaret Krever,** Marnalea Antiques, Campbellville, Ontario; **Dick and Alison Nicholson,** The British Toby, Markham, Ontario; **Mark Oliver,** Phillips, London, England; **Ed Pascoe,** Pascoe and Company, Miami, Florida, **Jamie and Mary Pole,** Seaway China Company, Marine City, Michigan; **Tom Power,** The Collector, London, England, **Nick Tzimas,** U.K. International Ceramics, Suffolk, England; **Stan Worrey,** Colonial House Antiques and Gifts, Berea, Ohio; **Princess and Barry Weiss,** Yesterdays, New City, New York

COLLECTORS

R.M. Banks, Leicestershire, England; **R.H.G. Benham,** Wiltshire, England; **Joan Gilman,** Leicestershire, England; **Scott M. Reichenberg,** North Smithfield, Rhode Island; **Patricia Winmill,** Essex, England

A SPECIAL NOTE TO COLLECTORS

We welcome and would appreciate any comments or suggestions in regard to the Charlton Standard Catalogue of Royal Doulton Jugs that you might have. If you would like to participate in pricing or supplying new data, such as information on unlisted jugs or varieties, please contact Jean Dale at (416) 488-4653.

CONTENTS

FOREWORD TO THE SECOND EDITION

This Second Edition has been expanded dramatically with its number of pages increasing over 50 percent. This increase is the direct result of the addition of two new segments of information. Firstly, the Limited Edition Loving Cups and Jugs have been added, as these popular collectables have caught the interest of many Doulton Collectors over the years. Secondly, early figure and toby jugs have been included. This second segment is more complicated and we consider the addition of these early pieces just the beginning. It will take us two or three editions before a complete listing of these jugs is reached.

The first figure jugs were issued circa 1820 at Lambeth. Chronologically these pieces do not belong in the tobies or character jug section of this book. However, in the interest of simplicity, they have been interspersed in this section. For example, if Nelson or Napolean were listed chronologically, they would nessecitate two different sections. As a result, we have taken the liberty of combining the Lambeth and early Burslem issues with the modern tobies and character jugs of the twentieth century. We apologize to those who would like to see a historical order preserved, but for those collectors who wish to easily trace the origins of their jugs, we believe our listing method will be easier to use.

THE COLLECTOR AND THIS BOOK

The purpose of this book is twofold. One purpose is to provide a timely price guide to Royal Doulton Jugs. A second purpose is to provide collectors with the comparative information and illustrations necessary to help them form a meaningful and rewarding collection.

Pricing jugs is difficult. It is an on going task and an explanation of our thoughts on pricing is needed.

The second purpose is reasonalby easy to acheive. With this and subsequent editions Charlton will be able to present the collector with a comprehensive technical guide on Jugs.

A price guide is just that, "a guide", it is a guide to the most current retail prices possible at the time of publication. It is not a fixed price list. It does not list a price at which dealers must sell their jugs. This publication is an indication of the current market price arrived at by submissions, price lists and auction results.

However, the Charlton Standard Catalogue of Royal Doulton Jugs goes a step farther than any guide has gone before in pricing. It shows current market prices in three regional areas, United Kingdom, United States and Canada in one catalogue.

When using this guide the collector must carefully assess the three market prices from a number of points:

1. The region of the prices listed.
2. The duties, taxes and shipping to move the jug from one region to another.
3. The foreign exchange calculations required to move between currencies.
   (Remembering that small amounts of funds convert at wide spreads.)

Even with these points taken into account there are major price differences between regional markets. The Royal Doulton Jug market is not elastic, there is not a uniform demand across all markets. There is also not a uniform supply in all markets. The U.K. market, which is older and supplied first by Doulton will have more product available at any one moment. Prices there, as a result, should be lower. Will dealers and collectors be able to use the guide to buy in the lowest market? Maybe. The seller will probably have the guide also and will immediately adjust to the higher market, especially when it is on the side to favour them. Careful examination of prices is called for, each market has its own peculiarities and prices can and do vary.

This guide will certainly give the collector an opportunity to explore prices more thoroughly and through that make an intelligent decision when purchasing jugs for their collection.

THE ORIGINS OF THE TOBY JUG
Louise Irvine

Pottery jugs in the image of human beings have been made since the dawn of civilisation and some impressive examples have survived from Greek and Roman times as well as from the ancient cultures of South America. In Medieval England, potters poked fun at their contemporaries by creating figurative jugs and these primitive vessels also provide interesting precedents for the Toby Jug, which first appeared in the Staffordshire Potteries in the late 18th century.

The toby jug traditionally represents a seated drinking character with a pot of foaming ale balanced on his knee. He is dressed in typical costume of the period, with long coat and knee breeches, and his large tricorn hat forms the spout of the jug. There are several theories as to the origin of his name. Some suggest a connection with Shakespeare's convivial character Sir Toby Belch, others believe the notorious Yorkshire toper Henry Elwes was the model. He died in 1761 having consumed some 2,000 gallons of Stingo, a particularly strong ale, and was known as 'Toby Fillpot'. Potters might also have been inspired by an old English drinking song *The Brown Jug*, written by the Reverend Francis Fawkes, which paid tribute to Toby Fillpot, 'a thirsty old soul' who excelled in boozing. The popular verses were first published in 1761 and were soon distributed in print form, accompanied by a caricature of an enthusiastic drinker with ruddy complexion and huge beer belly.

Admiral Lord Nelson figure jug produced
at the Doulton and Watts factory

By early years of the 19th century, the Staffordshire potters were producing many variations on the original toby type including standing figures flourishing pipes, sporting squires, jolly sailors and even female characters. Toby jugs were also made in other parts of England, notably London where the Lambeth potteries used their favoured brown salt-glaze stoneware material to produce genial tobies astride a barrel.

DOULTON LAMBETH JUGS

Brown stoneware tobies were amongst the earliest products of the Doulton and Watts factory which was established on the banks of the river Thames in London in 1815. As well as complete figure jugs, the company also produced face jugs of famous personalities. The most impressive and best known is their portrait of the great naval hero *Lord Nelson*. Two different models are marked with the company's early trade mark, Doulton and Watts. The complete bust stands 12 inches tall and the smaller head and shoulder design was made in three different sizes, the largest 7 1/2 inches tall. Replicas of both these models, clearly marked as such, were later made to celebrate the centenary of the Battle of Trafalgar in 1905 but even these are difficult to find today.

Stoneware portrait jug of Theodore Roosevelt
modelled by Leslie Harradine

Nelson's great antagonist Napoleon has also been portrayed as a stoneware jug and there are similar tributes to Wellington, the Iron Duke, but these are unmarked and could have been made by any of the London potters as they frequently copied each other's ideas. The Doulton pottery went on to honour many other military heroes, politicians and statesmen on flasks, jugs and vases but the idea of the face jug was not revived until the early 1900s when the celebrated modeller Leslie Harradine produced a stoneware portrait jug of *Theodore Roosevelt*, the 26th President of the United States. This was followed by a curious pair of *Veteran Motorist* jugs, an ugly *Highwayman*, a beaming *Old King Cole* and a humorous caricature of *Mr. Pecksniff* from Dickens' *Martin Chuzzlewit*. The pattern books also refer to a Wee Mac jug in 1908 but to date this has not materialised and there may well be others still to come to light. Harradine left the Lambeth studio in 1912 but his colleague Mark Marshall occasionally dabbled in the toby tradition, producing a *Soldier* toby jug and a face jug which bears a strong resemblance to *John Barleycorn*, the first character jug made at Royal Doulton's other factory in Burslem, Stoke-on-Trent.

Old King Cole modelled by Leslie Harradine

Charles Noke, the Burslem Art Director, was a regular visitor to Lambeth and was undoubtedly influenced by the achievements of the stoneware modellers. He was particularly impressed with the work of Harry Simeon, who contorted Toby Fillpots into a variety of useful shapes, including three styles of toby jug, tobacco jars, ashpots, inkwells, candlesticks, decanters and even a teapot. A publicity leaflet of the mid 1920s indicates that the Simeon toby jugs were available in several sizes with modelling variations and alternative colourways. In addition the waistcoat could be coloured in a bright red enamel for a surcharge of 25% on the list price.

Simeon's toby wares all feature the full seated figure with the exception of one model which depicts a happy smiling face on the 'Marriage Day' but when it is turned upside down, scowling features reveal what happens 'After Marriage'. The *Marriage* mug was made in three sizes and was included in the publicity leaflet for the rest of the stoneware toby collection. Although most of the Lambeth tobies were made of slip cast stoneware and produced in small editions they are very hard to find today and count amongst the rarest of the Royal Doulton jugs.

BURSLEM CHARACTER AND TOBY JUGS

The Doulton family extended their business to Burslem, Stoke-on-Trent in 1877 but initially they concentrated on the production of tablewares and other useful wares for the Victorian home. Gradually an art studio was developed and in 1889 Charles Noke, who had trained at the Worcester factory, was appointed as a modeller of ornamental vases, mainly for exhibition purposes. Before long Noke was also producing figure models and had embarked on a mission to revive the Staffordshire figurative tradition. In 1913, following the launch of his famous HN collection of figures he was promoted to Art Director and he soon turned his attention to the revival of the toby jug.

His first models were quite different in style from the traditional smoking topers with brimful tankards of ale. In 1918, he introduced a portrait of the great silent movie star *Charlie Chaplin* in the form of a large toby jug and this was followed a few years later by a similar portrait of *George Robey*, the popular music hall comedian. In both models the characters' bowler hats come off to reveal the jug underneath. George Robey, the Prime Minister of Mirth, visited the Burslem factory in 1925 and the toby jug was probably made at that time.

Another early toby jug depicts a *Huntsman* in scarlet, D4090, and this 1919 model was re-launched in more subdued colours as part of an extensive collection of tobies in 1950. The *Huntsman* was also issued in Kingsware, a distinctive treacle-brown ware which was developed by Noke in the

The Kingsware Huntsman
modelled by Charles Noke, 1919

early 1900s and used primarily for whisky flasks. A Kingsware *Squire* toby jug was also produced and a face jug of a *Highlander* was made around 1930 for D & J McCallum distillers in Edinburgh. It may have been this commission which gave Noke the idea for a collection of face jugs for by 1933 he had modelled two designs *John Barleycorn*, the personification of barley and *Old Charley*, a typical night watchman, and they were launched the following year.

With the help of his chief modeller, Harry Fenton, Noke quickly introduced more personalities from literature, legend, folk-lore and song and by 1935 the first models were also available in a small size (around 4 inches) as an alternative to the original large size (around 6 1/2 inches). A miniature size (around 2 1/2 inches) had been added to the range by 1939 and the following year the first tinies (1 1/4 inches) had been launched. These became the four standard sizes for the character jug range although the dimensions have altered over the years with some large size jugs now measuring over 7 1/2 inches. There have also been occasional medium or intermediate size jugs (around 4 1/2 inches), as with the *Dickens*, *Wild West* and *Beatles* collections and an extra large *Tony Weller* character jug but these are exceptions to the norm.

Although Charles Noke was in his mid-seventies when he introduced character jugs, his fertile imagination was still working overtime and by 1939 he had adapted the most popular personalities from the range to create a collection of useful gift items now known as the derivatives, for example musical jugs, wall vases, tobacco jars, ashtrays, sugar bowls and teapots. He also developed a new range of toby jugs, several of which were closely based on early models by Harry Simeon at Doulton's Lambeth factory, in particular *Double XX*, *Honest Measure* and *The Squire*.

The bombing of the Burslem studio during the Second World War briefly interrupted Noke's creative output but the conflict gave him opportunity to pay tribute to the great war leader Winston Churchill, the first contemporary personality to be portrayed as a character or toby jug. Unfortunately Noke's character jug portrait, an unusual two-handled model in white, was not considered a good likeness and was quickly withdrawn from the range. It was the first character jug to be discontinued and because of its brief production period it is now very sought after. Early in 1941 Noke made a couple of attempts to remodel and colour the portrait but only prototypes of these experiments are known to exist. Harry Fenton had considerably more success with his toby jug portrait of Churchill, which was launched in 1940 and remained in production for 50 years.

Charles Noke died in 1941, at the age of 83, and for several years Harry Fenton was the sole modeller. He continued to create excellent likenesses of contemporary characters, such as *Monty* and *Smuts*, but he was equally at home with historical or fictional characters, for example the *Samuel Johnson* and *Robin Hood* jugs which impart a vivid sense of reality. In 1949 Max Henk, who had been appointed as a tableware modeller, became interested in character jugs and his *Uncle Tom Cobbleigh* was introduced in 1952. When Fenton died in 1953, Henk was able to step into the breach and he

soon set a new style for character jugs which is most obvious in his approach to their handles. He fully exploited the handle's potential for elaborating on the story of the character portrayed, thus *Scaramouche* has his guitar and the handle of *The Ugly Duchess* is a flamingo, which she used as a croquet mallet in the story of Alice in Wonderland. Henk obviously loved delving into literature and legend for symbolic allusions such as these and they add a new dimension to character jugs for the curious collector.

Apart from his own work, Henk had responsibility for training the next generation of artists. Geoff Blower was generally regarded as Henk's protégé and even before he had completed his five year apprenticeship, he was contributing to the character jug range. His first jug in 1952 was *Lord Nelson* and he followed this with several other popular models, such as *Rip Van Winkle* which has been in production for nearly 40 years. Blower left the Burslem studio in 1956 to take up a career in teaching but on his retirement he began modelling character jugs again and worked on the *Collecting World* series. His former colleague Garry Sharpe also started his career at Doulton but moved overseas in 1960, by which time he had modelled some of the best selling character jugs in the range, including *Old Salt* and *Merlin*. Perhaps his success had something to do with Fenton's modelling tools which Henk gave him in 1953 with the challenging remark 'If there is any of Harry's magic left in these modelling tools, you certainly need it!'

Henk's third apprentice was David Biggs, who joined the team in 1958 after an art school training. Working on his first jug, the *Town Crier*, he soon found out how difficult it is to create one face which typifies a profession or a hobby but he then went on to specialise in this field, modelling the *Golfer*, the *Yachtsman*, the *Punch and Judy Man* and many other representative characters. When stuck for a particular expression, he would often reach for a mirror and manoeuvre his own face to achieve the desired affect.

To make way for all the exciting jugs from this new generation of modellers, around 30 early models were withdrawn from production in 1960. A few years later Royal Doulton decided to discontinue the traditional earthenware body and make all the jugs in the newly developed English Translucent China. David Biggs was given the task of making all the new, more detailed models of existing jugs, which were required for the new process, and several more jugs were withdrawn at this stage to avoid all the costly remodelling. The changeover took place between 1968 and 1970 but the fine china jugs were only made for a few years before earthenware production was resumed in 1973 at the newly acquired John Beswick factory. The fine china jugs are therefore highly valued by collectors and can be recognised most easily by the slight difference in size. Biggs continued to model new character jugs until the early 1970s but for the last twenty years he has concentrated on tableware modelling, only occasionally reviving his character jug design skills, notably for *W.C. Fields* and *Louis Armstrong* in the *Celebrity* series. Hopefully some new work will join the range in the future.

In 1972 a special studio was established for the development of figures and character jugs and Eric Griffiths was appointed the new Head of Sculpture, ultimately becoming Art Director. Griffiths was a portrait painter by training and he particularly enjoyed modelling famous people for the jug range, notably *Henry VIII*, *Mark Twain* and *Ronald Reagan*. He also portrayed *John Doulton*, the founder of the company, as the first character jug especially for members of the Royal Doulton International Collectors Club, which was founded in 1980. There have been many more exclusive commissions for members in the intervening years, including a revival of the tiny size for the *Beefeater* and *Old King Cole* jugs.

The 1980s was an exciting time for character jug fans. The Club provided a lot of useful information on the subject, stimulating many new collections, and the first major reference book by Desmond Eyles had just been published in 1979. Another informative book was produced by Jocelyn Lukins to celebrate the fiftieth anniversary of character jugs in 1984 and there were a number of price guides reflecting the buoyant market. New record prices were continuously being set in the salerooms and amongst the most exceptional was the *Toby Gillette* jug, which was modelled by Eric Griffiths in a limited edition of 3 for a popular British TV show, *Jim'll Fix It*. The jug sold for over £15,000 at Christie's auction rooms in 1984 to raise money for charity.

Several limited edition collections of character jugs were launched during the 1980s, beginning with the novel two-faced portraits for the *Antagonists* series by Michael Abberley, a young Royal Doulton figure painter who taught himself to model jugs in his spare time. The *Antagonists* were extremely popular and the edition of 9,500 was soon over-subscribed. Abberley followed his first success with another two-faced collection, the *Star-Crossed Lovers*, and he also worked on some unlimited series, including the *Wives of Henry VIII* and characters from *Shakespeare*.

Such was the popularity of character jugs by the mid 1980s that many independent companies requested special designs for advertising purposes. This was not a new idea as famous firms such as Charringtons had commissioned specially branded tobies in the 1930s and in 1956 the American industrialist Cliff Cornell even had a toby jug made in his own image to impress his customers. Thirty years later another American firm, Quaker Oats, ordered a character jug of *Mr Quaker* and Pick Kwik Wines and Spirits of Derby purchased a large range of character jug containers for their liquor during the 1980s. Mail order companies, fair organisers and leading retailers all wanted exclusive jugs for promotional events and colourways of existing jugs were sold in special editions. At first the very small editions were snapped up , as with the colourway of the *Mad Hatter* made to commemorate the opening of the Royal Doulton Shop at Higbees of Cleveland in 1985, but collectors eventually became jaded with the number of colourways and the company concentrated resources on new subjects instead.

Since the 1980s most new character jug subjects have been conceived as part of sets, thus creating interesting themes for collectors. In response to the demand for American subjects Royal Doulton introduced the *Wild West* and the *Celebrity* series. The anniversary of the Second World War led to several commemorative series, the *Heroic Leaders*, the *Armed Forces* and *Heroes of the Blitz* and other important historical events have inspired individual jugs, notably Columbus which was produced to mark the 500th anniversary of his famous voyage to the New World. Established themes have also been developed to create new series, for example the Beefeater was joined by lots of other London characters and Henk's early characters from *Alice's Adventures in Wonderland* were joined by *The Red Queen* and *The March Hare*. To date this is the only animal character in the range but the designer Bill Harper has also considered a grinning Cheshire Cat and White Rabbit so it will be interesting to see if any others appear in the future. Harper is perhaps best known as a figure modeller but he has produced a number of character jugs as well as the amusing *Doultonville* collection of 25 small size tobies, which were produced between 1983 and 1991.

Since 1992 there have also been limited edition toby jugs of traditional characters, such as the *Jester* and the *Clown*. These have been designed by Stan Taylor, a retired art teacher from Bristol, and he has been responsible for the majority of character jugs introduced since 1982. His subjects are extremely diverse, ranging from portraits of *Circus Performers* to typical characters encountered on a *Journey through Britain*, such as a *Postman* and a *Policeman*. He also allowed his imagination to run riot for his *Witch* and *Genie* jugs. These are now in demand having only been in production for 6 months because of the extensive withdrawal of character jugs at the end of 1991. The range was reduced from 157 models to 59 — all the early toby jugs were withdrawn and the miniature size of jug was discontinued altogether.

The rationalisation of the character jug range coincided with the appointment of a new Art Director, Amanda Dixon, who is in charge of all the Royal Doulton Design studios. She continues to commission character jugs from Stan Taylor and Bill Harper but other younger modellers from the John Beswick studio, notably Martyn Alcock and Warren Platt, have also been encouraged to try their hand at modelling jugs. They work under the guidance of Studio Manager Graham Tongue, who has several advertising jugs to his credit, including the superb portrait of *William Grant*.

As well as all this new talent, recent marketing initiatives have also been well received by collectors. The 'Character Jug of the Year' concept has proved very successful with huge sales for *Winston Churchill*, the 1992 exclusive. The prestige limited edition jugs with two or more handles have also been popular, notably the *Henry VIII* and *William Shakespeare* designs. After a brief period of concern about wide-ranging withdrawals and colourways, the future now looks very bright for character jug collectors.

BUILDING A COLLECTION

Collections start in many different ways. Often a surprise gift will be responsible for starting a life-long enthusiasm or it could be a legacy which starts an instant collection. Perhaps a chance discovery in an antique market might also spark off a new collector's curiosity and hunting for more will become an absorbing hobby. One thing is certain, the first acquisition is rarely alone for long.

A few dedicated collectors have acquired all the Royal Doulton character and toby jugs in the standard range and then gone on to add rare prototypes, colourways, modelling variations and unusual backstamps. However, this goal requires considerable time and energy as well as substantial financial resources. Most collectors are content to concentrate on specific themes, sizes or types of jugs and can build some fascinating collections in this way.

Collecting By Type

Lambeth Stoneware Jugs

The scarcity of the early jugs from the Lambeth factory has meant that they are not as widely publicised as the Burslem models. However, there is a committed group of collectors who specialise in English stonewares and seek out the Doulton tobies and face jugs along with other brown salt-glaze stoneware products, such as Reform flasks, Hunting jugs, bottles, mugs and jars. Competition is stiff, therefore, to include representative examples in Doulton jug collections. A little more accessible are the Lambeth toby wares, modelled by Harry Simeon, which were made in small editions during the 1920s. A number of collectors have specialised in this field, delighting in all the ingenious uses devised for Toby Fillpots, be it a candlestick, tobacco jar, ink pot or traditional jug. One of the largest collections, built up over 10 years, included more than 75 examples in various sizes and colour schemes. Collector's discoveries have added greatly to the archive information over the years but it is still impossible to produce a definitive list, which is part of the fun of collecting these Simeon tobies.

Toby Jugs

The term 'toby' is frequently used to describe all Royal Doulton jugs but strictly speaking it should only be applied to jugs in the form of a full seated or standing figure. Although Royal Doulton began by producing toby jugs at their Burslem factory, they are better known for their character jugs, which feature only the head and shoulders. Nevertheless, there is a lot of scope for collectors in the toby jug range alone.

Two of the earliest Burslem tobies are also the rarest, the large portraits of *Charlie Chaplin* and *George Robey* which stand around 11 inches tall. Most of the traditional tobies, with their tankards of foaming ale, were introduced in 1939 and the majority remained in production for over 50 years so they are relatively easy to find. The best-selling toby portrait of *Winston Churchill* is also readily available in three different sizes and should not be confused, as has often happened, with the rare *Churchill* character jug. Also confusing is the similarity between the *Winston Churchill* toby and the toby of *Cliff Cornell*. This American industrialist was a great admirer of Churchill and in 1956 he commissioned a portrait toby of himself in the image of the great statesman - even smoking a cigar. Three different colourways were produced in two sizes with Cornell wearing either a brown, blue or tan suit and various matching ties. The base was suitably inscribed to promote his Cleveland Flux company and he sent them to his

friends and associates as Thanksgiving gifts. Today they are becoming hard to find, particularly the tan suit variation which was made in smaller quantities than the others. Advertising toby jugs were also commissioned by Charrington's to promote their Toby Ale and three versions with different inscriptions have been recorded from the 1930s.

Completely different in style from the rest of the range are the little Dickens tobies (4 1/2 inches high) which verge on caricature. There are six characters to find in this desirable collection, which was produced between 1948 and 1960, and there is a lot of competition from Dickens fans. This whimsical style of toby jug was revived by Bill Harper for his *Doultonville* collection in 1983. He created 25 larger-than-life characters from the imaginary town of Doultonville for this appealing set and all have appropriate comical names. The rarest is *Albert Sagger, the Potter* which was only made for a six month period especially for Collectors Club members.

George Robey (c1925) and Charlie Chaplin (1918)
designed by Charles Noke, Art Director

In 1992 Royal Doulton launched their first limited edition toby jugs in a new style and size (5 1/2 inches). To date the collection comprises a *Jester*, a *Town Crier*, a *Clown* and *Father Christmas* and their instant popularity has inspired a revival of interest in Royal Doulton tobies.

Character Jugs

The standard character jug range has included around 300 different subjects, not to mention all the different sizes which have been available, so there is a lot of scope for collectors. It is the ambition of many keen collectors to find all of them but as the range expands, so the task becomes more daunting and choices have to be made.

The most accessible jugs are the ones in current production, which can be purchased in local china shops or by mail order through specialist dealers. The Doulton catalogues currently list around 40 different subjects, some of which are available in large size, some in small size and some in both. There are also limited editions, subject to availability, and a few special commissions from Lawleys by Post and other companies. This number changes every year as new designs are added and models are withdrawn from production.

Once a piece has been discontinued in the Doulton catalogues it is only available on the secondary market. Prices will depend on the demand for the retired model, which is often influenced by how long it was in production. Obviously there will be lots of *Bacchus* jugs around as it was made for over 30 years before being discontinued in 1991 whereas the *Genie* and the *Witch* jugs were in production for less than a year before being caught up in the sweeping withdrawals of 1991.

There are different styles of discontinued character jugs and it may be that a specific era or the work of a particular artist appeals. Harry Fenton, who was active in the 1930s and 40s, modelled rugged, wrinkly faces (with warts and all!) whereas in the 1950s and 60s his successor, Max Henk, favoured smoother complexions with exaggerated features. It was Henk and his assistants who saw the potential of the character jug's handle which had been mostly plain and functional in the early years, and many collectors delight in the creativity and ingenuity of the designs, which have included animals, birds, boats, various weapons, sporting equipment, musical instruments and even parts of buildings. Miniature faces or figures have often been incorporated in the handle and the latest representation of *Henry VIII* features all six of his wives on two handles - seven portraits in one jug! There has even been a prestigious three handled jug recently, *King Charles I*. Occasionally new handles have been modelled for promotional purposes or just to ring the changes and in the case of the *Santa Claus* and *Father Christmas* jug several different handles have been issued over the years.

Themes and Series

Part of the fun of collecting character jugs is researching the symbolism of the handles and finding out more about the characters behind the jugs. For bookworms, there have been lots of characters from literature, beginning with the novels of Charles Dickens, a particular favourite of the Art Director, Charles Noke. Just looking for all the different Dickens character jugs, tobies, derivatives and limited edition jugs could keep a collector very busy for several years. Those interested in England's past will find an abundance of Kings and Queens, colourful London characters and military heroes to create a historical pageant of jugs. As an island nation, the sea has been particularly important in British history and not surprisingly there are many sea-faring characters which could form part of a nautical collection. Patriotic Americans can look out for all the Presidents, Civil War Generals, Williamsburg pioneers, Hollywood film stars and Wild West cowboys represented in the collection. In many cases these have been presented in themed sub-collections, some in limited editions, and issued on an annual basis by Royal Doulton. A list of all the different self-contained series is listed below in alphabetical order for easy reference.

Alice in Wonderland
    The Cook and the Cheshire Cat; Mad Hatter; The March Hare; The Red Queen; Ugly Duchess; The Walrus and the Carpenter
Antagonists (limited)
    Chief Sitting Bull and George Armstrong Custer; Davy Crockett and Santa Anna; George Washington and George III; Ulysses S. Grant and Robert E. Lee
Armed Forces (limited)
    The Airman; The Sailor; The Soldier
Beatles
    George Harrison; John Lennon; Paul McCartney; Ringo Starr
Canadians (limited)
    The Airman; The Sailor; The Soldier
Canadian Centennial Series:
    The Lumberjack; North American Indian; The Trapper
Celebrity Series
    Clark Gable; Groucho Marx; Jimmy Durante; Louis Armstrong; Mae West; W.C. Fields
Characters from Life
    The Angler; The Baseball Player (style two); The Bowls Player; The Gardener (style two); The Golfer (style two); The Jockey (style two); The Snooker Player (style two)
Characters from Literature
    Aramis; Athos; D'Artagnan; Don Quixote; Falstaff; Long John Silver; Merlin; Porthos; Rip Van Winkle; Robin Hood; Scaramouche
Charles Dickens Tinies
    Artful Dodger; Betsy Trotwood; Bill Sykes; Charles Dickens (style one); David Copperfield; Fagin; Little Nell; Mr. Bumble; Mrs. Bardell; Oliver Twist; Scrooge; Uriah Heep
Circus Performers
    The Clown (style two); The Elephant Trainer; The Juggler; The Ringmaster
Collecting World (limited)
    The Antique Dealer; The Auctioneer; The Collector
Football Supporters
    Arsenal; Aston Villa; Celtic; Everton; Leeds United; Liverpool; Manchester United; Rangers
Great Generals (limited)
    Duke of Wellington; General Eisenhower; General Gordon
Henry VIII and his Wives
    Anne Boleyn; Anne of Cleves; Catherine of Aragon; Catherine Howard; Catherine Parr; Henry VIII; Jane Seymour; (Sir Thomas More)
Heroes of the Blitz (limited)
    A.R.P. Warden; Auxiliary Fireman; Home Guard

Heroic Leaders (limited)
 Earl Mountbatten of Burma; Sir Winston Churchill;
 Viscount Montgomery of Alamein
Journey through Britain (limited)
 The Engine Driver; The Fireman (style two);
 The Policeman; The Postman
London
 Beefeater; The Busker; Chelsea Pensioner;
 City Gent; The Guardsman; The London 'Bobby';
 Lord Mayor of London; Pearly King; Pearly Queen;
 Yeoman of the Guard
Mystical Characters
 Genie; Witch; The Wizard
Presidential (limited)
 Abraham Lincoln
Shakespearean
 Hamlet; Henry V; Macbeth; Othello; Romeo;
 William Shakespeare
Star-Crossed Lovers (limited)
 Antony and Cleopatra; King Arthur and Guinevere;
 Napoleon and Josephine; Samson and Delilah
Three Musketeers
 Aramis, Athos, D'Artagnan; Porthos
Wild West
 Annie Oakley; Buffalo Bill (style two); Doc Holliday;
 Geronimo; Wild Bill Hickock; Wyatt Earp
Characters from Williamsburg
 Apothecary; Blacksmith; Bootmaker; Gaoler;
 Guardsman; Gunsmith; Night Watchman

Collecting by Size

Potential display space is one of the factors to consider when embarking on a collection of character jugs as many subjects have been available in four different sizes - large, small, miniature and tiny. Some keen collectors purchase their favourite jugs in all the sizes along with the toby version and the various derivatives and in the case of Sairey Gamp, that makes 12 different portraits of her to collect!

The majority of collectors look out for one specific size of character jug and the large has tended to be the most popular. In the past Royal Doulton always launched the large size first and, if it was well received, smaller versions would follow within a few years. Sometimes the subject never appeared in the small or miniature sizes, much to the chagrin of those who were collecting these. In recent years, the Royal Doulton International Collectors Club has commissioned a number of small size jugs exclusively for their members and Lawleys by Post, the mail order division of the company, also prefer the small size for their special series and these are not produced in any other size.

The smaller the jug, the less detail it is possible to achieve and the costs do not decrease in proportion to the scale which has tended to make the miniature size character jug the least popular choice. In 1992 Royal Doulton discontinued this size jug altogether so there are now set limits to a miniature character jug collection. However, some models will be hard to find, notably *Trapper* and *Lumberjack*, which were not officially launched yet some examples have appeared on the market. On several occasions miniature prototypes were developed many years before they were put into production, as with *The Golfer* where the miniature followed 15 years after the large size or *Old Salt* where there was an interval of 23 years.

To date Royal Doulton have only produced 26 tiny size character jugs making this a diminutive collection in more ways than one. Their obvious appeal is reflected in the high prices commanded by the original set of 12, which are out of all proportion to their Lilliputian scale. The tinies require expert decorating skills and the artists have to balance the minute jugs on the end of their little fingers, which is very time consuming and consequently expensive. Such tiny jugs are also difficult to display in china shops which has meant that the recent models have been special commissions - a set a 12 *Dickens* characters for Lawleys by Post customers and the tiny *Beefeater* and *Old King Cole* jugs for members of the RDICC.

Limited and Special Edition
Character and Toby Jugs

Limited edition jugs are comparatively recent developments as the first character jug was not commissioned until 1978 and the first toby in 1992. It was Michael Doulton's first American tour that inspired the reproduction of the company's very first jug, *John Barleycorn* and it was issued in a limited edition of 7,500, appropriately numbered and marked on the base. A few years later, in 1983, the first limited edition collection was launched with *Grant and Lee* as the initial pair of *Antagonists*. The novel two-faced design proved to be very popular and the edition of 9,500 was quickly sold out. The other three jugs in the series were also very successful and so they were quickly followed in 1985 by the *Star Crossed Lovers*, another two-faced collection.

In 1984 Royal Doulton had the honour of designing a character jug portrait of President Ronald Reagan as a fund-raiser for the Republican National Committee and number 1 of the edition of 2,000 was presented to the President at the White House. This prestigious commission was followed by many other requests for special character jugs to promote various companies, products and events. A character jug of *Mr Quaker* was produced in a limited edition of 3,500 to mark the 85th year of Quaker Oats Limited in 1985 and the restricted distribution amongst this company's customers and employees has made this a very desirable jug today. Pick-Kwik Wines and Spirits of Derby commissioned a range of small size character jugs, some adapted as liquor containers, to promote their various whiskies. As well as the traditional pre-announced limited editions, they also issued collectors editions and special editions - new terms coined to describe commissions by independent companies which are not individually numbered limited editions in the strictest sense. Special editions have included colourways (discussed in the section on Colour Variations) and entirely new jugs, such as the *Collecting World* Series for Kevin Francis and the *Great Generals* series for UK International Ceramics.

There have also been occasional special commissions which are limited by time and distribution rather than by numbers. For example, in 1984 only members of the Royal Doulton International Collectors Club could purchase a small size *Henry Doulton* character jug and in 1986 the offer was a small Doultonville toby of *Albert Sagger, the Potter*. Similarly, only customers attending Michael Doulton's special appearances in 1988 and 1989 could buy the character jug portrait of him. In 1991 Royal Doulton launched their new 'Character Jug of the Year' concept which limits the model to one year's production and this has proved very popular.

In the last few years there has been a new approach to limited character jugs with the launch of several exceptionally complex and detailed models in low editions at premium prices. Some of these prestige jugs had two handles, or even three, and gold or silver embellishments. The first of this type was *Henry VIII*, issued in 1991 in a limited edition of 1,991 to mark the 500th anniversary of his birth. The edition was quickly oversubscribed, endorsing collectors very positive reactions to these ambitious designs. Another recent development which has generated a lot of interest is the collection of limited edition toby jugs which began in 1992 with the *Jester*.

Prototypes and Variations

Once all the standard range jugs have been acquired the ultimate challenge for many serious collectors is to find as many prototypes and variations as possible. This usually requires a very healthy bank balance as huge sums of money can change hands for these rare pieces.

Prototypes

Prototype jugs are the samples taken from the master mould and they are often described as pilots or trials. Usually two or three jugs are cast at this early stage, any more would wear down the detail in the master mould, and they are given different decorative treatments. If one of the prototypes is approved, then lots of production moulds will be made but if it is rejected the model will only exist in prototype form. There have been lots of character jugs and at least a few toby jugs which did not get past the prototype stage for various reasons.

In the 1920s Charles Noke modelled a toby jug of John Wesley, the founder of Methodism, but when the prototypes came from the kiln he had misgivings about the propriety of portraying a strict abstainer as a toby. He therefore abandoned the project, giving one of the prototype jugs to the decorator Ted Eley, another was later presented to the Museum of the Wesley Church in Tasmania.

During the 1930s most of the jugs that were modelled seem to have gone into production but the war interrupted several plans. In the Royal Doulton archives there are references to an *Old Scrooge* jug and one called *Red Wing* but no illustrations have survived. Harry Fenton modelled two portraits of a New Zealand *Maori*, one of which was approved in July 1939, but it did not subsequently go into the general range. A few examples survive in private collections around the world and the last one to come on the market in 1986 sold for £12,000. No records survive for the *Buffalo Bill* jug which presumably also dates from the war years and was modelled by Fenton.

The 1950s seem to have passed with only two casualties. *The Scarlet Pimpernell*, which was submitted by Geoff Blower, surfaced in 1987 and changed hands for over £15,000. Blower's colleague Garry Sharpe remembered his portrait of *Alice in Wonderland* being turned down in 1959 because of copyright restrictions but no examples have come to light so perhaps it did not get beyond the clay stage.

During the 1960s a rejected *Village Blacksmith* was rescued from a Doulton rubbish skip by a factory labourer and his family recently sold it at Phillips Auction rooms in London for over £7,000. It is probably the work of Design Manager Max Henk and it was given a pattern number D6549 in 1961 so it is strange that it was never launched.

David Biggs was responsible for many of the successful character jugs produced during the 1960s but several of his prototypes were rejected at the end of the decade, possibly because of the re-appraisal of the collection and the change-over to bone china production which took place at that time. He remembers submitting a *Fisherman* and a *Racing Driver* but these have not come to light. However, his model of *John Gilpin* (1968) and two colourways of *The Baseball Player* (1971) are in private collections and his ambitious *Pilgrim Father* is in the Royal Doulton archive.

Prototype of The Maori
modelled by Harry Fenton in 1939

Several new modellers joined the Design department in the 1970s and inevitably some of their early work was not accepted for production. Robert Tabbenor's character jug of *Uncle Tom Cobbleigh* was rejected in 1975 and Peter Gee's *Jester* toby in 1977. Although both artists later produced popular jugs, they made figure modelling their speciality. Michael Abberley's *Cabinet Maker of Williamsburg*, which he modelled in 1979, caused a lot of confusion as it was publicised in the

1981 catalogue but was never launched as it was decided to discontinue the Williamsburg range. Bill Harper's first character jug of a Pirate was rejected in 1976 but he has gone on to contribute a wide range of subjects to the range. Unfortunately his admirable portrait of *Pierre Trudeau* (1986) missed the boat as the Canadian Prime Minister had left office before the jug was ready to be launched. In 1987 Bill was keen to produce a *Canterbury Tales* series of jugs but it was felt that the *Miller* and *The Wife of Bath* were not sufficiently well known internationally and so they remain in prototype form in Royal Doulton's own collection. Bill also submitted a portrait of *Elvis Presley* for the *Celebrity* collection but it was not approved by the singer's estate. Several stars in this hapless series did not get beyond the prototype stage but they have found their way on to the market. In 1992 one of the *Marilyn Monroe* prototypes was auctioned in Canada for $17,500 and a *Humphrey Bogart* prototype has also changed hands recently for a significant sum. A portrait of *Clark Gable* had got beyond the prototype stage and several hundred had been made in 1984 before it was recalled for copyright reasons so although not unique it is still a rare model.

A few more jugs 'got away' in the late 1980s, including a portrayal of *Robin Hood* by Eric Griffiths, *Uncle Sam* by Harry Sales and a *Prison Warder* by Stan Taylor, and no doubt there will be more in the future although the Art Director's ideal is not to reach the expensive prototype stage until all the production problems have been ironed out. For this reason original clay models are smashed or left to dry out and crumble to dust if they do not come up to scratch.

Often the design of the character jug is basically acceptable but there are reservations about the handle. Usually this is resolved at the clay stage, as with the Collectors Club jug of *Henry Doulton* which originally incorporated a drainpipe in the handle to symbolise the firm's original achievements. It was felt that this was too mundane a reminder and the vase motif was emphasised instead. Occasionally alternative handles have been moulded and for the *Catharine of Aragon* character jug two different designs featuring a cornet and a scroll were considered before the version with the tower was agreed.

It is not only aesthetic considerations which lead to modifications, cost is also an important factor and handles occasionally need to be simplified. For example, the prototype of *Groucho Marx* included the other Marx brothers peeping out from behind his cigar and they were subsequently removed for the production model. Eagle-eyed collectors have often noticed other minor modifications. The original version of the *Fireman* character jug, which was used for publicity purposes, featured the badge of the London Fire Brigade but this was changed when permission to use it was not granted. Discrepancies such as these have always had a particular fascination for jug collectors and premium prices are paid when original version prototypes come up for sale.

Modelling Variations

If a character jug is altered once it has gone into production, it can no longer be described as a prototype but there is still a lot of interest in such modelling variations and there are more

of them around for collectors to find. The *Anne of Cleves* character jug is a celebrated example. When it was launched in 1980, the ears on the horse handle were erect but as these were easily chipped they were soon remodelled to lie flat. A premium is now paid for the first 'ears up' version. Similarly with the original handle of the *Macbeth* jug, the large protruding noses on the witches were prone to damage and consequently the heads were turned inwards. It would appear that only a few of the original jugs had been made before modification so the 'noses out' version is extremely rare.

Some of the early character jugs have also been modified although the reasons for the changes are not so apparent. Harry Fenton's *Granny*, which was introduced in 1935, was revamped within a few years. The proportions of her face were altered and a white frill was added to the front of her bonnet but the most significant addition was a prominent front tooth. This resulted in the original version being dubbed the 'Toothless Granny' and she commands considerably more in the marketplace than the second version which continued in production until 1983. Fenton's *Cavalier* also exists in two versions, the original from 1940 features a goatee beard, which is missing from the later version, but it now makes a big difference in price if he is bearded.

Style One: Hatless Drake

The war years seem to have been a period of change and reappraisal generally. Apart from the modifications already mentioned, *Drake* acquired a plumed hat making the original 'Hatless' version something of a rarity and *Pearly Boy* lost his relief modelled buttons to become plain *'Arry*. His companion *Pearly Girl* was not remodelled but was decorated differently to become *'Arriet*. The original *Pearly Boy and Girl* character jugs are now amongst the rarest production models to find.

Colour Variations

Changes of colour can make a significant difference to the desirability of jugs as has been seen with the *Pearly Girl*. The presence of a lime green and pink hat, as opposed to the drab green worn by *'Arriet*, will attract a substantial premium. *Pearly Boy* has also worn different coloured outfits and the blue version is considered to be much rarer than the brown. Another expensive variation is Fenton's *Old King Cole*. The original, which dates from 1939, has a yellow crown and the second common version an orange one. There are also slight modelling variations in the ruff but the colour differences are the most pronounced.

The *Clown* character jug features the most radical of the early colour changes. In the first version, introduced in 1937, he has a white painted face with bright red hair whilst the post-war version has natural flesh tones with white hair. There is also a brown hair variation which is contemporary with the red haired model. All the clowns are desirable additions to a collection but the red and brown haired versions are priced higher.

In the early years alternative colour schemes for character jugs were unusual but from the mid 1980s it became standard practice to offer the most popular models in different outfits. A few of these went into the general range but most were special commissions in limited editions. The first, in 1985, was a colourway of the large size *Mad Hatter* which was produced in an edition of 250 to celebrate the opening of the Royal Doulton room at Higbees department store in the US and it sold out on the day of issue. Many more special colourway editions followed this early success but their appeal gradually diminished until ultimately the practice ceased at the end of the decade.

During long production runs, colours have frequently been altered for technical reasons and the results of the new recipes are often noticed by serious collectors. The most obvious in recent years was the *Beefeater*, who received an on-glaze red jacket in 1987 instead of the early underglaze maroon shade. There have also been other modifications to this long-lived jug. In the first year or so of production the Royal Cypher GR was picked out in gold and this is now very rare. When Queen Elizabeth was crowned in 1953 the handle was altered again to feature her cypher ER.

Character and toby jugs are all painted individually by different artists and so inevitably there will be slight variations in colour between one and another even though everybody is following the same standard. Occasionally mistakes are made, colours might be reversed or omitted, and they can cause a lot of interest amongst collectors when they slip through the system. An interesting error was spotted in 1984 when the first *Custer and Sitting Bull* character jugs left the factory. The Indian chief was depicted with grey eyes and, when it was pointed out that this was genetically unlikely, the eyes were altered to brown. There are no prizes for guessing which variation is the most sought after! Around the same time a small quantity of *Henry V* jugs left the factory without the on-glaze red and gold decoration and initially they caused some excitement in the marketplace before it was realised they were seconds. Colour variations do not always command premium prices but it is still fun looking out for them.

DERIVATIVES

Novelty coupled with practicality became Charles Noke's maxim during the 1930s as his fertile imagination contorted many of his favourite character jug personalities into all sorts of useful items, including teapots, tobacco jars, ashtrays and wall vases. Collecting these derivatives, as they are known, can add another dimension to Doulton displays. It is possible to find *Old Charley* in 15 different guises, including character jugs, tobies and derivatives, and *Sairey Gamp* comes a close second in the variety of her appearances so putting together displays of these characters alone could be fun.

It may be that Noke was given the idea for the derivatives from the novel Toby wares made by Harry Simeon at the Lambeth studio and it is probably not a coincidence that the Burslem factory was also commissioned to model character decanters for Aspreys and Co. The resulting *Scotsman* and *Irishman* whisky containers were issued in 1934 and can be considered forerunners of the derivatives. Bookends, busts and napkin rings of Dickens personalities followed and although they have more in common with Noke's figures from the HN series, they are still sought after by jug enthusiasts.

The first true character jug derivatives were the ashtrays of 1936 which are essentially miniature size jugs with trays added. These must have been successful for larger ashbowls and tobacco jars were soon added to the range. Generally only minor modifications were required to suit the character jugs for their new purposes. The musical jugs, for instance, had an extended hollow base to accommodate the Thorens Swiss movement which played the appropriate tune. In contrast, Harry Fenton's creative powers were fully stretched to incorporate Sairey Gamp, Tony Weller and Old Charley into teapots! Although it is highly unlikely that these figurative teapots were used, they soon had matching sugar bowls. Perhaps milk jugs would have followed if it had not been for the outbreak of war which abruptly curtailed production of all these whimsical gift items. Consequently all the early derivatives are considered rare and hard to find.

It was not until the late 1950s that designers were once again able to turn their attention to the novelty gift market. A range of table lighters in the form of jug personalities was launched in 1958 and some of these now prove elusive. As well as the 14 lighters recorded in the catalogues, a prototype *Granny* lighter has also made an appearance in the market. Most of the post-war derivatives have been liquor containers made to order for various distillers and bottlers, including W. Walklate, Pick-Kwik and William Grant and perhaps there will be more in the future. The Royal Doulton International Collectors Club has also played its part in keeping the derivatives in focus by reviving the potty teapot tradition. In

Complete set of Sairey Gamp character jugs together with a sugar bowl and bust

1988 they commissioned the *Old Salt Teapot* especially for members and this led to the introduction of several new character teapots of *The Old Balloon Seller*, *Long John Silver* and *Falstaff*. As they were only in the range for a brief period they will eventually become as hard to find as some of the early derivatives.

Limited Edition Loving Cups and Jugs

A few years before the successful launch of character jugs, Charles Noke and Harry Fenton had already collaborated on a spectacular range of limited edition loving cups and jugs. These large, colourful pieces are vigorously modelled in low relief and they feature many of the characters who were later portrayed as jugs. Thus in terms of subject and style they are closely related to character and toby jugs and consequently many keen collectors seek them out as display centrepieces. Unfortunately they are not easy to find as most were only made for a short period during the 1930s and they were produced in very small editions of 300 to 1,000, some of which were never completed. Also it is inevitable that some have been broken in the intervening years so, not surprisingly, they are expensive when they do appear on the market.

These loving cups and jugs were Royal Doulton's very first limited edition pieces and, as such, represent the zenith of Noke's achievements as Art Director. The accompanying certificates of authenticity are almost as splendid as the items they describe with elaborate illustrations, ribboned seals and Noke's signature written in ink. Understandably many collectors have these documents framed as works of art in their own right. Further authentification and the unique number of the loving cup or jug appears on the base, which is usually equally decorative with appropriate motifs or symbols. Perhaps the most novel is the treasure chart on the base of *The Treasure Island Jug*.

The majority of the loving cups and jugs stand around 10 inches high and the scene unfolds in relief, painted in glowing underglaze colours. The handles are often ingeniously linked

to the subject, for instance the *John Peel* loving cup has a riding crop and fox head whilst the *Guy Fawkes* jug has a flaming torch. It is interesting that symbolic handles such as these later became a major feature of the character jug range.

Many of the subjects reflect Noke's literary interests, which he regularly explored in the series ware, figures and character jug collections, in particular the writings of Dickens and Shakespeare and popular adventure stories such as *The Three Musketeers* and *Treasure Island*. The exploits of real-life seafaring heroes, such as Drake, Nelson and Cook, were also celebrated in the range.

Wandering Minstrel Loving Cup

Noke realised at an early stage that these prestige pieces were ideal for commemorating important historical and royal events and so the bicentenary of the birth of George

Washington in 1932 was marked with a patriotic American jug, bedecked in stars and stripes, whilst the anniversary of the founding of New South Wales was recalled by the launch of the *Captain Phillip* jug. There was no shortage of royal events to celebrate during the 1930s and loving cups with portraits of the monarchs, emblazoned with flags and regalia, were issued for the Silver Jubilee of George V and the coronation of George VI. There are even three different coronation loving cups for Edward VIII who, of course, was never crowned but some of the editions had been sold before his abdication. Years later these ceremonial loving cups were revived for the Coronation and Silver Jubilee of Queen Elizabeth II in 1953 and 1977 respectively and perhaps they will be used again for important royal occasions in the future.

In 1982 the Royal Doulton International Collectors Club commissioned a loving cup in traditional style depicting *Pottery in the Past* and, as it was only made in small numbers for members, it is becoming increasingly difficult to find.

Collecting all the limited edition loving cups and jugs will prove to be something of a challenge and, as with all Royal Doulton wares, there are also some tantalising prototypes and variations. To date nobody has found the trials or *Roger Solemel, Cobbler* and *I.T. Wigg, Broom-man* but one lucky collector has a prototype *George Washington* presentation jug with a different stars and stripes handle. This variation was not recorded in the Royal Doulton archives and there may well be others to be found so happy hunting.

Making Character and Toby Jugs

Each Royal Doulton character and toby jug goes through the hands of many skilled and experienced individuals. From the designer to the painter to the kiln manager, each person is responsible for ensuring the quality of the finished article.

Today the diverse ideas for new jugs usually originate in the company's marketing department and, following discussions with the design managers, the modeller is briefed about the required subject. A great deal of research goes into the initial concept. If a historical personality is to be depicted, contemporary paintings, photographs and other records are studied to ensure accuracy in features and costume. For a fictional character, the designer needs to read the relevant book and consider any illustrations before embarking on sketches. Some Royal Doulton artists submit drawings of their proposed subject, others prefer to work directly with the modelling clay to visualise their ideas.

A careful balance must be achieved between portraiture and caricature, good humour and dignity to create a jug suitable for the Royal Doulton range. The symbolism of the handle, which is now such an important element of the design, also requires a lot of thought and ingenuity. When the modeller is completely satisfied with his work, it goes for approval to the Art and Marketing Directors who occasionally suggest modifications to improve the design or avert potting problems. It is vital that everybody is happy with the jug at this stage because the lines and details of this master model will determine the exact appearance of the finished piece.

The mould-maker then takes over and carefully disects the original to create plaster of Paris moulds of each part. Usually a four part mould is required for the head and the handle is moulded separately. A few sample jugs, known as prototypes, will be cast from the master mould for further discussion and colour trials. Ideally only two or three prototypes are produced as with each casting the intricate detail of the mould is gradually worn away. If the prototype is approved at one of the design conferences, a rubber working 'case' is made from the master mould and it is from this case that all the subsequent plaster of Paris production moulds are made.

In the casting department a liquid clay mixture known as slip is poured into the production moulds through a hole in the top. The porous plaster absorbs the water in the slip and a layer of solid clay is formed in the interior of the mould. When this has reached the required thickness, the excess slip is drained away and the mould is taken apart for the various cast sections to be extracted. The separate parts of the jug are assembled using slip as an adhesive and the rough edges and seams smoothed away in a process known as fettling.

After drying at a controlled temperature, the jugs are ready to receive their first firing in the electric tunnel kiln. This is known as the 'biscuit' firing because of the texture of the jug when it emerges from the kiln. On completion the fragile clay body has shrunk by about an eighth of its original size, becoming hard and durable.

The white biscuit jug is then taken to the decorating studio where special pigments suitable for underglaze painting are used. Painting directly onto the porous biscuit body gives the rugged character lines and wrinkles required in many jug subjects. Considerable care and expertise is required at this stage as some colours can change during the fixing process in the hardening — on kiln.

After this second, low-temperature firing, the jug is ready to be glazed and this is done by either spraying it with a liquid glass mixture or dipping it into a vat of the same mixture. The glossy, protective finish is achieved by firing the jug again, this time in a glost kiln. In many cases, this completes the process, but some brightly coloured jugs have a further coat of paint applied on top of the glaze and they need to be fired a fourth time to seal the colours permanently. Before leaving the factory, the finished jugs are inspected by the quality control staff to ensure there are no flaws and they are then packed for despatch all over the world.

Collectors are invited to see the jug making process at the John Beswick factory. For opening times and tour bookings contact: The Tour Organiser, John Beswick, Gold Street, Longton, Stoke-on-Trent ST3 2JP.

Bodies and Glazes

Stoneware

The first Doulton jugs were produced at the Lambeth factory in London and these were made of salt-glaze stoneware, a high fired ceramic body which is literally glazed with salt thrown into the kiln at peak temperatures. Bodies range from a plain buff to a rich brown, which is sometimes dipped in a darker coloured slip to create a two tone effect. Muted colours can be achieved in this high temperature process but only the Simeon toby wares were additionally coloured with a bright red on-glaze enamel colour.

Earthenware, Kingsware and China

The first character and toby jugs produced at Royal Doulton's factory in Nile Street, Burslem were mostly made of white earthenware, although the treacle-coloured Kingsware body was used for some early commissions. For a brief period, between 1968 and 1973, character jugs were made in English Translucent China, a porcelain body pioneered by Doulton chemists in 1959. All the jugs had to be remodelled for this process and so collectors will notice differences in detail between earthenware and ETC jugs. However, the most obvious variation is the size as the china body fires about 1/2 an inch smaller than the earthenware.

Following Royal Doulton's acquisition of the John Beswick factory, it was decided to concentrate the production of jugs at this location in Longton and the earthenware body was revived. Consequently, since 1973 new models have been produced in earthenware and painted under the glaze although some recent designs also have on-glaze decoration, particularly to achieve bright reds, blues or metallic effects.

In the early 1980s there was some research at the Nile Street factory to revive the china body for character jugs in order to cope with the demand for the *Antagonists* and *Beatles* collections and, although the experiment was short-lived, occasional china examples come on to the market.

White Jugs

From time to time white glazed versions of standard character jugs appear on the market and these are highly valued by collectors. Most were made from the late 1930s to the early 1950s when wartime restrictions prohibited the production of decorated china for the UK market. It is believed that white biscuit jugs with slight flaws, which could not be decorated for the export market, were glazed for sale to company employees.

These white substandard jugs should not be confused with the white character jug portrait of Winston Churchill which was originally conceived undecorated, no doubt because of the UK embargo. Examples are rare because it did not remain in production for long.

During the 1930s D&J McCallum, the whisky distillers, commissioned a white version of their *Highlander* jug as well as the better known Kingsware variety. Numbers were limited to around 1,000 and they are hard to find today. Fifty years later Pick-Kwik Wines and Spirits of Derby commissioned two undecorated variations in their extensive range of promotional jugs. Only 100 of each were made of the *Micawber* character jug and spirit container for internal promotional use.

Occasionally modern white character jugs have turned up at local auctions and markets but it would appear that these have 'escaped' from the factory in an undecorated state and been glazed to cater for the strong market demand for white jugs.

Care and Repair

Character and toby jugs are relatively robust and easy to look after. The glaze seals and protects the colours permanently and occasional dusting will maintain the shiny finish. If the jugs are displayed on open shelves it is a good idea to fill the interior with crumpled tissue paper as this catches the dust and can be replaced easily at cleaning times. When necessary, jugs can be washed in luke-warm water using a mild detergent then rinsed thoroughly and dried naturally or buffed with a soft cloth. Care should be taken not to knock jugs against the tap or each other - the rims and handles are the most vulnerable parts. If an accident does happen, there are professional restorers who can make 'invisible' repairs to chips and cracks, even hairlines.

Obviously when buying on the secondary market, it is advisable to check very carefully for restorations such as these as they are not immediately obvious to the naked eye. Expert dealers have many different ways of spotting repairs. Rarely do they carry an ultra-violet lamp which will highlight problem areas, instead they become sensitive to the different vibrations given by the softer restored areas when tapped with a metallic object or even bitten with the teeth! Reputable dealers will stand by any guarantees they give regarding restorations. Prices should reflect the level of damage sustained and the quality of the restoration.

Occasionally old jugs have been used as containers and these can appear at flea markets quite dirty and stained. If washing fails, petroleum jelly will usually remove stubborn rust marks. It is worth persevering — apparently the rare coloured *Churchill* character jug, which made over £16,000 at auction in 1989, had originally been used as a storage jar under the kitchen sink.

A Guide to Backstamps and Dating

The marks on the base of a character jug can be a useful guide for dating the piece, particularly if it has been in production for a while. However, it is impossible to be precise as stocks of old-style backstamps continued to be used up after changes had been implemented. Nevertheless, jugs can usually be placed in a specific time period and, very occasionally, if there is a date code, an exact year of manufacture can be determined.

The Royal Doulton Trademark

Most prominent on the base is the Royal Doulton factory mark which has featured a lion standing on a crown ever since the company was awarded the Royal Warrant in 1901. It is unusual for a jug not to have a Royal Doulton trademark but occasionally prototypes have been found with a blank base and these have been authenticated by the company in Stoke-on-Trent.

Lion and Crown
Backstamp 1901 to 1930s

Made in England
was added in the 1930s

The early Royal Doulton trademark is found on some of the first Burslem toby jugs, such as *Charlie Chaplin*, and on the *McCallum* character jugs. By the early 1930s the words 'Made in England' had been incorporated in the lion and crown trademark and this style of backstamp has been recorded, with no other information, on some of the first character jugs. Most of the toby jugs issued between 1939 and 1950 are marked with this backstamp and the title of the character portrayed. Copyright information was either non-existent or kept to a minimum, unlike the character jugs.

The 1930s

In order to protect their designs from being copied, Royal Doulton registered them at the UK patent office and the resulting registration number (eg *RdNo782778* for John Barleycorn) is often printed underneath the backstamp. The year the jug was registered can be worked out from the table of numbers published by the patent office. Usually registration was a year before the jug went into production but on occasion the number was not issued in time and the words 'Reg. applied for' were added to the backstamp. (This has also been found misspelt 'Registeration'). It should be noted that the registration number does not give the date of manufacture for a specific piece, only when the design was first protected.

Registered Mark below backstamp
Printed numberal '14' stands for 1941

Regd in Australia
Name in inverted commas

Around 1938 Royal Doulton also began to register their designs in Australia and the information *Regd in Australia* was added to the backstamp.

By the late 1930s the name of the jug in inverted commas was usually included above the registration number. (eg "*The Cavalier*"). Jugs produced during the 1930s might also have a hand-painted D pattern number which was added by the decorator when the jug was completed. This practice continued until the Second World War.

All the above details will help date a piece to the 1930s but the only way to determine the exact year of manufacture is with the date code it it has one. This numbering system began in 1928 with the number 1. The date code number is immediately to the right of the lion and crown symbol and the year of manufacture can be calculated by adding it to 1927. Thus the code number 11 will give a date of 1938 and 15 indicates 1942. This code system can be found on character jugs from the 1930s and 40s.

The 1940s and 1950s

A capital *A* on the left of the lion and crown symbol is known as the A mark and it is a kiln control mark denoting a specific type of earthenware body known as Georgian. Sometimes an A mark appears on a character jug without any other information. It was used on a variety of Royal Doulton products between 1939 and 1955 so its presence on character jugs will date the piece to within that time period.

'A' to the left of the
Lion and Crown

Gone Away
D 6531
COPR 1959
DOULTON & CO LIMITED
Rd No 893844
Rd No 39659
Rd No 8316
Rd No 417/59

Copyright mark

After the war Royal Doulton found it necessary to register their designs in more of their main export markets and a new style backstamp was devised in 1947. This gives a copyright date for Doulton and Co Limited and four different registration numbers for the UK, Australia, South Africa and New Zealand. A few jugs introduced in 1950 only have three registration numbers.

From c1952 a printed D pattern number appears above the copyright date and a few years later the inverted commas around the character's name were dropped. Several different typefaces appear to have been used.

The 1960s and 1970s

New UK copyright laws in 1966 gave protection without separate design registrations in each country. Protection was extended to articles previously registered and as the period of registration ran out, the relevant numbers were withdrawn from the backstamp. By c1973 the lists had disappeared altogether and a new copyright symbol was adopted *C in place of Copr*. From 1975 the company's new name *Royal Doulton Tableware Ltd* began to appear in the copyright notice and many collectors were puzzled by this reference to tableware on gift items.

The 1980s and 1990s

A large elegant script was adopted for the character names in the early 1980s and by 1983 the first reference to hand made and hand decorated had been included underneath. The new Doultonville tobies also adopted this improved style. An entirely new design of backstamp was introduced in 1984, featuring the new styling for the company name *Royal Doulton*, the subject of the jug in bold capitals, the modeller's facsimile signature and the words 'Hand made and hand decorated' forming an arch around the lion and crown. These changes were implemented in order to acknowledge the talents of individual artists and to seek public recognition of the specialist production skills involved. Initials or dots and dashes on the base are decorator's marks but no records exist to identify these.

Doultonville
Tobies backstamp

The Fireman
Backstamp

In the last ten years backstamps have become increasingly interesting and attractive as evocative images and typefaces are chosen to capture the spirit of the subject matter, for example the *Journey through Britain* series has lots of novel backstamp motifs, including a hose for the *Fireman* jug and postage stamp for the *Postman*. The *Celebrity* collection has a Hollywood billboard typeface and relevant quotes from the characters portrayed. This is not a completely new idea as one of the earliest jugs *Mephistopheles* was inscribed with a quotation about the devil by Rabelais. Not all the jugs carry this inscription, however and keen collectors are prepared to pay a slight premium for this feature.

Promotional and Commemorative Backstamps

There are many other interesting backstamp variations which ardent collectors will seek out. During the 1930s several independent companies commissioned standard character jugs with their name printed on the base for promotional purposes and this can now add to the value of the jug. Amongst the names to look for are Coleman's, Bentall's, Darley and Sons, and the Salt River Cement Works. In 1967, to celebrate the Canadian Centenary, the *North American Indian* and *Trapper* jugs were launched in North America only with a special backstamp and this was deleted for worldwide sales the following year. The presence of this commemorative backstamp will double the price of these jugs.

Coleman's Compliments
Backstamp

Winston Churchill
Prime Minister of
Great Britain 1940

This practice of pre-releasing has continued in recent years for Royal Doulton's important customers. For example the first two jugs in the *Celebrity* series, *W.C. Fields* and *Mae West* were produced in a Premier Edition for American Express and a small premium is payable for this backstamp.

Generally speaking the backstamps on toby jugs do not excite collectors, the exception being the portrait of *Winston Churchill* which originally had a backstamp commemorating 'Winston Churchill Prime Minister of Great Britain 1940.' This was deleted after 1940 and so jugs with this mark are very rare and consequently expensive.

Other Guides to Dating

Much can obviously be gleaned from the backstamp as to the age of a character jug but occasionally there are some other clues. It used to be the practice with large size jugs to continue painting inside the rim and this is referred to as bleeding by collectors. As this method was discontinued by 1973 it is possible to date jugs with this trait before then. Having checked the rim, look into the character's eyes! It is not as strange as it sounds for early style modelling was to indent the iris and this continued until the early 1960s. For a few years between 1968 and 1973, character jugs were produced in a type of porcelain known as ETC so pieces in this body must have been made during this short period.

Other clues are specific to certain models, for example early versions of *Auld Mac* have 'Owd Mac' on the backstamp and also impressed in the tammy. *Toby Philpots* was spelt with a double 't' until c1952 so those spelt Toby Philpotts date from the 1930s or 40s. *The Beefeater* has a couple of unique clues. Until c1953 it was called 'Beefeaters' on the backstamp and following the coronation of Queen Elizabeth in 1953, the handle was remodelled with a new Royal cypher. (See Modelling Variations).

Seconds

Seconds character jugs are no longer sold through retailers but examples do tend to appear in the marketplace, following sales to Royal Doulton employees. Jugs which have not been approved by the company's quality control department have their backstamps defaced. Nowadays a hole is drilled into the interlacing D device of the trademark but in the past a cross was scratched through.

WHERE TO BUY

Discontinued Royal Doulton toby and character jugs can be found in antique shops, markets and fairs as well as auction houses. Specialist dealers in Royal Doulton jugs attend many of the venues and events below.

UNITED KINGDOM

Auction Houses

Phillips
101 New Bond Street
London W1

Christie's South Kensington
85 Old Brompton Road
London SW5

Bonhams
Montpelier Street
London SW7

Sotheby's
Summer's Place
Billingshurst, West Sussex

Louis Taylor
Percy Street
Hanley, Stoke-on-Trent

Peter Wilson
Victoria Gallery
Market Street
Nantwich, Cheshire

Antique Fairs

UK Doulton Collectors Fair
Park Lane Hotel
Piccadilly
London W1

Stafford International Doulton Fair
Stafford County Showground
Stafford

Antique Markets

Portobello Road Market
London W11
Saturday only

New Caledonian Market
Bermondsey Square
London SE1
Friday morning

Alfie's Antique Market
13-25 Church Street
London NW8
Tuesday - Saturday

Camden Passage Market
(off Upper Street)
London N1
Wednesday and Saturday

USA

Auction Houses

Phillips New York
406 East 79th Street
New York, NY 10021

Antique Fairs

Florida Doulton Convention
Sheraton Design Centre
Fort Lauderdale, Florida

Doulton Show
Sheraton Poste House
Cherry Hill, New Jersey

Doulton Show
Holiday Inn
Independence, Ohio

CANADA

Auction Houses

D & J Ritchies
429 Richmond Street
Toronto, Ontario M5A 1R1

Antique Shows

The International Doulton Collectors Weekend
Sheraton Toronto East Hotel
2035 Kennedy Road
Scarborough, Ontario

Antique Markets

Harbourfront Antique Market
390 Queen's Quay West
Toronto, Ontario
(Tuesday - Sunday)

PLACES TO VISIT

John Beswick Studio
Gold Street
Longton
Stoke-on-Trent ST3 2JP

CLUBS AND SOCIETIES

The Royal Doulton Collectors Club was founded in 1980 to provide an information service on all aspects of the company's products, past and present. The Club's magazine 'Gallery' is published four times a year and local branches also publish newsletters. There are also several regional groups in the USA, which meet for lectures and other events and some publish newsletters. Contact the USA branch for further information.

Headquarters and UK Branch

Royal Doulton
Minton House
London Road
Stoke-on-Trent, ST4 7QD

Canadian Branch

Royal Doulton Canada Inc.
850 Progress Avenue
Scarborough, Ontario
M1H 3C4

USA Branch

Royal Doulton USA Inc.
P.O. Box 1815
Somerset, New Jersey
08873

Australia Branch

Royal Doulton Australia Pty Ltd.
17 - 23 Merriwa Street, Gordon
Australia NSW 2072

New Zealand Branch

Royal Doulton
P.O. Box 2059
Auckland, New Zealand

FURTHER READING

Figures and Character Jugs

Royal Doulton Figures by Desmond Eyles, Richard Dennis and Louise Irvine
The Charlton Standard Catalogue of Royal Doulton Figurines by Jean Dale
Collecting Character and Toby Jugs by Jocelyn Lukins
The Original Price Guide to Royal Doulton Discontinued Character Jugs by Princess and Barry Weiss
The Character Jug Collectors Handbook by Kevin Pearson
The Doulton Figure Collectors Handbook by Kevin Pearson

General

The Doulton Story by Paul Atterbury and Louise Irvine
Royal Doulton Series Wares by Louise Irvine (Vols 1 - 4)
Royal Doulton Bunnykins Figures by Louise Irvine
Bunnykins Collectors Book by Louise Irvine
Limited Edition Loving Cups and Jugs by Louise Irvine and Richard Dennis
Doulton for the Collector by Jocelyn Lukins
Doulton Kingsware Flasks by Jocelyn Lukins
Collecting Doulton Animals by Jocelyn Lukins
Doulton Burslem Advertising Wares by Jocelyn Lukins
Doulton Lambeth Advertising Wares by Jocelyn Lukins
The Doulton Lambeth Wares by Desmond Eyles
The Doulton Burslem Wares by Desmond Eyles
Hannah Barlow by Peter Rose
George Tinworth by Peter Rose
Sir Henry Doulton Biography by Edmund Gosse
Phillips Collectors Guide by Catherine Braithwaite
Discovering Royal Doulton by Michael Doulton
Royal Doulton by Jennifer Queree
Doulton Divvy Magazine by Betty Weir and David Gilman
Collecting Doulton Magazine Edited by Alan Blakeman, BBR Publishing
Thorndon Antiques and Fine China Ltd. by David Harcourt

TOBY JUGS

ALBERT SAGGER THE POTTER

THE DOULTONVILLE COLLECTION
ONE OF TWENTY-FIVE

Issued for the Royal Doulton International Collectors Club in 1986.

ALBERT SAGGER THE POTTER
FROM THE DOULTONVILLE COLLECTION
EXCLUSIVELY FOR
COLLECTORS CLUB
© 1986 ROYAL DOULTON (U.K.)
MODELLED BY

Designer: William K. Harper
Handle: Plain
Colourway: Brown apron, white shirt, dark green cap,
light green vase

Backstamp: Doulton / RDICC

Doulton Number	Size	Backstamp	Height	Intro.	Discon.	Current Market Value U.K. £	U.S. $	Can. $
D6745	Small	Doulton/RDICC	4"	1986	1986	60.00	100.00	150.00

ALDERMAN MACE THE MAYOR

THE DOULTONVILLE COLLECTION
ONE OF TWENTY-FIVE

Designer: William K. Harper	**Backstamp:** Doulton
Handle: Plain	
Colourway: Red coat trimmed with gold, white collar and scarf, black hat trimmd with gold and white feathers	

Doulton Number	Size	Backstamp	Height	Intro.	Discon.	Current Market Value U.K. £	U.S. $	Can. $
D6766	Small	Doulton	4"	1987	1991	30.00	60.00	75.00

THE BEST IS NOT TOO GOOD

STYLE ONE: *LAMBETH - FOURTEEN BUTTONS*

Issued in 1920, this jug was the fore runner of "The Best is Not Too Good" by Harry Fenton. This earlier version of The Best is Not Too Good by Harry Simeon is wider than the later version by Harry Fenton. Other noticeable differences between the two jugs are the white hair, closed mouth, dark mug, dark waistcoat with fourteen light coloured buttons, smooth face and the hand enclosing the pipe of the Harry Simeon jug, whereas the Harry Fenton jug has dark hair, white teeth on a smiling face, light coloured mug, no tie, a dark waiscoat with eleven buttons, a detailed face and the index finger holds the pipe.

Photograph Not Available At Press Time

Designer: Harry Simeon		**Backstamp:** Doulton Lambeth
Model: Unknown		
Handle: Plain		
Colourway: Unknown		
Inscription: No inscription around base		

Doulton Number	Size	Backstamp	Height	Intro.	Discon.	U.K. £	U.S. $	Can. $
						Current Market Value		
D —	Small	Doulton	4 1/2"	1920	Unknown	200.00	350.00	425.00

Miscellaneous "The Best Is Not Too Good" Items
Tobacco Jar

Designer: Harry Simeon   **Backstamp:** Doulton Lambeth
Model No.: 8593
Colourway: Blue coat, green hat and trousers,
white waistcoat with double row of
green buttons, brown lid
Inscription: No inscription around base

Doulton Number	Size	Backstamp	Height	Intro.	Discon.	Current Market Value		
						U.K. £	U.S. $	Can. $
D —		Doulton	4 1/2"	Unknown		500.00	750.00	1000.00

Miscellaneous "The Best Is Not Too Good" Items
Liquor Flask

"The Man in the Bottle" is of the same style as the "The Best is Not Too Good" toby jug except, of course, the man is enclosed in a circular frame. The neck of this flask is hallmarked Sterling silver. The outer edge of the flask is blue.

Designer:	Harry Simeon	
Model No.:	Unknown	
Colourway:	**Face of Jug:** White haired man wearing blue jacket, green-brown trousers, orange waistcoat with double row of white buttons, white stockings and necktie, black shoes	
	Back of Jug: Back of blue jacket and lower section of hair; blue-white buttons and coat flaps	
Inscription:	No inscription around base	

Backstamp: Doulton Lambeth

Doulton Number	Size	Backstamp	Height	Intro.	Discon.	Current Market Value U.K. £	U.S. $	Can. $
D —		Doulton	8 1/2"	Unknown		500.00	750.00	1000.00

THE BEST IS NOT TOO GOOD

STYLE TWO: BURSLEM - ELEVEN BUTTONS

This jug is modelled on an earlier Harry Simeon, Lambeth design of about 1920, there are, however, several different and obvious features noticeable on the later piece. See page No. 4 for an outline of these differences.

The Best is not too good.

Designer:	Harry Fenton
Model No.:	8338
Handle:	Plain
Colourway:	Green jacket, burgundy trousers, mustard waistcoat with double row of black buttons; Brown hat with gold trim
Inscription:	The Best Is Not Too Good

Backstamp: Doulton Burslem

Doulton Number	Size	Backstamp	Height	Intro.	Discon.	Current Market Value		
						U.K. £	**U.S. $**	**Can. $**
D6107	Small	Doulton	4 1/2"	1939	1960	180.00	300.00	400.00

BETTY BITTERS THE BARMAID

THE DOULTONVILLE COLLECTION
ONE OF TWENTY-FIVE

Designer: William K. Harper   **Backstamp:** Doulton
Handle: Plain
Colourway: Green blouse, burgundy skirt, yellow hair

| Doulton | | | | | | Current Market Value | | |
Number	Size	Backstamp	Height	Intro.	Discon.	U.K. £	U.S. $	Can. $
D6716	Small	Doulton	4"	1984	1990	40.00	65.00	75.00

CAP'N CUTTLE

DICKENS TOBIES
ONE OF SIX

Designer: Harry Fenton
Handle: Plain
Colourway: Light brown suit, blue highlights on
jacket lapels and waistcoat

Backstamp: Doulton

Doulton Number	Size	Backstamp	Height	Intro.	Discon.	Current Market Value		
						U.K. £	U.S. $	Can. $
D6266	Small	Doulton	4 1/2"	1948	1960	120.00	200.00	230.00

CAPTAIN PROP THE PILOT

THE DOULTONVILLE COLLECTION
ONE OF TWENTY-FIVE

Designer: William K. Harper

Handle: Plain

Colourway: Brown coat and gloves, grey cap, cream scarf

Backstamp: Doulton

Doulton Number	Size	Backstamp	Height	Intro.	Discon.	Current Market Value U.K. £	U.S. $	Can. $
D6812	Small	Doulton	4"	1989	1991	40.00	55.00	75.00

CAPT. SALT THE SEA CAPTAIN

THE DOULTONVILLE COLLECTION
ONE OF TWENTY-FIVE

Designer: William K. Harper
Handle: Plain
Colourway: Blue-black coat, blue-black cap trimmed with yellow

Backstamp: Doulton

Doulton Number	Size	Backstamp	Height	Intro.	Discon.	Current Market Value U.K. £	U.S. $	Can. $
D6721	Small	Doulton	4"	1985	1991	30.00	55.00	75.00

CHARLIE

The figure of Charlie Chaplin has a removable bowler hat. He stands on a green base and the lettering incised in the base "Charlie."

Designer: Unknown   **Backstamp:** Doulton
Handle: Plain
Colourway: Black suit and bowler hat, green and red
plaid waistcoat, red-brown tie; green base

Doulton Number	Size	Backstamp	Height	Intro.	Discon.	Current Market Value		
						U.K. £	U.S. $	Can. $
D —	Large	Doulton	11 1/4 "	1918	Unknown	1,750.00	3,000.00	3,500.00

CHARLIE CHEER THE CLOWN

THE DOULTONVILLE COLLECTION
ONE OF TWENTY-FIVE

Designer: William K. Harper
Handle: Plain
Colourway: Orange jacket, blue tie, green cap, yellow hair,
pink sausages

Backstamp: Doulton

Doulton Number	Size	Backstamp	Height	Intro.	Discon.	Current Market Value		
						U.K. £	U.S. $	Can. $
D6768	Small	Doulton	4"	1987	1991	30.00	55.00	75.00

CHARRINGTON & CO. LTD.

According to The Bass Museum, Burton-on-Trent, Staffordshire, these jugs originated from Hoare & Co, a London Brewery. This brewery was purchased and then closed in 1933 by Charringtons, another London Brewery. The original Charrington toby jugs were made by Doulton but there are no records of the numbers manufactured. The three variations below were made as promotional pieces for Charrington & Co., Mile End, London. They differ only in the wording on their bases and were in production from the 1930s.

VARIATION No. 1: Inscription around Base: Toby Ale

Designer: Hoare & Co. Ltd		**Backstamp:** Doulton
Handle: Plain		
Colourway: Black hat, green coat and maroon trousers		

Doulton Number	Size	Inscription	Height	Intro.	Discon.	Current Market Value U.K. £	U.S. $	Can. $
D8074	Large	Toby Ale	9"	1934	1938	175.00	400.00	500.00

VARIATION No. 2: Inscription around Base: One Toby Leads to Another

Doulton Number	Size	Inscription	Height	Intro.	Discon.	Current Market Value		
						U.K. £	U.S. $	Can. $
D —	Large	One Toby	9"	1937	1938	225.00	450.00	550.00

VARIATION No. 3: Inscription around Base: Charrington's Toby

Doulton Number	Size	Inscription	Height	Intro.	Discon.	Current Market Value		
						U.K. £	U.S. $	Can. $
D —	Large	Charrington's	9 1/4"	1939	1938	375.00	600.00	750.00

CLIFF CORNELL

In 1956 an American industrialist commissioned these toby jugs as gifts to friends and associates. The inscription on base reads: Greetings Cliff Cornell "Famous Cornell Fluxes" Cleveland Flux Company

Approximately 500 pieces were issued for the large size blue and dark brown jugs and 375 pieces for the small sizes. The numbers produced of the light brown jug are unknown.

VARIATION No. 1: Colourway: Tan suit

GREETINGS

CLIFF CORNELL

"FAMOUS CORNELL FLUXES"

CLEVELAND FLUX COMPANY

Designer: Unknown
Handle: Plain
Colourway: Light brown suit, brown and cream striped tie

Backstamp: Doulton

Doulton Number	Size	Variation	Height	Intro.	Discon.	Current Market Value U.K. £	U.S. $	Can. $
D —	Large	Var. 1	9"	1956	1956	300.00	500.00	600.00
D —	Small	Var. 1	5 1/2"	1956	1956	300.00	400.00	500.00

VARIATION No. 2   VARIATION No. 3

VARIATION No. 2: Colourway: Dark blue suit, red tie with cream polka dots.

Doulton Number	Size	Variation	Height	Intro.	Discon.	Current Market Value		
						U.K. £	U.S. $	Can. $
D —	Large	Var. 2	9"	1956	1956	225.00	350.00	425.00
D —	Small	Var. 2	5 1/2"	1956	1956	200.00	350.00	550.00

VARIATION No. 3: Colourway: Dark brown suit, green, black and blue designed tie.

Doulton Number	Size	Variation	Height	Intro.	Discon.	Current Market Value		
						U.K. £	U.S. $	Can. $
D —	Large	Var. 3	9"	1956	1956	225.00	350.00	400.00
D —	Small	Var. 3	5 1/2"	1956	1956	200.00	350.00	450.00

THE CLOWN

Issued in limited edition of 3,000.

Royal Doulton®
THE CLOWN
D 6935
Modelled by

Stanley James Taylor

© 1992 ROYAL DOULTON
ISSUED IN A LIMITED
EDITION OF 3,000.
THIS IS Nº 129

Designer: Stanley J. Taylor
Handle: Plain, black
Colourway: Green shirt, blue trousers, yellow bow-tie
with blue polka dots, yellow and red drum.

Backstamp: Doulton

Doulton Number	Size	Backstamp	Height	Intro.	Discon.	Current Market Value U.K. £	U.S. $	Can. $
D6935	Small	Doulton	5 1/2"	1993	Ltd. Ed.	69.95	175.00	225.00

DR. PULSE THE PHYSICIAN

THE DOULTONVILLE COLLECTION
ONE OF TWENTY-FIVE

Designer: William K. Harper	**Backstamp:** Doulton
Handle: Plain	
Colourway: Light brown jacket, grey hair	

Doulton Number	Size	Backstamp	Height	Intro.	Discon.	Current Market Value		
						U.K. £	U.S. $	Can. $
D6723	Small	Doulton	4"	1985	1991	30.00	55.00	75.00

FALSTAFF

BACKSTAMP B

Designer:	Charles Noke
Model No.:	8328
Handle:	Plain
Colourway:	Burgundy clothes, black hat with burgundy feathers

Backstamps: A. Sir John Falstaff
B. Falstaff

Doulton Number	Size	Backstamp	Height	Intro.	Discon.	Current Market Value U.S. £	U.S. $	Can. $
D6062	Large	Doulton	8 1/2"	1939	1991	60.00	125.00	175.00
D6063	Small	Doulton	5 1/4"	1939	1991	30.00	75.00	90.00

FAT BOY

DICKENS TOBIES
ONE OF SIX

Designer: Harry Fenton
Handle: Plain
Colourway: Brown

Backstamp: Doulton

Doulton Number	Size	Backstamp	Height	Intro.	Discon.	Current Market Value U.S. £	U.S. $	Can. $
D6264	Small	Doulton	4 1/2"	1948	1960	120.00	200.00	230.00

FATHER CHRISTMAS

A holly wreath is incorporated into the backstamp of the Father Christmas toby jug. Issued in a limited edition of 3,500 each jug is issued with a certificate of authenticity.

Designer: William K. Harper
Handle: Plain
Colourway: Red and white

Backstamp: Doulton

Doulton Number	Size	Backstamp	Height	Intro.	Discon.	Current Market Value		
						U.S. £	U.S. $	Can. $
D6940	Small	Doulton	5 1/2"	1993	Current	49.95	125.00	225.00

FLORA FUCHSIA THE FLORIST

THE DOULTONVILLE COLLECTION
ONE OF TWENTY-FIVE

Designer: William K. Harper
Handle: Plain
Colourway: Light blue uniform, brown hair; red,
yellow and white flowers

Backstamp: Doulton

Doulton Number	Size	Backstamp	Height	Intro.	Discon.	Current Market Value		
						U.K. £	U.S. $	Can. $
D6767	Small	Doulton	4"	1987	1990	40.00	75.00	85.00

FRED FEARLESS THE FIREMAN

THE DOULTONVILLE COLLECTION
ONE OF TWENTY-FIVE

Designer: William K. Harper
Handle: Plain
Colourway: Dark blue uniform wih green buttons,
yellow helmet

Backstamp: Doulton

Doulton Number	Size	Backstamp	Height	Intro.	Discon.	Current Market Value		
						U.K. £	U.S. $	Can. $
D6809	Small	Doulton	4"	1989	1991	30.00	55.00	75.00

FRED FLY THE FISHERMAN

THE DOULTONVILLE COLLECTION
ONE OF TWENTY-FIVE

Designer: William K. Harper   **Backstamp:** Doulton
Handle: Plain
Colourway: Light brown coat, tan hat, grey fish and net

Doulton Number	Size	Backstamp	Height	Intro.	Discon.	Current Market Value		
						U.K. £	U.S. $	Can. $
D6742	Small	Doulton	4"	1986	1991	30.00	55.00	75.00

GEORGE ROBEY

The hat is detachable. "George Robey", a star of the British Music Hall, entertained thousands during his long career, is incised on the base.

Designer: Charles Noke
Handle: Plain
Colourway: Black suit and hat, grey shirt and green base

Backstamp: Doulton

Doulton Number	Size	Backstamp	Height	Intro.	Discon.	Current Market Value U.K. £	U.S. $	Can. $
D —	Large	Doulton	9 3/4"	c.1925	Unknown	1,750.00	3,000.00	3,500.00

HAPPY JOHN

HAPPY JOHN

Designer: Harry Fenton
Handle: Plain
Colourway: Black hat, light green coat, yellow scarf with blue polka dots, and orange breeches

Backstamp: Doulton

Doulton Number	Size	Backstamp	Height	Intro.	Discon.	Current Market Value U.K. £	U.S. $	Can. $
D6031	Large	Doulton	8 1/2"	1939	1991	60.00	125.00	175.00
D6070	Small	Doulton	5 1/4"	1939	1991	30.00	65.00	95.00

HONEST MEASURE

It is hard to concieve that the original "Honest Measure" Jug does not exist in the form of a toby jug and that the only use made of this design was for a ink pot and jam pot.

This photograph is reconstructed from the ink pot on the next page.

Designer: Harry Simeon   **Backstamp:** Doulton Lambeth
Model No.: Unknown
Colourway: Unknown

Doulton Number	Size	Backstamp	Height	Intro.	Discon.	Current Market Value		
						U.K. £	U.S. $	Can. $
D —		Doulton Lambeth			Unknown			

Note: This is the first attempt to catalogue the Harry Simeon designs within a pricing catalogue. We have adopted the name "Honest Measure" for this jug as Fenton, who adopted Simeon's designs, was the first to name them. It seemed logical for cataloguing purposes to carry the name back to the original design. There will be errors. We need information to correct these errors for the third edition of this book. All assistance is greatly appreciated.

Miscellaneous "Honest Measure" Items
Inkpot with Detachable Hat

Designer: Harry Simeon   **Backstamp:** Doulton Lambeth
Model No.: 553
Colourway: Brown coat and stockings;
Black trousers and shoes

Doulton Number	Size	Backstamp	Height	Intro.	Discon.	Current Market Value		
						U.K. £	U.S. $	Can. $
D —		Doulton Lambeth	2 3/4"		Unknown	200.00	300.00	400.00

Miscellaneous "Honest Measure" Items
Jam Pot with Detachable Hat

Designer: Harry Simeon	**Backstamp:** Doulton Lambeth
Model No.: 552	
Colourway: Green-brown coat, green-black waistcoat	
black trousers, shoes and hat	

Doulton Number	Size	Backstamp	Height	Intro.	Discon.	Current Market Value U.K. £	U.S. $	Can. $
D —		Doulton Lambeth	4 "	Unknown		250.00	375.00	500.00

HONEST MEASURE

Honest Measure

Designer: Harry Fenton
Handle: Plain
Colourway: Green coat, orange waistcoat with black buttons, burgundy trousers, brown hat with gold trim
Inscription: "Honest Measure: Drink at Leisure"

Backstamp: Doulton

Doulton Number	Size	Backstamp	Height	Intro.	Discon.	Current Market Value		
						U.K. £	U.S. $	Can. $
D6108	Small	Doulton	4 1/4"	1939	1991	30.00	70.00	95.00

THE HUNTSMAN

VARIATION No. 1: Burslem
       Colourways: Bright Orange Coat

Designer: Charles Noke   **Backstamp:** Doulton Burslem
Model No.: 4090
Handle: Plain
Colourway: Bright orange coat, yellow waistcoat;
            Silver rim around top of hat

Doulton Number	Size	Variation	Height	Intro.	Discon.	Current Market Value		
						U.K. £	U.S. $	Can. $
D4090	Large	Var. 1	8 "	c.1919	Unknown	Extremely Rare		

VARIATION No. 2: Burslem
            Colourways: Red Coat

This variation may be found with or without the Sterling silver rim around the hat. The variety recorded has a silver rim.

Designer:	Charles Noke
Model No.:	4090
Handle:	Plain
Colourway:	Red coat with yellow buttons, yellow waistcoat, White shirt

Backstamp: Doulton Burslem

Doulton Number	Size	Variation	Height	Intro.	Discon.	Current Market Value U.K. £	Current Market Value U.S. $	Current Market Value Can. $
D —	Large	Var. 2	7 3/4"	c. 1919	1930	500.00	750.00	900.00

VARIATION No. 3 : Doulton
                     Colourway: Kingsware - Browns

Designer: Charles Noke   **Backstamp:** Doulton
    Handle: Plain
Colourway: Browns

Doulton Number	Size	Variation	Height	Intro.	Discon.	Current Market Value		
						U.K. £	**U.S. $**	**Can. $**
D —	Large	Var. 3	7 1/4"	1910	c.1927	500.00	1,000.00	1,000.00

VARIATION No. 4: Doulton
Colourway: Black hat, Maroon coat

This is the Harry Fenton adaption of Noke's original design.

THE HUNTSMAN

Designer: Harry Fenton
Handle: Plain
Colourway: Black hat, maroon coat, white shirt,
Gold waistcoat, grey trousers

Backstamp: Doulton

Doulton Number	Size	Variation	Height	Intro.	Discon.	Current Market Value U.K. £	U.S. $	Can. $
D6320	Large	Var. 4	7"	1950	1991	60.00	115.00	175.00

JESTER

Issued in a Limited Edition of 2500.

Royal Doulton®
THE JESTER
D 6910
Modelled by
Stanley James Taylor.
© 1991 ROYAL DOULTON
ISSUED IN A LIMITED
EDITION OF 2,500.
THIS IS N°. *633*

Designer: Stanley J. Taylor
Handle: Plain, black   **Backstamp:** Doulton
Colourway: Mauve and brown costume with yellow bobbles

Doulton Number	Size	Backstamp	Height	Intro.	Discon.	Current Market Value		
						U.K. £	U.S. $	Can. $
D6910	Medium	Doulton	5"	1992	Ltd. Ed. (1993)	75.00	135.00	175.00

JOHN WESLEY

PROTOTYPE

Designer: Charles Noke
Handle: Plain
Colourway: Black

Backstamp: Doulton

Doulton Number	Size	Backstamp	Height	Intro.	Discon.	Current Market Value U.K. £	U.S. $	Can. $
D ---	Large	Doulton	Unknown	c.1925			Unique	

JOLLY TOBY

Designer: Harry Fenton   **Backstamp:** Doulton
Handle: Riding crop
Colourway: Black hat, burgundy coat, yellow vest

Doulton Number	Size	Backstamp	Height	Intro.	Discon.	Current Market Value		
						U.K. £	U.S. $	Can. $
D6109	Medium	Doulton	6"	1939	1991	40.00	75.00	115.00

LEN LIFEBELT THE LIFEBOATMAN

THE DOULTONVILLE COLLECTION
ONE OF TWENTY-FIVE

Designer: William K. Harper
Handle: Plain
Colourway: Yellow life jacket and sou'wester, blue
sweater and white life buoy

Backstamp: Doulton

Doulton Number	Size	Backstamp	Height	Intro.	Discon.	Current Market Value U.K. £	U.S. $	Can. $
D6811	Small	Doulton	4"	1989	1991	30.00	55.00	75.00

MADAME CRYSTAL THE CLAIRVOYANT

THE DOULTONVILLE COLLECTION
ONE OF TWENTY-FIVE

Designer: William K. Harper
Handle: Plain
Colourway: Green headscarf, burgundy skirt,
mauve shawl with blue fringe

Backstamp: Doulton

Doulton Number	Size	Backstamp	Height	Intro.	Discon.	Current Market Value U.K. £	U.S. $	Can. $
D6714	Small	Doulton	4"	1984	1989	40.00	75.00	95.00

MAJOR GREEN THE GOLFER

THE DOULTONVILLE COLLECTION
ONE OF TWENTY-FIVE

Backstamp: Doulton

Designer: William K. Harper
Handle: Plain
Colourway: Light brown waistcoat, yellow shirt and green cap

Doulton Number	Size	Backstamp	Height	Intro.	Discon.	Current Market Value		
						U.K. £	U.S. $	Can. $
D6740	Small	Doulton	4"	1986	1991	30.00	55.00	75.00

MIKE MINERAL THE MINER

THE DOULTONVILLE COLLECTION
ONE OF TWENTY-FIVE

Designer: William K. Harper
Handle: Plain
Colourway: Light green shirt, grey helmet, blue scarf
and light brown belt

Backstamp: Doulton

Doulton Number	Size	Backstamp	Height	Intro.	Discon.	Current Market Value		
						U.K. £	U.S. $	Can. $
D6741	Small	Doulton	4"	1986	1989	50.00	75.00	85.00

MISS NOSTRUM THE NURSE

THE DOULTONVILLE COLLECTION
ONE OF TWENTY-FIVE

Designer: William K. Harper   **Backstamp:** Doulton
Handle: Plain
Colourway: Blue uniform, white apron, blue and white cap

Doulton Number	Size	Backstamp	Height	Intro.	Discon.	Current Market Value		
						U.K. £	U.S. $	Can. $
D6700	Small	Doulton	4"	1983	1991	30.00	50.00	75.00

MISS STUDIOUS THE SCHOOLMISTRESS

THE DOULTONVILLE COLLECTION
ONE OF TWENTY-FIVE

Designer: William K. Harper   **Backstamp:** Doulton
Handle: Plain
Colourway: Yellow blouse, green waistcoat and dark burgundy skirt

Doulton Number	Size	Backstamp	Height	Intro.	Discon.	Current Market Value		
						U.K. £	U.S. $	Can. $
D6722	Small	Doulton	4"	1985	1989	35.00	75.00	75.00

MONSIEUR CHASSEUR THE CHEF

THE DOULTONVILLE COLLECTION
ONE OF TWENTY-FIVE

Designer: William K. Harper   **Backstamp:** Doulton
Handle: Plain
Colourway: White chefs coat and hat, blue scarf

Doulton Number	Size	Backstamp	Height	Intro.	Discon.	Current Market Value		
						U.K. £	U.S. $	Can. $
D6769	Small	Doulton	4"	1987	1991	30.00	60.00	75.00

MR. BRISKET THE BUTCHER

THE DOULTONVILLE COLLECTION
ONE OF TWENTY-FIVE

Designer: William K. Harper
Handle: Plain
Colourway: Pale blue shirt, white apron and yellow hat with brown band

Backstamp: Doulton

Doulton Number	Size	Backstamp	Height	Intro.	Discon.	Current Market Value		
						U.K. £	U.S. $	Can. $
D6743	Small	Doulton	4"	1986	1991	30.00	60.00	75.00

MR. FURROW THE FARMER

THE DOULTONVILLE COLLECTION
ONE OF TWENTY-FIVE

Designer: William K. Harper
Handle: Plain
Colourway: Dark brown coat, cream trousers and light brown hat

Backstamp: Doulton

Doulton Number	Size	Backstamp	Height	Intro.	Discon.	Current Market Value U.K. £	U.S. $	Can. $
D6701	Small	Doulton	4"	1983	1989	40.00	65.00	85.00

MR. LITIGATE THE LAWYER

THE DOULTONVILLE COLLECTION
ONE OF TWENTY-FIVE

Designer: William K. Harper
Handle: Plain
Colourway: Black robes, yellow waistcoat, grey wig and trousers

Backstamp: Doulton

Doulton Number	Size	Backstamp	Height	Intro.	Discon.	Current Market Value		
						U.K. £	U.S. $	Can. $
D6699	Small	Doulton	4"	1983	1991	30.00	55.00	75.00

MR. MICAWBER

DICKENS TOBIES
ONE OF SIX

Designer: Harry Fenton	**Backstamp:** Doulton
Handle: Plain	
Colourway: Browns	

Doulton Number	Size	Backstamp	Height	Intro.	Discon.	Current Market Value		
						U.K. £	U.S. $	Can. $
D6262	Small	Doulton	4 1/2"	1948	1960	120.00	200.00	230.00

MR. PICKWICK

DICKENS TOBIES
ONE OF SIX

Designer: Harry Fenton
Handle: Plain
Colourway: Browns

Backstamp: Doulton

Doulton Number	Size	Backstamp	Height	Intro.	Discon.	Current Market Value U.K. £	U.S. $	Can. $
D6261	Small	Doulton	4 1/2"	1948	1960	120.00	200.00	230.00

MR. TONSIL THE TOWNCRIER

THE DOULTONVILLE COLLECTION
ONE OF TWENTY-FIVE

Designer: William K. Harper

Handle: Plain

Colourway: Burgundy coat trimmed with gold, brown hat trimmed with gold, white scarf

Backstamp: Doulton

Doulton Number	Size	Backstamp	Height	Intro.	Discon.	Current Market Value		
						U.K. £	U.S. $	Can. $
D6713	Small	Doulton	4"	1984	1991	30.00	55.00	75.00

MRS. LOAN THE LIBRARIAN

THE DOULTONVILLE COLLECTION
ONE OF TWENTY-FIVE

Designer:	William K. Harper	**Backstamp:** Doulton
Handle:	Plain	
Colourway:	Dark green blouse trimmed with white, light green skirt, yellow book	

Doulton Number	Size	Backstamp	Height	Intro.	Discon.	Current Market Value U.K. £	U.S. $	Can. $
D6715	Small	Doulton	4"	1984	1989	35.00	50.00	85.00

OLD CHARLIE

Old Charlie.

Designer: Harry Fenton   **Backstamp:** Doulton
Handle: Plain
Colourway: Brown hat, green coat and burgundy trousers

Doulton Number	Size	Backstamp	Height	Intro.	Discon.	Current Market Value U.K. £	U.S. $	Can. $
D6030	Large	Doulton	8 1/2"	1939	1960	150.00	275.00	350.00
D6069	Small	Doulton	5"	1939	1960	100.00	175.00	215.00

PAT PARCEL THE POSTMAN

THE DOULTONVILLE COLLECTION
ONE OF TWENTY-FIVE

Designer: William K. Harper

Handle: Plain

Colourway: Dark blue uniform trimmed with red, grey postbag

Backstamp: Doulton

Doulton Number	Size	Backstamp	Height	Intro.	Discon.	Current Market Value		
						U.K. £	U.S. $	Can. $
D6813	Small	Doulton	4"	1989	1991	30.00	50.00	75.00

REV. CASSOCK THE CLERGYMAN

THE DOULTONVILLE COLLECTION
ONE OF TWENTY-FIVE

Designer: William K. Harper	**Backstamp:** Doulton
Handle: Plain	
Colourway: Black coat, grey shirt, brown cap	

Doulton Number	Size	Backstamp	Height	Intro.	Discon.	Current Market Value		
						U.K. £	U.S. $	Can. $
D6702	Small	Doulton	4"	1983	1990	30.00	55.00	85.00

SAIREY GAMP

DICKENS TOBIES
ONE OF SIX

Designer: Harry Fenton
Handle: Plain
Colourway: Browns

Backstamp: Doulton

Doulton Number	Size	Backstamp	Height	Intro.	Discon.	Current Market Value		
						U.K. £	U.S. $	Can. $
D6263	Small	Doulton	4 1/2"	1948	1960	125.00	225.00	250.00

SAM WELLER

DICKENS TOBIES
ONE OF SIX

Designer: Harry Fenton   **Backstamp:** Doulton
  Handle: Plain
Colourway: Browns

Doulton Number	Size	Backstamp	Height	Intro.	Discon.	Current Market Value		
						U.K. £	U.S. $	Can. $
D6265	Small	Doulton	4 1/2"	1948	1960	120.00	200.00	230.00

SEATED TOBY

STYLE ONE: *KNEES TOGETHER*

Designer: Harry Simeon   **Backstamp:** Doulton Lambeth
Model No.: 8599
Handle: Plain
Colourway: Blue coat with white buttons and pocket flaps;
green trousers, green sleeve cuffs with white
buttons; white stockings; black shoes and hat

Doulton Number	Size	Backstamp	Height	Intro.	Discon.	Current Market Value U.K. £	U.S. $	Can. $
D —		Doulton Lambeth	3 1/8"		Unknown	100.00	150.00	200.00

Note: This is the first attempt to catalogue the Harry Simeon designs. There will be errors. We need information to correct these errors for the third edition of this book. All assistance is greatly appreciated.

Miscellaneous "Seated Toby" Items
Candlestick

Designer: Harry Simeon	**Backstamp:** Doulton Burslem
Model No.: 559	
Colourway: Blue coat with gold buttons, blue hat, orange trousers, pale blue stockings; black shoes, dark brown base	

Doulton Number	Size	Backstamp	Height	Intro.	Discon.	Current Market Value U.K. £	U.S. $	Can. $
D —		Doulton	3 3/4"			150.00	225.00	300.00

SEATED TOBY

STYLE TWO: *KNEES APART*

It is hard to concieve that Style Two does not exist in the form of a toby jug and that the only use made of this design was for a candlestick.

This photograph is reconstructed from the candlestick holder on the next page.

Designer: Harry Simeon   **Backstamp:** Unknown
Model No.: Unknown
Colourway: Unknown

Doulton Number	Size	Backstamp	Height	Intro.	Discon.	Current Market Value		
						U.K. £	U.S. $	Can. $

Details Not Available

Miscellaneous "Seated Toby" Items
Candlestick

VARIATION No. 1: Colourway: Blue coat, cream waistcoat

Designer: Harry Simeon
Colourway: Blue coat, cream waistcoat, black hat
and stockings, blue candle well, dark
brown base

Backstamp: Doulton Lambeth

VARIATION No. 2: Colourway: Cream coat with blue buttons and
pocket flaps, blue hat and stockings, tan
waistcoat; blue candle well, dark brown base

VARIATION No. 3: Colourway: Blue coat with white buttons and pocket
flaps; brown waistcoat with white lapels and buttons,
dark green candle well and saucer of base, brown
base

Doulton Number	Colourway	Height	Intro.	Discon.	Current Market Value U.K. £	U.S. $	Can. $
D —	Var. 1	2 1/2"		Unknown	175.00	250.00	350.00
D —	Var. 2	2 1/2"		Unknown	175.00	250.00	350.00
D —	Var. 3	2 1/2"		Unknown	175.00	250.00	350.00

SEATED TOBY

STYLE THREE: ARMCHAIR VARIETY

VARIATION No. 1: Colourway: Blue coat, white waistcoat

Designer: Harry Simeon

Model No.: 858

Handle: None

Colourway: Blue coat, white waistcoat with brown buttons, dark brown hat and trousers, brown chair

Backstamp: Doulton Lambeth

Doulton Number	Var.	Backstamp	Height	Intro.	Discon.	Current Market Value U.K. £	U.S. $	Can. $
D —	Var. 1	Doulton Lambeth	4"		Unknown	200.00	325.00	400.00

VARIATION No. 2: Colourway: Brown-blue coat, orange waistcoat

Designer:	Harry Simeon
Model No.:	543
Handle:	None
Colourway:	Brown-blue coat, orange waistcoat with black buttons, Dark brown trousers and hat, brown chair

Backstamp: Doulton Lambeth

Doulton Number	Var.	Backstamp	Height	Intro.	Discon.	Current Market Value		
						U.K. £	U.S. $	Can. $
D —	Var. 2	Doulton Lambeth	4"		Unknown	200.00	325.00	400.00

VARIATION No. 3: Colourway: Royal blue coat, burgundy waistcoat

Designer:	Harry Simeon
Model No.:	543
Handle:	None
Colourway:	Royal blue coat, burgundy waistcoat with grey buttons, green trousers, dark blue hat, green-blue chair

Backstamp: Doulton Lambeth

Doulton Number	Var.	Backstamp	Height	Intro.	Discon.	Current Market Value		
						U.K. £	U.S. $	Can. $
D —	Var. 3	Doulton Lambeth	4"		Unknown	200.00	325.00	400.00

VARIATION No. 4: Ye Olde Cock Tavern
Colourway: Brown-green coat, rust waistcoat

Around base: "Ye Olde Cock Tavern 22 Fleet Street Founded 1549"

Designer: Harry Simeon	**Backstamp:** Doulton Lambeth
Model No.: 551	
Handle: None	
Colourway: Brown-green coat, rust waistcoat, black trousers, blue hat, brown chair	

Doulton Number	Var.	Backstamp	Height	Intro.	Discon.	Current Market Value		
						U.K. £	U.S. $	Can. $
D —	Var. 4	Doulton Lambeth	6"		Unknown	300.00	450.00	600.00

SGT. PEELER THE POLICEMAN

THE DOULTONVILLE COLLECTION
ONE OF TWENTY-FIVE

Designer:	William K. Harper
Handle:	Plain
Colourway:	Blue-black uniform

Backstamp: Doulton

Doulton Number	Size	Backstamp	Height	Intro.	Discon.	Current Market Value		
						U.K. £	U.S. $	Can. $
D6720	Small	Doulton	4"	1985	1991	30.00	50.00	75.00

SHERLOCK HOLMES

"Issued to Commemorate the 50th Anniversary of the Death of Sir Arthur Conan Doyle (1859 - 1930)" is the inscription of the base of this jug.

© ROYAL DOULTON
TABLEWARE LTD. 1980

Sherlock Holmes

D.6661
ISSUED TO COMMEMORATE
THE 50th ANNIVERSARY
OF THE DEATH OF
SIR ARTHUR CONAN DOYLE
(1859 - 1930)

Designer: Robert Tabbenor
Handle: Plain, black
Colourway: Green hat and cloak, green-brown coat

Backstamp: Doulton

Doulton Number	Size	Backstamp	Height	Intro.	Discon.	Current Market Value		
						U.K. £	U.S. $	Can. $
D6661	Large	Doulton	9"	1981	1991	60.00	100.00	125.00

SIR FRANCIS DRAKE

"Issued to commemorate the 400th Anniversary of the circumnavigation of the world." is the inscription on the base of this jug.

© ROYAL DOULTON
TABLEWARE LTD. 1980

Sir Francis Drake

D.6660
ISSUED TO COMMEMORATE
THE 400th ANNIVERSARY
OF THE CIRCUMNAVIGATION
OF THE WORLD

Backstamp: Doulton

Designer: Michael Abberley
Handle: Plain
Colourway: Black hat with white feather,
yellow with brown tunic, tan boots

Doulton Number	Size	Backstamp	Height	Intro.	Discon.	Current Market Value U.K. £	U.S. $	Can. $
D6660	Large	Doutlon	9"	1981	1991	60.00	100.00	125.00

THE SQUIRE

VARIATION No. 1: Kingsware - Browns; Sterling silver rim around neck of jug

The Squire
B6319
COPR 1950
DOULTON & CO LIMITED

Designer:	Unknown	**Backstamp:**	Doulton
Handle:	Plain		
Colourway:	Browns		

Doulton Number	Var.	Backstamp	Height	Intro.	Discon.	Current Market Value U.K. £	U.S. $	Can. $
D —	Var. 1	Doulton	6"	c.1910	Unknown	375.00	500.00	750.00

Note: We believe there is a possibility that an early "Squire" exists in earthenware c.1910. If anyone has any further information regarding this jug we would appreciate hearing from them.

VARIATION No. 2: **Colourways: Green coat, brown hat; Bone China**

Designer: Harry Fenton
Handle: Plain
Colourway: Brown hat, green coat, mustard waistcoat
with black buttons

Backstamp: Doulton

Doulton Number	Size	Variation	Height	Intro.	Discon.	Current Market Value		
						U.K. £	U.S. $	Can. $
D6319	Medium	Var. 2	6"	1950	1969	250.00	425.00	450.00

THE STANDING MAN

STYLE ONE: *SMILING FACE; FIVE BUTTONS ON WAISTCOAT;*
NO BUTTONS ON COAT

Designer: Harry Simeon   **Backstamp:** Doulton Lambeth
Model No.: 8572
Handle: Plain
Colourway: Blue-green coat with brown collar and cuffs,
brown trousers, orange waistcoat with five
white buttons, brown hat

Doulton Number	Size	Backstamp	Height	Intro.	Discon.	Current Market Value U.K. £	U.S. $	Can. $
D —	Large	Doulton Lambeth	8 3/4"	c.1925	Unknown	250.00	375.00	500.00
D —	Medium	Doulton Lambeth	7"	c.1925	Unknown	200.00	300.00	400.00
D —	Small	Doulton Lambeth	4 1/2"	c.1925	Unknown	150.00	225.00	300.00

THE STANDING MAN

STYLE TWO: *SOMBRE FACE; FIVE BUTTONS ON WAISTCOAT; TWO BUTTONS ON COAT*

VARIATION No. 1: Colourways: White buttons on waistcoat

Designer: Harry Simeon
Model No.: 8572
Handle: Plain
Colourway: Blue coat with brown collar and cuffs,
two white buttons at top of coat,
brown waistcoat with five white buttons,
brown hat

Backstamp: Doulton Lambeth

Doulton Number	Size	Backstamp	Height	Intro.	Discon.	Current Market Value U.K. £	U.S. $	Can. $
D —	Large	Doulton Lambeth	8 3/4"	c.1925	Unknown	250.00	375.00	500.00
D —	Medium	Doulton Lambeth	6 1/4"	c.1925	Unknown	200.00	300.00	400.00
D —	Small	Doulton Lambeth	4 1/2"	c.1925	Unknown	150.00	225.00	300.00
D —	Tiny	Doulton Lambeth	2 3/4"	c.1925	Unknown	100.00	150.00	200.00s

VARIATION No. 2: Colourways: Dark brown overglaze; gold buttons on waistcoat

Designer: Harry Simeon   **Backstamp:** Doulton Lambeth
Model No.: 8572
Handle: Plain
Colourway: Blue coat with brown collar and cuffs,
two white buttons at top of coat,
brown waistcoat with five gold buttons,
brown hat

Doulton Number	Size	Backstamp	Height	Intro.	Discon.	Current Market Value		
						U.K. £	U.S. $	Can. $
D —	Large	Doulton Lambeth	8 3/4"	c.1925	Unknown	300.00	450.00	600.00

TOBY XX

(WITH HANDLE)

STYLE ONE: *SALTGLAZE EARTHENWARE; HAND HOLDS JUG OF ALE*

VARIATION No. 1: Lambeth; Light brown overall, no overglaze

*Photograph
Not Available
At Press Time*

Designer: Unknown   **Backstamp:** Doulton Lambeth
   Handle: Lower section of hair tied with a bow at the base
Colourway: Light brown overall, with darker brown
                 highlights around hat, jacket and base

Doulton Number	Var.	Backstamp	Height	Intro.	Discon.	Current Market Value U.K. £	U.S. $	Can. $
D —	Var. 1	Lambeth	14 1/2"	1863	Unknown	300.00	450.00	600.00
D —	Var. 1	Lambeth	8 1/2"	1863	Unknown	250.00	375.00	500.00

VARIATION No. 2: Lambeth; Light brown overall with dark brown overglaze on upper section

Designer: Unknown   **Backstamp:** Doulton Lambeth
Reg. No.: 169753
Handle: Lower section of hair tied with a bow at the base
Colourway: Light brown lower section, dark brown upper section

Doulton Number	Var.	Backstamp	Height	Intro.	Discon.	Current Market Value U.K. £	U.S. $	Can. $
D —	Var. 2	Lambeth	8 1/2"	1863	Unknown	200.00	300.00	400.00

VARIATION No. 3: Burslem; Light brown overall with chocolate brown overglaze on upper section

Designer: Unknown   **Backstamp:** Doulton Burslem
Handle: Lower section of hair tied with a bow at the base
Colourway: Light brown lower section, chocolate brown
upper section

Doulton Number	Var.	Backstamp	Height	Intro.	Discon.	Current Market Value U.K. £	U.S. $	Can. $
D —	Var. 3	Burslem	10 1/2"	1863	Unknown	200.00	300.00	400.00

TOBY XX

(WITH HANDLE)

STYLE TWO: *PAINTED EARTHENWARE; HAND HOLDS JUG OF ALE*

VARIATION No. 1: Lambeth
 Colourways: Blue coat, green shirt, white bow tie

Designer: Harry Simeon	**Backstamp:** Doulton Lambeth
Model No.: 589	
Handle: Strands of hair	
Colourway: Blue coat, green collar and cuffs, green trousers and shirt, white bow tie, stockings and frilled cuffs, brown hat, brown barrel	

Doulton Number	Var.	Backstamp	Height	Intro.	Discon.	Current Market Value U.K. £	U.S. $	Can. $
D —	Var. 1	Lambeth	7"	c.1925	Unknown	250.00	375.00	500.00

VARIATION No. 2: Lambeth
          Colourways: Blue coat, brown shirt and bow tie

Designer: Harry Simeon	**Backstamp:** Doulton Lambeth
Model No.: 8592	
Handle: Strands of hair	
Colourway: Blue coat, brown collar, shirt, cuffs and trousers, brown bow tie, white stockings and frilled cuffs, dark brown hat, brown barrel	

Doulton Number	Var.	Backstamp	Height	Intro.	Discon.	Current Market Value U.K. £	U.S. $	Can. $
D —	Var. 2	Lambeth	8"	c.1925	Unknown	250.00	375.00	500.00

VARIATION No. 3: Lambeth
            Blue coat, orange shirt, white bow tie

Designer:	Harry Simeon
Model No.:	8590
Handle:	Strands of hair
Colourway:	Blue coat, green-brown collar and cuffs, orange shirt, green trousers, white bow tie and frilled cuffs, brown hat, brown barrel

Backstamp: Doulton Lambeth

Doulton Number	Var.	Backstamp	Height	Intro.	Discon.	Current Market Value U.K. £	U.S. $	Can. $
D —	Var. 3	Lambeth	7 3/4"	c.1925		250.00	375.00	500.00

Miscellaneous "Toby XX" Items
Liquor container: Stands on silver-plated stand with tap
"Finnigans Limited Manchester"

Designer: Unknown
Model No.: 8589
Handle: None
Colourway: Blue coat, dark brown collar, cuffs and trousers, orange waistcoat, white bow tie, frilled cuffs and stockings, dark brown hat with green on top, brown barrel

Backstamp: Doulton Lambeth

Doulton Number	Size	Backstamp	Height	Intro.	Discon.	Current Market Value		
						U.K. £	U.S. $	Can. $
D —	Large	Lambeth	10 1/4"	c.1890	Unknown	500.00	750.00	1,000.00

TOBY XX

(WITH HANDLE)

STYLE FOUR: CHINA; BURSLEM; BURGUNDY COAT

Style No. 4 is a modification of the 1925 design by Harry Simeon. "Toby XX" is also known as "The Man on the Barrel" and "Double XX."

"Toby XX."
Rᵈ Nº 837178.
Regᵈ in Australia

Designer: Harry Fenton	**Backstamp:** Doulton
Model No.: 8337	
Handle: Plain	
Colourway: Burgundy coat, orange shirt, blue bow tie, black trousers, dark brown hat, green-grey hair and handle, cream barrel	

Doulton Number	Size	Backstamp	Height	Intro.	Discon.	Current Market Value U.K. £	U.S. $	Can. $
D6088	Medium	Doulton	7"	1939	1969	150.00	375.00	375.00

TOBY XX

(WITHOUT HANDLE)

STYLE FIVE: SALTGLAZE; EARTHENWARE; HANDS REST ON KNEES

VARIATION No. 1: Lambeth; Light brown overall, no overglaze;
Dark brown hat

Designer:	Unknown	**Backstamp:** Doulton Lambeth
Model No.:	8547	
Handle:	None	
Colourway:	Light brown, dark brown hat	

Doulton Number	Var.	Backstamp	Height	Intro.	Discon.	Current Market Value U.K. £	U.S. $	Can. $
D —	Var. 1	Lambeth	5 3/4"	Unknown		200.00	300.00	400.00

VARIATION No. 2: Lambeth, Light brown overall with dark brown overglaze on upper half

Designer: Unknown	**Backstamp:** Doulton Lambeth
Model No.: 8547	Phillips Oxford St. London
Handle: None	
Colourway: Brown from base to chest,	
dark brown from chest to top of hat	

Doulton Number	Var.	Backstamp	Height	Intro.	Discon.	U.K. £	U.S. $	Can. $
						Current Market Value		
D —	Var. 2	Lambeth/Phillips	6"	Unknown		200.00	300.00	400.00

TOBY XX

(WITHOUT HANDLE)

STYLE SIX: PAINTED EARTHENWARE

VARIATION No. 3: Lambeth; Colourways: Orange waistcoat

Designer: Harry Simeon
Model No.: 8591
Handle: None
Colourway: Blue coat, green cuffs and trousers, orange waistcoat with white buttons, black shoes, dark brown trousers, brown barrel

Backstamp: Doulton Lambeth

Doulton Number	Var.	Backstamp	Height	Intro.	Discon.	Current Market Value		
						U.K. £	U.S. $	Can. $
D —	Var. 3	Lambeth	5 1/2"		Unknown	250.00	375.00	500.00

VARIATION No. 4: Lambeth; Colourways: Green waistcoat

Designer: Harry Simeon	**Backstamp:** Doulton Lambeth
Model No.: 8591	
Handle: None	
Colourway: Blue coat, green cuffs and trousers green waistcoat with white buttons, black shoes, dark brown hat	

Doulton Number	Var.	Backstamp	Height	Intro.	Discon.	Current Market Value U.K. £	U.S. $	Can. $
D —	Var. 4	Lambeth	5 1/2"		Unknown	250.00	375.00	500.00

VARIATION No. 5: Colourways: White waistcoat

Designer: Harry Simeon	**Backstamp:** Doulton Lambeth
Model No.: 547	
Handle: None	
Colourway: Green-brown coat and trousers, white waistcoat with black buttons, black hat and shoes, brown barrel	

Doulton Number	Var.	Backstamp	Height	Intro.	Discon.	Current Market Value U.K. £	U.S. $	Can. $
D —	Var. 5	Lambeth	5 3/4"		Unknown	250.00	375.00	500.00

TOWN CRIER

Issued in a Limited Edition of 2500.

Royal Doulton®
TOWN CRIER
D 6920
Modelled by

Stanley James Taylor

© 1992 ROYAL DOULTON
ISSUED IN A LIMITED
EDITION OF 2,500.
THIS IS N⁰ 770

Designer: Stanley J. Taylor
Handle: Plain, black
Colourway: Scarlet great coat trimmed with
yellow, black tricorn hat trimmed
with yellow, white feather

Backstamp: Doulton

Doulton Number	Size	Backstamp	Height	Intro.	Discon.	Current Market Value		
						U.K. £	U.S. $	Can. $
D6920	Medium	Doulton	5"	1992	Ltd. Ed.	69.95	190.00	250.00

WINSTON CHURCHILL

WINSTON CHURCHILL
PRIME MINISTER
OF GREAT BRITAIN
— 1940 —

BACKSTAMP A

WINSTON CHURCHILL

BACKSTAMP B

Designer: Harry Fenton
Handle: Plain
Colourway: Black hat, brown overcoat, black-green suit

Backstamps: A. "Winston Churchill Prime Minister of Great Britain 1940"
Model No. 8360 B
B. "Winston Churchill" only

Doulton Number	Size	Backstamp	Height	Intro.	Discon.	Current Market Value		
						U.K. £	U.S. $	Can. $
D6171	Large	Doulton - A	9"	1940	1940	175.00	300.00	350.00
D6171	Large	Doulton - B	9"	1941	1991	60.00	110.00	135.00
D6172	Medium	Doulton - A	5 1/2"	1940	1940	125.00	200.00	250.00
D6172	Medium	Doulton - B	5 1/2"	1941	1991	40.00	65.00	85.00
D6175	Small	Doulton - A	4"	1940	1940	110.00	175.00	215.00
D6175	Small	Doulton - B	4"	1941	1991	30.00	55.00	70.00

Old Charley Teapot
D6017

CHARACTER JUGS

ABRAHAM LINCOLN

PRESIDENTIAL SERIES
ONE OF ONE
PRESIDENTS OF THE UNITED STATES. THIS IS THE FIRST

First in a series of Presidents of the United States of America, issued in a limited edition of 2500. The handle is the American flag and Lincoln's famous speech that begins "Four score and seven years ago..."

Royal Doulton®

PRESIDENTIAL SERIES
ABRAHAM LINCOLN
D 6936
Modelled by
Stanley James Taylor

© 1992 ROYAL DOULTON
A SPECIALLY COMMISSIONED
LIMITED EDITION OF 2,500
THIS IS NO. 767

Designer: Stanley J. Taylor
Handle: U.S. Flag & Gettysburg Address
Colourway: Black & White

Backstamp: Doulton

Doulton Number	Size	Backstamp	Height	Intro.	Discon.	Current Market Value		
						U.K. £	U.S. $	Can. $
D6936	Large	Doulton	6 3/4"	1992	Ltd. Ed.	125.00	190.00	195.00

ADMIRAL LORD NELSON

STYLE ONE: *NELSON MODELLED TO THE CHEST*

VARIATION No. 1: Lambeth Original; 1821 - 1830

Produced in the 1820's by Doulton and Watts in Lambeth. Although originally called figure mugs this jug must be considered one of the first character jugs.

Designer: Unknown	**Backstamps:** A. Doulton & Watts,
Handle: Rope	B. Doulton & Watts,
Colourway: Saltglaze; light tan	Lambeth Pottery London

Doulton Number	Size	Backstamp	Height	Intro.	Discon.	Current Market Value U.K. £	U.S. $	Can. $
D ---	Large	Doulton / Watts	6 - 7 1/2"	1821	1830	300.00	450.00	600.00
D ---	Small	Doutlon / Watts	5"	1821	1830	250.00	375.00	500.00
D ---	Miniature	Doulton / Watts	2 1/2"	1821	1830	200.00	300.00	400.00

VARIATION No. 2: Burslem Replica; Centenary of The Battle of Trafalgar; 1905

Produced in Burslem to commemorate the 100th Anniversary of the great naval Battle of Trafalgar in which Nelson defeated the French fleet. This variation is a replica of the first jug made at the Lambeth factory (1820-1831) and bears the incised lion and crown backstamp of Royal Doulton used by the Burslem factory. The inscription in the base of the jugs reads "Replica of the Original Jug Made by Doulton & Watts Lambeth".

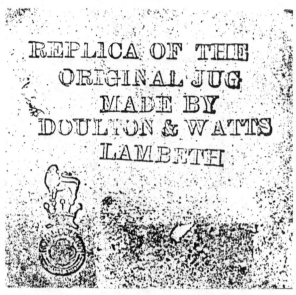

Designer: Unknown	**Backstamp:**	Doulton Burslem
Handle: Rope		
Colourway: Saltglaze		

Doulton Number	Size	Backstamp	Height	Intro.	Discon.	Current Market Value U.K. £	U.S. $	Can. $
D —	Large	Doulton Burslem	6"	1905	Unknown	250.00	375.00	500.00

ADMIRAL LORD NELSON

STYLE TWO: *NELSON MODELLED TO THE WAIST*

VARIATION No. 1: Lambeth Original; 1845

The inscription around the base of this jug reads "England Expects Every Man to do his Duty".

Designer:	Unknown	
Handle:	Hair tied with a bow	
Colourway:	Saltglaze, light brown	

Backstamp: Doulton & Watts, Lambeth Pottery London

Doulton Number	Size	Backstamp	Height	Intro.	Discon.	Current Market Value U.K. £	U.S. $	Can. $
D —	Large	Doulton / Watts	11 3/4"	1845	Unknown	500.00	750.00	1,000.00

ADMIRAL LORD NELSON

VARIATION No. 2: Burslem Replica; 1905

This jug is a replica of the original jug produced in 1845. It was produced to commemorate the 100th Anniversary of the Battle of Trafalgar.

Designer: Unknown	**Backstamp:** Doulton Burslem
Handle: Hair tied with a bow	
Colourway: Saltglaze, light brown	

Doulton Number	Size	Backstamp	Height	Intro.	Discon.	Current Market Value U.K. £	U.S. $	Can. $
D —	Large	Doulton Burslem	11 3/4"	1905	Unknown	400.00	600.00	800.00

THE AIRMAN
(Royal Air Force)

ARMED FORCES SERIES
ONE OF THREE

A member of the armed forces, an airman works particularly for the Royal Air Force as either a pilot or another member of the crew. This series pays tribute to those servicemen of the Royal Air Force, Army and Navy who fought in the Second World War.

STYLE ONE: WHITE SCARF WITHOUT CYPHER

Hand made and hand decorated

Royal Doulton®
THE AIRMAN
D 6870
Modelled by

William K. Harper

© 1990 ROYAL DOULTON

Designer: William K. Harper
Handle: German fighter plane
shot down in flames
Colourway: Light brown cap and dark brown flight
jacket with cream collar, white scarf

Backstamp: Doulton

Doulton Number	Size	Backstamp	Height	Intro.	Discon.	Current Market Value U.K. £	U.S. $	Can. $
D6870	Small	Doulton	4 1/2"	1991	Current	28.95	78.00	100.00

THE AIRMAN
(Royal Canadian Air Force)

THE CANADIANS SERIES
ONE OF THREE

Commissioned by The British Toby of Ontario, Canada, in a limited edition of 250 pieces. Sold originally as part of a set of three at $465.00 Canadian funds.

STYLE TWO: *RED SCARF WITH R.C.A.F. CYPHER*

Designer:	William K. Harper
Handle:	German fighter plane shot down in flames
Colourway:	Dark brown cap and flight jacket with biege collar, red scarf with cypher

Backstamp: Doulton / British Toby

Doulton Number	Size	Backstamp	Height	Intro.	Discon.	Current Market Value		
						U.K. £	U.S. $	Can. $
D6903	Small	Doulton/British	4 1/2"	1991	1991	120.00	140.00	165.00

THE ANGLER

CHARACTERS FROM LIFE SERIES
ONE OF SEVEN

Angling, meaning to fish with hook and bait, is the preferred term used by sport fishermen. A pastime known for its popularity, angling was a fitting choice of subject for the Characters from Life Series.

Royal Doulton®
THE ANGLER
D 6866
Modelled by
Stanley James Taylor
© 1990 ROYAL DOULTON

Designer: Stanley J. Taylor
Handle: A fish and lure
Colourway: Green jacket, brown hat, cream pullover

Backstamp: Doulton

Doulton Number	Size	Backstamp	Height	Intro.	Discon.	Current Market Value U.K. £	U.S. $	Can. $
D6866	Small	Doulton	4"	1990	Current	28.95	78.00	100.00

ANNE BOLEYN

HENRY VIII AND HIS SIX WIVES SERIES
ONE OF EIGHT

Anne (1502-1536) became the second wife of Henry VIII in a secret ceremony performed in January, 1533. Their marriage was officially sanctioned in May by the Archbishop of Canterbury, Thomas Cranmer, and she was crowned Queen on June 1, 1533 in Westminster Hall. Unable to produce the son Henry VIII desired Anne was imprisoned in the tower of London on false grounds of adultery. She was beheaded, with a sword on May 19, 1536 in a courtyard of the Tower of London. (The modeller use of an axe for the handle was incorrect.) Anne Boleyn was the mother of Queen Elizabeth the First, born September 7, 1533.

Designer:	Douglas V. Tootle	
Handle:	An axe and chopping block	**Backstamp:** Doulton
Colourway:	Black and grey	

Doulton						Current Market Value		
Number	Size	Backstamp	Height	Intro.	Discon.	U.K. £	U.S. $	Can. $
D6644	Large	Doulton	7 1/4"	1975	1990	60.00	110.00	155.00
D6650	Small	Doulton	3 1/2"	1980	1990	40.00	65.00	90.00
D6651	Miniature	Doulton	2 1/2"	1980	1990	40.00	65.00	65.00

ANNE OF CLEVES

HENRY VIII AND HIS SIX WIVES SERIES
ONE OF EIGHT

In a political arrangement by Thomas Cromwell, Anne (1515-1557) was chosen to marry Henry VIII. Upon seeing his dull and unattractive betrothed, whom he later referred to as his 'Flanders Mare', Henry attempted unsuccessfully to break the contract. Anne became his fourth wife on January 6, 1540, for only a brief time. Henry had the marriage annulled on July 8th of that year and gave Anne a pension for life.

VARIATION No. 1:   **Handle:** **Horse's ears pointing up.**
The original design of the handle had the ears of the horse pointing upwards.

| **Designer:** | **Large Size:** Michael Abberley | **Backstamp:** Doulton |
| | **Small & Miniature Size:** Peter Gee | |

Handle: Head of a horse
Colourway: Black and red

Doulton Number	Size	Variation	Height	Intro.	Discon.	Current Market Value U.K. £	U.S. $	Can. $
D6653	Large	Var. 1	7 1/4"	1980	1981	135.00	250.00	300.00

VARIATION No. 2:   Handle: Horse's ears flat against head. It was found that during the packaging and shipping of the jug, the horse's ears tended to break off. The design was then changed to have the ears of the horse lying flat against the head.

VARIATION 2, EARS FLAT   VARIATION 1, EARS POINTING UP

Royal Doulton
ANNE OF CLEVES
D 6653
Modelled by

© ROYAL DOULTON TARLEWARE
LIMITED 1979

LARGE JUG BACKSTAMP

Royal Doulton©
ANNE OF CLEVES
D 6753
Designed by M Abberley
Modelled by

PeterAGee

© 1979 ROYAL DOULTON (UK

SMALL JUG BACKSTAMP

Doulton Number	Size	Variation	Height	Intro.	Discon.	Current Market Value		
						U.K. £	U.S. $	Can. $
D6653	Large	Var. 2	7 1/4"	1980	1990	65.00	120.00	155.00
D6753	Small	Var. 2	4 1/4"	1987	1990	40.00	75.00	90.00
D6754	Miniature	Var. 2	2 1/2"	1987	1990	40.00	60.00	65.00

ANNIE OAKLEY

THE WILD WEST COLLECTION
ONE OF SIX

Phoebe Anne Moses (1860-1926) learned to shoot at the age of eight and helped support her family by killing game for a hotel in Cincinatti, Ohio. At fifteen, she defeated professional marksman Frank Butler in a shooting contest. She married him in 1876 and became a regular performer in shooting exhibitions, using the stage name Annie Oakley. She was a star of Buffalo Bill's Wild West Show from 1885 until 1901, when she was injured in a train accident and forced to retire. During WW I she trained American soldiers in marksmanship.

Royal Doulton

THE WILD WEST
Collection

ANNIE OAKLEY
D6732
Modelled by

Stanley James Taylor.

© ROYAL DOULTON TABLEWARE
LIMITED 1984

Designer: Stanley J. Taylor   **Backstamp:** Doulton
Handle: Rifle and belt
Colourway: Yellow hair, cream hat, brown tunic

Doulton Number	Size	Backstamp	Height	Intro.	Discon.	Current Market Value U.K. £	U.S. $	Can. $
D6732	Mid	Doulton	5 1/4"	1985	1989	45.00	90.00	110.00

THE ANTIQUE DEALER

THE COLLECTING WORLD
ONE OF THREE

In the world of collecting, the Antique dealer is involved with old and valuable furniture, paintings, and other decorative items which he buys and sells to the public.

Commissioned by Kevin Francis Ceramics Ltd. (KFC) in 1988. Issued in a limited edition of 5,000 pieces. It is interesting to note that the Kevin Francis Jugs have the handle on the right side.

Original Concept by Kevin Pearson and Geoff Blower

Royal Doulton®
THE ANTIQUE DEALER
D 6807
Modelled by

A Special Edition of 5000
From "The Collecting World" series
Produced by Royal Doulton
for Kevin Francis Ceramics
© 1988 ROYAL DOULTON
AND KEVIN FRANCIS CERAMICS

Designer: Geoff Blower
Handle: Flintlock handgun and candlestick
Colourway: Black hat, blue coat

Backstamp: Doulton / Kevin Francis

Doulton Number	Size	Backstamp	Height	Intro.	Discon.	Current Market Value U.K. £	U.S. $	Can. $
D6807	Large	Doulton/KFC	7 1/4"	1988	Ltd. Ed.	75.00	150.00	195.00

ANTONY AND CLEOPATRA

PROTOTYPE

A prototype of this Character Jug exists with Antony having a pudgy face, wide eyes and brown hair and Cleopatra with lighter make-up around the eyes, lighter beads around her neck and a dark red head-dress. Only one is known to exist.

| | | PROTOTYPE | | | REGULAR ISSUE | | | |

Doulton Number	Size	Variation	Height	Intro.	Discon.	Current Market Value		
						U.K. £	U.S. $	Can. $
D6728	Large	Prototype	7 1/4"	1984	1984	Unique		

ANTONY AND CLEOPATRA

THE STAR-CROSSED LOVERS COLLECTION
(TWO FACED JUG), ONE OF FOUR.

Marcus Antonius (83-30 B.C.) was a skilled soldier and co-ruler of Rome with Caesar's nephew Octavian from 43 to 32 B.C.

Cleopatra (68-30 B.C.) was well known for her charm and beauty. She was Queen of Egypt and ally and lover of Julius Caesar. In 41 B.C. Antony and Cleopatra met and fell in love, marrying in 37 B.C. Antony gave to Cleopatra and their children a share of his Roman provinces in 34 B.C., a move which enraged Octavian who waged war on the couple, pursuing them in their defeat to Alexandria.

Antony, hearing a rumour of Cleopatra's death, stabbed himself in grief. He was carried to her and died in her arms. Cleopatra in turn committed suicide, apparently from fear of Octavian, by placing an asp on her chest.

Issued in 1985 in a limited edition of 9,500 pieces.

Designer: Michael Abberley
Handle: Eagle's head, dagger and shield/Asp and harp
Colourway: Black, grey, brown
Backstamp: Doulton

Doulton Number	Size	Backstamp	Height	Intro.	Discon.	Current Market Value		
						U.K. £	U.S. $	Can. $
D6728	Large	Doulton	7 1/4"	1985	Ltd. Ed. (1990)	80.00	95.00	175.00

APOTHECARY

CHARACTERS FROM WILLIAMSBURG
ONE OF SEVEN

Along with the other characters in the Williamsburg series, the apothecary was central to colonial life in 18th century America. The term "apothecary," replaced by modern day "pharmacist," referred to a seller and dispenser of drugs.

Designer: Max Henk
Handle: Mortar and pestle
Colourway: Green coat with white cravat, white wig

Backstamp: Doulton

Doulton Number	Size	Backstamp	Height	Intro.	Discon.	Current Market Value U.K. £	U.S. $	Can. $
D6567	Large	Doulton	7"	1963	1983	60.00	110.00	150.00
D6574	Small	Doulton	4"	1963	1983	40.00	70.00	85.00
D6581	Miniature	Doulton	2 1/2"	1963	1983	40.00	60.00	75.00

ARAMIS

THE "THREE MUSKETEERS," ONE OF FOUR.
NOW PART OF THE CHARACTERS FROM LITERATURE, ONE OF ELEVEN.

One of the three musketeers, Aramis joined Athos, Porthos and D'Artagnan in a fictional life of adventure in Alexandre Dumas' 19th century novel, led by their code "All for one, and one for all".

VARIATION No. 1: Colourway: Black hat, white feather, brown tunic.

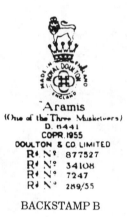

Aramis
((One of the Three Musketeers)
D. 6441
COPR. 1955
DOULTON & CO. LIMITED
R♦ N♤ 877527
R♦ N♤ 34108
R♦ N♤ 7247
R♦ N♤ 289/55

BACKSTAMP B

Designer:	Max Henk	
Handle:	Handle of a sword	
Colourway:	Black hat, white feather, brown tunic	

Backstamps: A. Doulton
            B. Doulton/One of the Three
            Musketeers; The wording "One of
            the Three Musketeers" was
            included to enlighten the unknow-
            ledgeable that "Aramis" was one of
            the famous Musketeers.

Doulton Number	Size	Backstamp	Height	Intro.	Discon.	Current Market Value U.K. £	U.S. $	Can. $
D6441	Large	Var. 1A	7 1/4"	1956	1991	60.00	100.00	145.00
D6441	Large	Var. 1B	7 1/4"	1956	1970	60.00	110.00	145.00
D6454	Small	Var. 1B	3 1/2"	1956	1991	35.00	55.00	80.00
D6508	Miniature	Var. 1A	2 1/2"	1960	1991	30.00	40.00	60.00

VARIATION No. 2:   Colourway: Yellow hat, maroon tunic. Commissioned by Peter Jones
China Ltd., England. Issued in 1988 in a limited edition of 1,000.

Backstamp: Doulton / Peter Jones China Ltd.

Doulton Number	Size	Backstamp	Height	Intro.	Discon.	Current Market Value		
						U.K. £	U.S. $	Can. $
D6829	Large	Doulton/Jones	7 1/4"	1988	Ltd. Ed.	75.00	125.00	225.00

'ARD OF 'EARING

With hand held to cup his ear, this cockney gentleman is a comic representation of the popular euphemism for deafness. This jug was discontinued in 1967 and has since increased in value and has become difficult to find.

Designer:	David Biggs
Handle:	A hand held to the ear
Colourway:	Dark purple tricorn; green, white and yellow clothing

Backstamp: Doulton

Doulton Number	Size	Backstamp	Height	Intro.	Discon.	Current Market Value		
						U.K. £	U.S. $	Can. $
D6588	Large	Doulton	7 1/2"	1964	1967	650.00	1,200.00	1,450.00
D6591	Small	Doulton	3 1/2"	1964	1967	450.00	875.00	950.00
D6594	Miniature	Doulton	2 1/2"	1964	1967	475.00	1,200.00	1,250.00

(ARP) WARDEN

HEROES OF THE BLITZ
ONE OF THREE.

The ARP (Air Raid Police) were charged with the responsibility of insuring that people were as secure as possible during an air raid. Armed only with his whistle he would patrol the streets enforcing the "lights out please" signal and see that all citizens took cover as quickly as possible. Commissioned by Lawleys By Post in a limited edition of 9,500 sets.

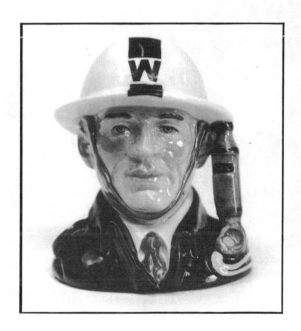

Designer:	Stanley J. Taylor	**Backstamp:** Doulton
Handle:	Grey whistle	
Colourway:	Dark blue jacket, white helmet with black stripe and the initial "W" (Warden)	

Doulton Number	Size	Backstamp	Height	Intro.	Discon.	Current Market Value U.K. £	U.S. $	Can. $
D6872	Small	Doulton	4"	1991	Ltd. Ed.	50.00	125.00	110.00

'ARRIET

'Arriet is a coster or costermonger, a cockney woman who sold fruits and vegetables from a barrow in the streets of London.

'Arriet is a derivative of Pearly Girl. Please see page No. 356 for the Pearly Girl character jug.

"'arriet"

COPR.1946
DOULTON & CO LIMITED
R^dN^o 6 47682
R^dN^o 2 3909
R^dN^o 132/46
R^dN^o 5195

Designer: Harry Fenton
Handle: Hat feather
Colourway: Green hat, brown coat, yellow scarf

Backstamp: Doulton

Doulton Number	Size	Backstamp	Height	Intro.	Discon.	Current Market Value		
						U.K. £	U.S. $	Can. $
D6208	Large	Doulton	6 1/2"	1947	1960	130.00	225.00	265.00
D6236	Small	Doulton	3 1/4"	1947	1960	60.00	110.00	140.00
D6250	Miniature	Doulton	2 1/4"	1947	1960	50.00	85.00	110.00
D6256	Tiny	Doulton	1 1/4"	1947	1960	80.00	200.00	240.00

'ARRY

'Arriet's husband 'Arry is also a costermonger, plying his trade in London.

'Arry is a derivative of Pearly Boy. Please see page No. 333 for the Pearly Boy character jug. The original design of 'Arry featured the word "Blimey" across the back but it was never produced.

Designer: Harry Fenton   **Backstamp:** Doulton
Handle: Plain
Colourway: Brown hat and coat, red and yellow scarf

Doulton Number	Size	Backstamp	Height	Intro.	Discon.	Current Market Value U.K. £	U.S. $	Can. $
D6207	Large	Doulton	6 1/2"	1947	1960	130.00	225.00	265.00
D6235	Small	Doulton	3 1/2"	1947	1960	60.00	110.00	140.00
D6249	Miniature	Doulton	2 1/2"	1947	1960	50.00	85.00	100.00
D6255	Tiny	Doulton	1 1/2"	1947	1960	80.00	200.00	240.00

ARSENAL (FOOTBALL CLUB)

THE FOOTBALL SUPPORTERS
ONE OF EIGHT

Designer: Stanley J. Taylor
Handle: Team coloured scarf
Colourway: Red and white uniform

Backstamp: Doulton

Doulton Number	Size	Backstamp	Height	Intro.	Discon.	Current Market Value		
						U.K. £	U.S. $	Can. $
D6927	Mid	Doulton	5"	1992	Current	35.00	125.00	95.00

ARTFUL DODGER

CHARLES DICKENS COMMEMORATIVE SET
DICKENS TINIES, ONE OF TWELVE

The Artful Dodger is a member of a gang of thieves who meet and enlist Oliver Twist in Dickens' novel of Victorian London.

Issued to commemorate the 170th Anniversary of the birth of Charles Dickens. There are twelve jugs in this set each issued with a certificate of authenticity. A mahogany display shelf completes the set. The set was first sold by Lawleys By Post in the U.K. during 1982 to 1988 and in 1985 forward in North America and Australia.

Artful
Dodger
D 6678

Designer: Peter Gee   **Backstamp:** Doulton
Handle: Plain
Colourway: Yellow and black

Doulton Number	Size	Backstamp	Height	Intro.	Discon.	Current Market Value U.K. £	U.S. $	Can. $
D6678	Tiny	Doulton	1 1/2"	1982	1989	30.00	45.00	55.00
		Display for 12 Tinies				65.00	45.00	50.00

ARTHUR WELLESLEY
FIRST DUKE OF WELLINGTON

Arthur Wellesley, 1769 - 1852, had a distinguished military career and was endowed with numerous honours including the title of First Duke of Wellington after the battle of Toulouse, France in 1814. He became a Member of Parliament in 1806 and Prime Minister in 1827.

Produced in the 1820's by Doulton and Watts in Lambeth this jug is also considered a figure mug.

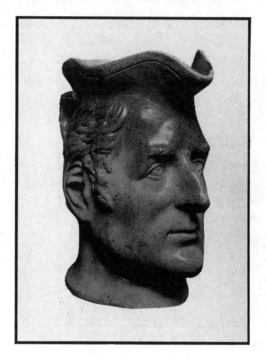

Designer: Unknown	**Backstamp:**	Doulton & Watts, Lambeth Pottery
Handle: Plain		London
Colourway: Saltglaze; light tan		

Doulton Number	Size	Backstamp	Height	Intro.	Discon.	Current Market Value U.K. £	U.S. $	Can. $
D —	Large	Doulton / Watts	7 1/2"	1821	1830	300.00	450.00	600.00

ASTON VILLA (FOOTBALL CLUB)

THE FOOTBALL SUPPORTERS
ONE OF EIGHT

Royal Doulton®
**FOOTBALL SUPPORTER'S
CHARACTER JUG.**
D 6931
Modelled by
Stanley James Taylor.
© 1992 ROYAL DOULTON
"ASTON VILLA"

Designer: Stanley J. Taylor
Handle: Team coloured scarf
Colourway: Maroon and blue uniform

Backstamp: Doulton

Doulton Number	Size	Backstamp	Height	Intro.	Discon.	Current Market Value		
						U.K. £	U.S. $	Can. $
D6931	Mid	Doulton	5"	1992	Current	35.00	125.00	95.00

ATHOS

THE "THREE MUSKETEERS", ONE OF FOUR.
NOW PART OF THE CHARACTERS FROM LITERATURE, ONE OF ELEVEN.

First issued as one of four in The Three Musketeers Series, Athos is now incorporated into the larger series Characters From Literature. Under the banner of "All for one and one for all," Athos was one of the original musketeers in the 19th century novel by Alexandre Dumas.

VARIATION No. 1:   **Mould:**   Feathers along rim of hat.
                               Colourway: Black hat, white feather, green tunic with gold trim.

Athos
D 6439
©DOULTON & CO LIMITED 1955

BACKSTAMP A

Athos
(One of the "Three Musketeers")
D 6452
COPR 1955
DOULTON & CO LIMITED
Rd No 677528
Rd No 34106
Rd No 7245
Rd No 290/55

BACKSTAMP B

Designer: Max Henk
Handle: Upper half of a sword
Colourway: Black hat, white feather, green tunic with gold trim.

Backstamps: A. Doulton
                  B. Doulton/One of the Three Musketeers
                  The wording "One of the Three Musketeers" was included in the early backstamp to enlighten the unknowledgeable that "Athos" was one of the famous Musketeers.

Doulton Number	Size	Backstamp	Height	Intro.	Discon.	Current Market Value U.K. £	U.S. $	Can. $
D6439	Large	Doulton	7 1/4"	1956	1991	55.00	100.00	145.00
D6439	Large	Doulton/One	7 1/4"	1956	1991	55.00	110.00	145.00
D6452	Small	Doulton/One	3 3/4"	1956	1991	35.00	55.00	80.00
D6509	Miniature	Doulton/One	2 1/2"	1960	1991	30.00	40.00	60.00

VARIATION No. 2:   Mould: **Feathers run along rim of hat.**
                        Colourway: **Black hat, white feather, yellow tunic with blue trim.**

VARIATION No. 3:   Mould: **Feathers above rim of hat.**
                        Colourway: **Black hat, white feather, yellow tunic with blue trim.**

There were two different moulds used in the production of the Jones colourway, Variation 2 and Variation 3. A total of 1,000 jugs were issued but the numerical breakdown between the two varieties is unknown..

VARIATION No. 2   VARIATION No. 3

Designer: Max Henk
Handle: Upper half of a sword
Colourway: Black hat, white feather, yellow tunic with blue trim.

Backstamp: Doulton/Peter Jones China Ltd. Commissioned by Peter Jones China Ltd., England. Issued in 1988 in a limited edition of 1,000.

Royal Doulton®
ATHOS
D 6827
Modelled by

© 1955 ROYAL DOULTON
NEW COLOURWAY 1988
SPECIAL COMMISSION 1000
PETER JONES CHINA
LEEDS AND WAKEFIELD

Doulton Number	Size	Variation	Height	Intro.	Discon.	Current Market Value		
						U.K. £	U.S. $	Can. $
D6827	Large	Var. 2	7 1/4"	1988	Ltd. Ed.	65.00	110.00	165.00
D6827	Large	Var. 3	7 1/4"	1988	(incl. in above)	75.00	150.00	185.00

THE AUCTIONEER

THE COLLECTING WORLD
ONE OF THREE.

Unlike a store or market, an auction requires a prospective buyer to bid a price on an item, the object being sold to the individual offering the highest bid. The auctioneer presents the merchandise, controls the bidding and declares the buyer of each item.

Commissioned by Kevin Francis Ceramics Ltd. (KFC). Issued in 1988 in a limited edition of 5,000, this jug again has the Kevin Francis characteristic of the right handed handle.

Designer: Geoff Blower	
Handle: Auctioneer's gavel and (HN687) The Bather	**Backstamp:** Doulton / Kevin Francis
Colourway: Green coat and bow tie, light brown cap	

Doulton Number	Size	Backstamp	Height	Intro.	Discon.	Current Market Value		
						U.K. £	U.S. $	Can. $
D6838	Large	Doulton/KFC	6 1/4"	1988	Spec. Ed. (1991)	85.00	160.00	195.00

AULD MAC

Sir Harry Lauder, a 20th century singer/comedian, sang a song which inspired this piece. His Scotsman Mac found the prices too high in London because every time he made a move, "Bang Went Saxpence". The phrase is incised on back of his hat below "Auld Mac."

"OWD MAC"   "AULD MAC"

BACKSTAMP A

Auld Mac
D.5823

BACKSTAMP B

Designer: Harry Fenton
Handle: A Brier
Colourway: Green tam, brown coat

Backstamps: A. Doulton - "OWD MAC"
"Owd Mac" incised in the tam and printed in the backstamp c. 1937.
B. Doulton - "AULD MAC"
"Auld Mac" incised in the tam in 1938, but "Owd Mac" continued in the backstamp until approximately 1940.
C. Doulton - "AULD MAC"
"Auld Mac" incised in tam and printed in backstamp.

Doulton Number	Size	Backstamp	Height	Intro.	Discon.	Current Market Value U.K. £	U.S. $	Can. $
D5823	Large	A "Owd"/"Owd"	6 1/4"	1937	c. 1937	250.00	300.00	350.00
D5823	Large	B "Auld/Owd"	6 1/4"	1938	1940	70.00	250.00	300.00
D5823	Large	C "Auld/Auld"	6 1/4"	1940	1986	60.00	100.00	150.00
D5824	Small	A "Owd"/"Owd"	3 1/4"	1937	1937	80.00	150.00	175.00
D5824	Small	B "Auld/Owd"	3 1/4"	1938	1940	40.00	150.00	175.00
D5824	Small	C "Auld/Auld"	3 1/4"	1940	1985	30.00	55.00	70.00
D6253	Miniature	C "Auld/Auld"	2 1/4"	1946	1985	30.00	50.00	70.00
D6257	Tiny	C "Auld/Auld"	1 1/4"	1946	1960	110.00	235.00	225.00

Miscellaneous "Auld Mac" Items

Doulton Number	Item	Height	Intro.	Discon.	Current Market Value U.K. £	U.S. $	Can. $
D5889	Musical Jug	6 1/4"	1938	c. 1939	300.00	800.00	925.00
D6006	Ash Bowl	3"	1938	1960	75.00	125.00	140.00

Note: Tune to the Musical Jug: "The Campbells are Coming".

AUXILIARY FIREMAN

HEROES OF THE BLITZ
ONE OF THREE

Large numbers of volunteer firemen were needed during the bombing of London and other cities of Great Britain during WWII to assist the regular firemen. It was through the courage of the Auxiliary Fire Service (A.F.S.) that the incendiary fires of the air raids were held in check. Commissioned by Lawleys By Post in a limited edition of 9,500 sets.

Designer: Stanley J. Taylor
Handle: Hose and nozzle
Colourway: Black jacket, grey helmet with white initials "A.F.S."

Backstamp: Doulton

Doulton Number	Size	Backstamp	Height	Intro.	Discon.	Current Market Value U.K. £	U.S. $	Can. $
D6887	Small	Doulton	4"	1991	Ltd. Ed.	60.00	125.00	110.00

BACCHUS

In Roman mythology, Bacchus, son of Zeus, was the god of wine and nature. He traditionally inspired men and women to music and poetry. "Bacchanalia", the harvest celebrations to honour him were reputed to be such orgies of excess that the Roman government had them banned.

Some of the earlier versions of the miniature jug had the leaves on the vine handle painted green. There is no current premium value for this variety.

Bacchus
D 6505
COPR 1958
DOULTON & CO LIMITED
Rd No 889570
Rd No 38226
Rd No 8036
Rd No 423/58

BACKSTAMP A

CITY OF
STOKE-ON-TRENT
JUBILEE YEAR
1959-1960
WITH THE COMPLIMENTS OF
LORD MAYOR AND LADY MAYORESS
ALDERMAN HAROLD CLOWES O.B.E. J.P
AND
MISS CHRISTINE CLOWES

BACKSTAMP B

Designer: Max Henk
Handle: Grapevine
Colourway: Maroon robes, green leaves and purple grapes adorn the head

Backstamps: A. Doulton
B. Doulton / City of Stoke-on-Trent Jubilee Year 1959 - 1960
"With the compliments of Lord Mayor and Lady Mayoress Alderman Harold Clowes, O.B.E., J.P. and Miss Christine Clowes"

Doulton Number	Size	Backstamp	Height	Intro.	Discon.	Current Market Value U.K. £	U.S. $	Can. $
D6499	Large	Doulton	7"	1959	1991	50.00	95.00	155.00
D6499	Large	Doulton/City	7"	1959	1960	475.00	800.00	950.00
D6505	Small	Doulton	4"	1959	1991	35.00	55.00	80.00
D6521	Miniature	Doulton	2 1/2"	1960	1991	30.00	45.00	65.00

Miscellaneous "Bacchus" Items

Doulton Number	Item	Height	Intro.	Discon.	Current Market Value U.K. £	U.S. $	Can. $
D6505	Table Lighter	3 1/2"	1964	1974	125.00	350.00	275.00

BAHAMAS POLICEMAN

Famous for their crisp, white uniforms, the constabulary of the Bahamas has become known for its courteous and friendly demeanor in the warm, sunny streets of Nassau.

Royal Doulton®

BAHAMAS POLICEMAN
D 6912
Modelled by

© 1991 ROYAL DOULTON

ISLAND GALLERIA

An Island Galleria Exclusive

Designer: William K. Harper
Handle: Tassle
Colourway: White and red

Backstamp: Doulton / Island Galleria
Commissioned by Island Galleria
Nassau, Bahamas in a special
edition of 1000 jugs.

Note: The D number 6912 is also the numerical designation of The Snake Charmer.

Doulton Number	Size	Backstamp	Height	Intro.	Discon.	Current Market Value		
						U.K. £	U.S. $	Can. $
D6912	Large	Doulton/Island	7"	1992	Sp. Ed.	125.00	250.00	275.00

BASEBALL PLAYER

Only two of the jugs are known to exist. They are test pieces and were never put into production. Both jugs are different.

STYLE ONE: HANDLE: BAT AND BALL

VARIATION No. 1: Colourway: Blue / green jersey, red sleeves and cap.

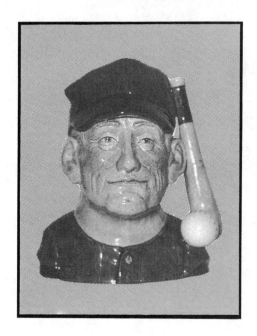

Designer: David Biggs		**Backstamp:** Doulton
Handle: Bat and ball		
Colourway: Blue / green jersey, red sleeves and cap.		

Doulton Number	Size	Variation	Height	Intro.	Discon.	Current Market Value U.K. £	U.S. $	Can. $
D6624	Large	Var. 1	7 1/2"	1970	1970		Extremely Rare	

VARIATION No. 2: Colourway: Striped blue and black jersey and cap.

Doulton Number	Size	Variation	Height	Intro.	Discon.	Current Market Value U.K. £	U.S. $	Can. $
D6624	Large	Var. 2	7 1/2"	1970	1970		Extremely Rare	

THE BASEBALL PLAYER

CHARACTERS FROM LIFE
ONE OF SEVEN

The "great American pastime" of baseball is an obvious choice in a series inspired by favourite hobbies.

STYLE TWO: HANDLE: BALL, BAT AND GLOVE.

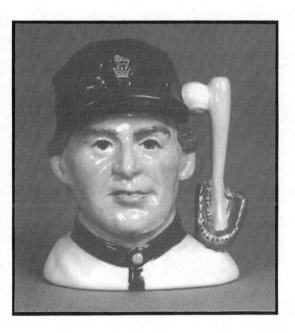

BACKSTAMP A

BACKSTAMP B

Designer: Stanley J. Taylor
Handle: Ball, bat and glove
Colourway: Dark blue cap and white jersey

Backstamps: A. **Doulton**
For General Issue: 1991.
B. **Doulton/Britannia Limited**
Commissioned by Britannia Limited
to celebrate the 5th anniversary of
their Doulton Convention and Sale,
January 1991. Issued in a special
edition of 500 pieces.

Doulton Number	Size	Backstamp		Height	Intro.	Discon.	U.K. £	Current Market Value U.S. $	Can. $
D6878	Small	Doulton		4 1/4"	1991	1992	45.00	75.00	100.00
D6878	Small	Doulton/Britannia		4 1/4"	1991	Sp. Ed.	65.00	80.00	100.00

BEEFEATER

THE LONDON COLLECTION, ONE OF TEN.
THE CURRENT BEEFEATER IS INCLUDED IN THIS SERIES.

The Yeomen of the Guard and warders of the Tower of London are colloquially referred to as Beefeaters. The name "Beefeater" came from a visiting Grand Duke who was astonished by the large amounts of beef the Yeoman Guards ate. He nicknamed them "Beefeaters." The monarch's cypher at the base of the handle, G.R., is an abbreviation of George Rex, for King George VI. In 1953, after his death, the cypher was changed to E.R., (Elizabeth Regina), for Queen Elizabeth II and continues today.

VARIATION No. 1: Handle: Pink with a "GR" cypher.

"Beefeaters"

COPR 1946.
DOULTON & CO LIMITED
RdNo 847680
RdNo 23907
RdNo 119/46
RdNo 5193

Designer:	Harry Fenton/Robert Tabbenor	**Backstamp:** Doulton / "Beefeaters"
Handle:	Pink with a "GR" cypher.	The pluralized name was used on all
Colourway:	Black hat, white ruff, pink tunic.	three size jugs from 1947 through
		1953.

Doulton Number	Size	Variation	Height	Intro.	Discon.	Current Market Value U.K. £	U.S. $	Can. $
D6206	Large	Var. 1	6 1/2"	1947	1953	70.00	150.00	175.00
D6233	Small	Var. 1	3 1/4"	1947	1953	50.00	80.00	100.00
D6251	Miniature	Var. 1	2 1/2"	1947	1953	40.00	60.00	75.00

VARIATION No. 2: Handle: Yellow with a "GR" cypher.

Backstamp: Doulton/"Beefeaters"

Doulton Number	Size	Variation	Height	Intro.	Discon.	Current Market Value		
						U.K. £	U.S. $	Can. $
D6206	Large	Var. 2	6 1/2"	1947	1947	900.00	2,500.00	1,750.00
D6233	Small	Var. 2	3 1/4"	1947	1947	800.00	2,000.00	1,500.00

VARIATION No. 3: Handle: Pink with an "ER" cypher.

Beefeaters
COPR.1946
DOULTON & CO LIMITE
RdNo 847680
RdNo 23907
RdNo 119/46
RdNo 5193

BACKSTAMP A

Beefeater
D 6206
COPR 1946
DOULTON & CO LIMITED

BACKSTAMP B

Royal Doulton
BEEFEATER
D6233
Modelled by

H Fenton

© ROYAL DOULTON TABLEWARE
LIMITED 1946

BACKSTAMP B

BACKSTAMP C

Backstamps: A. Doulton/"Beefeaters"
The plural name was found only on early versions of the "ER" jugs.
B. Doulton/"Beefeater"
In late 1953 the backstamp was adjusted and the singular "Beefeater" name was incorporated.
C. Doulton/"Beefeater"
"Fired in the last firing of a traditional Bottle Oven 1978 Longton Stoke-on-Trent, England"

Doulton Number	Size	Variation	Height	Intro.	Discon.	Current Market Value		
						U.K. £	U.S. $	Can. $
D6206	Large	Var. 3A	6 1/2"	1953	1953	60.00	110.00	135.00
D6206	Large	Var. 3B	6 1/2"	1953	1987	55.00	100.00	125.00
D6206	Large	Var. 3C	6 1/2"	1978	1978	750.00	1,250.00	1,500.00
D6233	Small	Var. 3A	3 1/4"	1953	1953	40.00	60.00	75.00
D6233	Small	Var. 3B	3 1/4"	1953	1987	30.00	50.00	65.00
D6251	Miniature	Var. 3A	2 1/2"	1953	1953	35.00	50.00	65.00
D6251	Miniature	Var. 3B	2 1/2"	1953	1987	30.00	40.00	50.00

VARIATION No. 4:   Designer: Harry Fenton
Modeller: Robert Tabbenor
Handle: Scarlet with an "ER" cypher
Colourway: Black hat, white ruff, scarlet tunic

VARIATION No. 3   VARIATION No. 2   VARIATION No. 4

Backstamps: A. Doulton/"Beefeater"
B. Doulton/Royal Doulton International Collectors Club

A "Tiny" Beefeater was issued in 1988 and offered for sale to the members of the RDICC. Robert Tabbenor miniaturized Fenton's design of 1947.

Doulton Number	Size	Backstamp	Height	Intro.	Discon.	Current Market Value U.K. £	U.S. $	Can. $
D6206	Large	Var. 4A	6 1/2"	1987	Current	49.95	142.50	160.00
D6233	Small	Var. 4A	3 1/4"	1987	Current	25.00	78.00	90.00
D6251	Miniature	Var. 4A	2 1/2"	1987	1991	45.00	40.00	60.00
D6806	Tiny	Var. 4B	1 1/2"	1988	1988	45.00	125.00	85.00

Miscellaneous "Beefeater" Items

Doulton Number	Item	Height	Intro.	Discon.	Current Market Value U.K. £	U.S. $	Can. $
D6233	Table Lighter	3 1/2"	1958	1973	125.00	150.00	175.00

BEEFEATER (with keys)

PROTOTYPE

The jug was designed by Dick Nicholson for a proposed commission by PWC Publishing. The head was from the standard Beefeater originally modelled by Harry Fenton with the handle being the keys from the Simon the Cellarer that was remodelled by Harry Sales to fit the Beefeater.

Due to cost and quantitiy requirements the project was dropped.

Variation No. 3 was not returned to Doulton and is now in a U.S. collection.

VARIATION No. 1: Colourway: Grey keys, blue hat

VARIATION No. 2: Colourway: Yellow keys, blue hat, name highlighted in yellow

VARIATION No. 3: Colourway: Yellow keys, black hat with on glaze red and blue band

Designer:	**Head:** Harry Fenton	**Backstamp:** Doulton
	Keys: Remodelled by Harry Sales	
Handle:	See colourway variations above	
Colourway:	Scarlet tunic, white ruff, black hat	

Doulton Number	Size	Backstamp	Height	Intro.	Discon.	U.K. £	Current Market Value U.S. $	Can. $
D —	Large	Var. 1	6 1/2"	1988	1988		Unique	
D —	Large	Var. 2	6 1/2"	1988	1988		Unique	
D —	Large	Var. 3	6 1/2"	1988	1988		Unique	

BENJAMIN FRANKLIN

An American publicist, scientist and statesman, Ben Franklin (1706-1790) was a signatory to the peace between Britain and the U.S.A. following the war of Independence. In 1748 he left his printing business to his foreman and devoted his life to science. His most famous discovery, that lightning is electricity, was accomplished with the simple objects of a knife and a metal key. It lead to the invention of the lightning rod, still used today to divert lightning harmlessly into the ground.

This jug was modelled for "The Queen's Table," Royal Doulton's Exhibit at the United Kingdom Showcase at Walt Disney's Epcot Centre in Orlando, Florida. The jug was sold exclusively to Epcot tourists visiting the exhibition during 1982. It was released for general sale in 1983.

Royal Doulton
Benjamin Franklin
D.6695
Hand made and Hand decorated
© ROYAL DOULTON
TABLEWARE LTD. 1982

Designer: Eric Griffiths
Handle: A kite and key
Colourway: Black coat, white shirt, blue scarf

Backstamp: Doulton

Doulton Number	Size	Backstamp	Height	Intro.	Discon.	Current Market Value		
						U.K. £	U.S. $	Can. $
D6695	Small	Doulton	4"	1982	1989	45.00	80.00	85.00

BETSY TROTWOOD

CHARLES DICKENS COMMEMORATIVE SET
DICKENS TINIES, ONE OF TWELVE.

In Dickens' novel "David Copperfield," Betsy is David's curt yet loving aunt.

Issued to commemorate the 170th Anniversary of the birth of Charles Dickens. There are twelve jugs in this set, each issued with a certificate of authenticity. A mahogany display shelf completes the set. The set was first sold by Lawleys By Post in the U.K. during 1982 to 1988, and in 1985 forward in North America and Australia.

Betsy Trotwood
D 6685

Designer: Michael Abberley
Handle: Plain
Colourway: Yellow, white and black

Backstamp: Doulton

Doulton Number	Size	Backstamp		Height	Intro.	Discon.	Current Market Value		
							U.K. £	**U.S. $**	**Can. $**
D6685	Tiny	Doulton		1 1/2"	1982	1989	30.00	50.00	60.00
		Display for 12 Tinies					65.00	45.00	50.00

BILL SYKES

CHARLES DICKENS COMMEMORATIVE SET
DICKENS TINIES, ONE OF TWELVE.

In Dickens' "Oliver Twist," Sykes is a cruel cohort of Fagin and his band of child thieves.

Issued to commemorate the 170th Anniversary of the birth of Charles Dickens. There are twelve jugs in this set, each issued with a certificate of authenticity. A mahogany display shelf completes the set. The set was first sold by Lawleys By Post in the U.K. during 1982 to 1988, and in 1985 onward in North America and Australia.

Bill Sykes
D 6684

Designer: Michael Abberley
Handle: Plain
Colourway: Green and dark blue

Backstamp: Doulton

Doulton Number	Size	Backstamp	Height	Intro.	Discon.	Current Market Value		
						U.K. £	U.S. $	Can. $
D6684	Tiny	Doulton	1 1/2"	1982	1989	30.00	50.00	60.00
		Display for 12 Tinies				65.00	45.00	50.00

BLACKSMITH

PROTOTYPE

A large prototype of the Blacksmith with older features, different hat and hair style. Only one copy known to exist.

Designer: David Biggs
Handle: Hammer, anvil and pliers
Colourway: Beige, white and black

Backstamp: Doulton

Doulton Number	Size	Backstamp	Height	Intro.	Discon.	Current Market Value		
						U.K. £	U.S. $	Can. $
Not Issued	Large	Doulton	7 1/4"	c. 1963			Unique	

BLACKSMITH

CHARACTERS FROM WILLIAMSBURG
ONE OF SEVEN.

In 18th Century Williamsburg, Virginia, the blacksmith was an essential part of colonial life. Working a forge he made horseshoes and other iron tools needed to cultivate the land.

Character Jugs from Williamsburg®

Blacksmith
D 6571
COPR 1962
DOULTON & CO LIMITED
Rd No 906341
Rd No 43648
Rd No 9227
Rd No 283.62

Designer: David Biggs
Handle: Hammer, anvil and pliers
Colourway: Salmon hat, white shirt, light brown apron

Backstamp: Doulton

Doulton Number	Size	Backstamp	Height	Intro.	Discon.	Current Market Value		
						U.K. £	U.S. $	Can. $
D6571	Large	Doulton	7 1/4"	1963	1983	60.00	110.00	160.00
D6578	Small	Doulton	4"	1963	1983	40.00	70.00	95.00
D6585	Miniature	Doulton	2 1/2"	1963	1983	35.00	60.00	80.00

BONNIE PRINCE CHARLIE

Grandson of James II, the "Young Pretender" (1720-1788) was born Charles Edward Stuart in Rome. He became the hopeful leader of the Jacobites, adherents to the Stuart line and led them in an unsuccessful uprising in 1745. After being defeated at Culloden Moor in 1746, he escaped to France with the help of Flora McDonald. Charles roamed Europe, a drunkard, until settling in Rome where he passed the remainder of his life.

Royal Doulton®
BONNIE PRINCE CHARLIE
D 6858
Modelled by
Stanley James Taylor.
© 1989 ROYAL DOULTON

Designer: Stanley J. Taylor
Handle: Crown atop thistles
Colourway: Blue plaid tam, red coat trimmed with yellow collar, white ruffles at the neck

Backstamp: Doulton

Doulton Number	Size	Backstamp	Height	Intro.	Discon.	Current Market Value		
						U.K. £	U.S. $	Can. $
D6858	Large	Doulton	6 1/2"	1990	Current	63.00	175.00	250.00

BOOTMAKER

PROTOTYPE

A large size prototype of the Bootmaker with younger features, different hair, handle and hat designs. Only one copy known to exist.

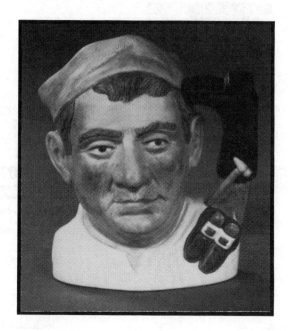

Designer: David Biggs
Handle: A boot, hammer and a
pair of shoes at the base
Colourway: Beige cap, white shirt and black shoes

Backstamp: Doulton

Doulton Number	Size	Backstamp	Height	Intro.	Discon.	Current Market Value		
						U.K. £	U.S. $	Can. $
Not Issued	Large	Doulton	7 1/2"	c. 1963		Unique		

BOOTMAKER

CHARACTERS FROM WILLIAMSBURG
ONE OF SEVEN

This 18th Century American craftsman differed from a cobbler by his product. Although he may have made shoes as well as boots, it is doubtful he would have done so often as Virginia winters were much too harsh for such delicate footwear.

Designer: David Biggs
Handle: A boot, hammer and a pair of shoes at the base
Colourway: Salmon cap, white shirt

Character Jugs from Williamsburg

Bootmaker
D 6 5 7 2
COPR 1962
DOULTON & CO LIMITED
Rd No 906342
Rd No 43449
Rd No 9228
Rd No 282/62

Backstamp: Doulton

Doulton Number	Size	Backstamp	Height	Intro.	Discon.	Current Market Value		
						U.K. £	U.S. $	Can. $
D6572	Large	Doulton	7 1/2"	1963	1983	60.00	100.00	160.00
D6579	Small	Doulton	4"	1963	1983	40.00	70.00	95.00
D6586	Miniature	Doulton	2 1/2"	1963	1983	35.00	65.00	80.00

BOWLS PLAYER

CHARACTERS FROM LIFE
ONE OF SEVEN

Bowls is a British game played on a flat green in lanes (rink) or crown green. Sir Francis Drake is reputed to have been playing bowls when the Spanish Armada was sighted in the English Channel.

Royal Doulton®
THE BOWLS PLAYER
D 6896
Modelled by
Stanley James Taylor
© 1991 ROYAL DOULTON

Designer: Stanley J. Taylor
Handle: Bowl, jack and measure
Colourway: White and yellow

Backstamp: Doulton

Doulton Number	Size	Backstamp	Height	Intro.	Discon.	Current Market Value		
						U.K. £	U.S. $	Can. $
D6896	Small	Doulton	4"	1991	Current	28.95	78.00	110.00

BUFFALO BILL

William Frederick Cody (1846-1917) was a scout, plainsman, soldier in the Civil War, hotelier, rancher and showman. His expert marksmanship while working as a buffalo hunter earned him his nickname Buffalo Bill. In 1883, Cody and others formed "Buffalo Bill's Wild West Show," a theatrical shooting exhibition which became very successful and travelled through the U.S. and Europe.

STYLE ONE: *"W.F. CODY BUFFALO BILL"*

This jug was piloted but never put into production. Only three jugs are known to exist. "W.F. Cody Buffalo Bill" is incised on the right shoulder in raised letters.

Designer: Unknown   **Backstamp:** Doulton
Handle: A rifle and buffalo head
Colourway: Brown hat, grey moustache and goatee

Doulton Number	Size	Backstamp	Height	Intro.	Discon.	Current Market Value U.K. £	U.S. $	Can. $
D —	Large	Doulton	7 1/2"	Unknown			Extremely Rare	

BUFFALO BILL

THE WILD WEST COLLECTION
ONE OF SIX

STYLE TWO: *BUFFALO BILL*

Designer: Robert Tabbenor

Handle: Buffalo head and horn

Colourway: Light brown hat and buckskin jacket

Backstamp: Doulton

Doulton Number	Size	Backstamp	Height	Intro.	Discon.	Current Market Value		
						U.K. £	U.S. $	Can. $
D6735	Mid	Doulton	5 1/2"	1985	1989	50.00	85.00	110.00

THE BUSKER

THE LONDON COLLECTION
ONE OF TEN

PROTOTYPE

The prototype jug of The Busker had a one-man band for the handle, however this was considered too complex for production and was replaced by a concertina.

*Photograph
Not Available
At Press Time*

Designer: Stanley J. Taylor **Backstamp:** Doulton
Handle: One-man band
Colourway: Grey cap, green coat, yellow scarf

Doulton Number	Size	Backstamp	Height	Intro.	Discon.	Current Market Value U.K. £	U.S. $	Can. $
D —	Large	Doulton	6 1/2"	c.1988			Unique	

THE BUSKER

THE LONDON COLLECTION
ONE OF TEN

Finding its roots with the early wandering minstrels, busking is still widely practiced today. Entertaining for money in public places has long been an honourable way for artists to support themselves while gaining public exposure for their work.

Royal Doulton®
THE BUSKER
D 6775
Modelled by
Stanley James Taylor
© 1987 ROYAL DOULTON

Designer: Stanley J. Taylor
Handle: An open concertina
Colourway: Grey cap, green coat, yellow scarf

Backstamp: Doulton

Doulton Number	Size	Backstamp	Height	Intro.	Discon.	Current Market Value U.K. £	U.S. $	Can. $
D6775	Large	Doulton	6 1/2"	1988	1991	65.00	95.00	125.00

BUZFUZ

This is an excellent example of the literary character designs of early Character Jugs. In Dickens' "Pickwick Papers," Sergeant Buzfuz was the counsel of Mrs. Bardell in the breach of promise suit she brought against Mr. Pickwick.

Designer: Leslie Harradine / Harry Fenton

Handle: Plain

Colourway: White collar, brown waistcoat, dark green coat, black robe.

Backstamp: Doulton

Doulton Number	Size	Backstamp	Height	Intro.	Discon.	Current Market Value U.K. £	U.S. $	Can. $
D5838	Mid	Doulton	5 1/2"	1938	1948	120.00	175.00	200.00
D5838	Small	Doulton	4"	1948	1960	60.00	110.00	125.00

Miscellaneous "Buzfuz" Items

Doulton Number	Item	Height	Intro.	Discon.	Current Market Value U.K. £	U.S. $	Can. $
D5838	Table Lighter	3 1/2"	1958	1959	125.00	225.00	250.00
D6048	Bust	3"	1939	1960	65.00	90.00	110.00

CABINET MAKER

CHARACTERS FROM WILLIAMSBURG

PROTOTYPE

In 1980 plans to continue the Williamsburg series were still in force. A new jug, the Cabinet Maker was announced in 1981 based on the prototype. The Williamsburg series was cancelled in 1983 and the new jug was never put into production.

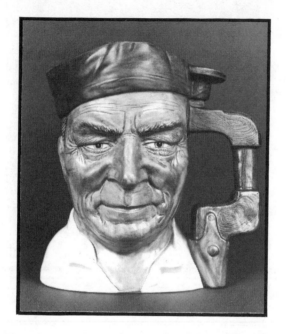

Designer: Michael Abberley
Handle: Brace
Colourway: Red, white and brown

Backstamp: Doulton

Doulton Number	Size	Backstamp	Height	Intro.	Discon.	Current Market Value		
						U.K. £	U.S. $	Can. $
D6659	Large	Doulton	7 1/2"	1979	1979		Unique	

CAP'N CUTTLE

The wonderful characters of Dickens' novels were the inspiration of many early jug designs. Captain Edward Cuttle was an eccentric English gentleman in "Dombey and Son," (1846), who is best known for saying "When found, make a note of it."

Designer: Leslie Harradine / Harry Fenton
Handle: Plain
Colourway: Blue-black coat, grey-green hat, white collar, green bow-tie

Backstamp: Doulton

Doulton Number	Size	Backstamp	Height	Intro.	Discon.	Current Market Value U.K. £	U.S. $	Can. $
D5842	Mid	Doulton	5 1/2"	1938	1948	120.00	175.00	210.00
D5842	Small	Doulton	4"	1948	1960	60.00	115.00	125.00

Miscellaneous "Cap'n Cuttle" Items

Doulton Number	Item	Height	Intro.	Discon.	Current Market Value U.K. £	U.S. $	Can. $
D5842	Table Lighter	3 1/2"	1958	1959	145.00	250.00	275.00

CAPT AHAB

Captain Ahab sailed the whaler, "Pequod" in Herman Melville's great 19th century American classic "Moby Dick". He lost a leg and then his life in pursuit of the great white whale who triumphed in the chase and sunk his ship.

Capt Ahab
D 6522
COPR 1958
DOULTON & CO LIMITED
Rd No 889571
Rd No 38227
Rd No 8037
Rd No 422/58

Designer: Garry Sharpe
Handle: A grey whale
Colourway: Blue cap and black coat, white sweater

Backstamp: Doulton

Doulton Number	Size	Backstamp	Height	Intro.	Discon.	Current Market Value U.K. £	U.S. $	Can. $
D6500	Large	Doulton	7"	1959	1984	60.00	115.00	155.00
D6506	Small	Doulton	4"	1959	1984	35.00	60.00	95.00
D6522	Miniature	Doulton	2 1/2"	1960	1984	30.00	50.00	70.00

Miscellaneous "Capt Ahab" Items

Doulton Number	Item	Height	Intro.	Discon.	Current Market Value U.K. £	U.S. $	Can. $
D6506	Table Lighter	3 1/2"	1964	1973	160.00	325.00	350.00

CAPT HENRY MORGAN

A privateer and head of buccaneer pirates in the West Indies, Morgan (1635-1688) carried out commissions from the British Authorities. His attack on Panama in 1671 violated a peace treaty between England and Spain. Sent to England to stand trial, he was instead knighted and became Lieutenant Governor of Jamaica where he remained until his death.

Capt Henry Morgan
D 6467
COPR 1957
DOULTON & CO LIMITED
Rd No 886231
Rd No 37211
Rd No 7853
Rd No 388/57

Designer: Garry Sharpe
Handle: Sails of a ship
Colourway: Black tricorn, blue collar trimmed with gold

Backstamp: Doulton

Doulton Number	Size	Backstamp	Height	Intro.	Discon.	Current Market Value U.K. £	U.S. $	Can. $
D6467	Large	Doulton	6 3/4"	1958	1982	60.00	115.00	165.00
D6469	Small	Doulton	3 1/2"	1958	1982	40.00	60.00	95.00
D6510	Miniature	Doulton	2 1/2"	1960	1982	35.00	50.00	70.00

CAPT HOOK

Captain Hook is the villian and nemesis of Peter Pan in J.M. Barrie's famous story. Peter Pan cut off Hook's hand and fed it to a crocodile, who liked it so much he followed the captain around in hopes of eating the rest of him. Hook managed to keep eluding his predator because the crocodile had accidentally swallowed a clock that ticked inside him and ruined the element of suprise in his attacks.

Designer: Max Henk / David Biggs
Handle: An alligator and clock
Colourway: Blue tricorn trimmed with yellow, green coat trimmed with yellow, white ruffles at the neck

Backstamp: Doulton

Doulton Number	Size	Backstamp	Height	Intro.	Discon.	Current Market Value		
						U.K. £	U.S. $	Can. $
D6597	Large	Doulton	7 1/4"	1965	1971	300.00	550.00	695.00
D6601	Small	Doulton	4"	1965	1971	200.00	375.00	450.00
D6605	Miniature	Doulton	2 1/2"	1965	1971	200.00	400.00	495.00

THE CARDINAL

Cardinals are the spiritual leaders of the Roman Catholic church. The traditional red robes worn by this sacred group have come to signify both their holiness and their power. Since 1059, The Sacred College of Cardinals has been responsible for electing the Pope.

This jug does have minor colour variations in the hair. The earliest jugs had hair that was brown while later jugs had hair that was either grey or white. This jug was produced with and without the pink highlighting on the raised character name.

Designer: Charles Noke
Handle: Tassle (Part of clerics robes)
Colourway: Scarlet robes, Purple handle

The Cardinal

Backstamp: Doulton

Doulton Number	Size	Backstamp	Height	Intro.	Discon.	Current Market Value U.K. £	U.S. $	Can. $
D5614	Large	Doulton	6 1/2"	1936	1960	80.00	150.00	195.00
D6033	Small	Doulton	3 1/2"	1939	1960	50.00	80.00	115.00
D6129	Miniature	Doulton	2 1/4"	1940	1960	40.00	60.00	95.00
D6258	Tiny	Doulton	1 1/2"	1947	1960	110.00	250.00	225.00

CATHERINE OF ARAGON

HENRY VIII AND HIS SIX WIVES
ONE OF EIGHT

Daughter of Ferdinand and Isabella of Spain, Catherine (1485-1536) was married to Arthur, Prince of Wales, in a political arrangement between the two countries. When Arthur died shortly after their wedding, she was married to Henry VIII to continue the arrangement. This first marriage for Henry lasted 24 years until he became restless at the lack of a male heir and sought out Anne Boleyn. In 1527 Henry attempted to have his marriage annulled, a move that led to his excommunication by the Pope and, eventually, to the English Reformation. Catherine was banished from the Royal Court and lived until the age of 50, unhappy and lonely.

Designer: Alan Maslankowski
Handle: A tower
Colourway: Red, gold, black and white

Backstamp: Doulton

Doulton Number	Size	Backstamp	Height	Intro.	Discon.	Current Market Value U.K. £	U.S. $	Can. $
D6643	Large	Doulton	7"	1975	1989	60.00	115.00	155.00
D6657	Small	Doulton	4"	1981	1989	45.00	75.00	90.00
D6658	Miniature	Doulton	2 3/4"	1981	1989	35.00	80.00	65.00

CATHERINE HOWARD

HENRY VIII AND HIS SIX WIVES
ONE OF EIGHT

Niece to the Duke of Norfolk, Catherine (1521-1542) became Henry VIII's fifth wife on July 28, 1540 in a marriage arranged by her family. In 1541 Henry accused her of adultery and had her beheaded in the Tower of London.

Royal Doulton
CATHERINE HOWARD
D 6645
Modelled by

Peter A Gee.

© ROYAL DOULTON TABLEWARE
LIMITED 1977

Designer: Peter Gee
Handle: An axe
Colourway: Brown, gold and white

Backstamp: Doulton

Doulton Number	Size	Backstamp	Height	Intro.	Discon.	Current Market Value U.K. £	U.S. $	Can. $
D6645	Large	Doulton	7"	1978	1989	60.00	120.00	155.00
D6692	Small	Doulton	4"	1984	1989	40.00	75.00	90.00
D6693	Miniature	Doulton	2 1/2"	1984	1989	35.00	80.00	65.00

CATHERINE PARR

HENRY VIII AND HIS SIX WIVES
ONE OF EIGHT

Catherine (1512-1548) became Henry VIII's last wife on July 12, 1543 after being twice widowed herself. She came to wield considerable power in the Royal Court, serving for a time as Queen regent in 1544 and overseeing the start of Edward VI's reign. After Henry's death in 1547, she married Baron Seymour of Sudeley but died during childbirth the following year.

Royal Doulton®
CATHERINE PARR
D 6752
©1980 ROYAL DOULTON (UK)

Royal Doulton
CATHERINE PARR
D 6664
Modelled by

Michael Abberley

© ROYAL DOULTON TABLEWARE
LIMITED 1980

Designer: Michael Abberley
Handle: Bible and pulpit
Colourway: Black, brown and gold

Backstamps: Doulton

Doulton Number	Size	Backstamp	Height	Intro.	Discon.	Current Market Value		
						U.K. £	U.S. $	Can. $
D6664	Large	Doulton	6 3/4"	1981	1989	60.00	135.00	195.00
D6751	Small	Doulton	4"	1987	1989	40.00	100.00	90.00
D6752	Miniature	Doulton	2 1/2"	1987	1989	35.00	125.00	65.00

THE CAVALIER

During the English Civil War, the cavaliers were Royalist soldiers who fought for Charles I. They became known for their off-hand gallantry and haughtiness, an attitude today still described as "cavalier."

STYLE ONE: *CAVALIER WITH GOATEE*

Designer: Harry Fenton
Handle: Handle of a sword
Colourway: Green hat, white ruff

Backstamp: Doulton

Doulton Number	Size	Backstamp	Height	Intro.	Discon.	Current Market Value U.K. £	U.S. $	Can. $
D6114	Large	Doulton	7"	1940	1950	1,450.00	3,500.00	3,500.00

THE CAVALIER

Originally listed in Royal Doulton's product guide as "The Laughing Cavalier" presumably after the famous Frans Hals painting.

STYLE TWO: *CAVALIER WITHOUT GOATEE*

Slight colour changes along with alterations to the ruff (collar) and removal of the goatee occurred in 1950.

Designer: Harry Fenton
Handle: Handle of a sword
Colourway: Green hat, white ruff

Backstamp: Doulton

Doulton Number	Size	Backstamp	Height	Intro.	Discon.	Current Market Value U.K. £	U.S. $	Can. $
D6114	Large	Doulton	7"	1950	1960	80.00	150.00	195.00
D6173	Small	Doulton	3 1/4"	1941	1960	50.00	65.00	110.00

CELTIC (FOOTBALL CLUB)

THE FOOTBALL SUPPORTERS
ONE OF EIGHT

Royal Doulton®
**FOOTBALL SUPPORTER'S
CHARACTER JUG.**
D 6925
Modelled by
Stanley James Taylor
© 1992 ROYAL DOULTON
"CELTIC"

Designer: Stanley J. Taylor
Handle: Team coloured scarf
Colourway: Green and white uniform

Backstamp: Doulton

Doulton Number	Size	Backstamp	Height	Intro.	Discon.	Current Market Value U.K. £	U.S. $	Can. $
D6925	Mid	Doulton	5"	1992	Current	35.00	125.00	95.00

CHARLES DICKENS

CHARLES DICKENS COMMEMORATIVE SET
DICKENS TINIES, ONE OF TWELVE.

Issued to commemorate the 170th Anniversary of the birth of Charles Dickens. There are twelve jugs in this set, each issued with a certificate of authenticity. A mahogany display shelf completes the set. The set was first sold by Lawleys By Post in the U.K. during 1982 to 1988, and in 1985 onward in North America and Australia.

STYLE ONE: HANDLE: PLAIN

**Charles
Dickens**
D 6676

Designer: Eric Griffiths
Handle: Plain
Colourway: Grey and black

Backstamp: Doulton

Doulton Number	Size	Backstamp	Height	Intro.	Discon.	Current Market Value		
						U.K. £	U.S. $	Can. $
D6676	Tiny	Doulton	1 1/2"	1982	1989	45.00	60.00	80.00
		Display for 12 Tinies				65.00	45.00	50.00

CHARLES DICKENS

ROYAL DOULTON INTERNATIONAL COLLECTORS CLUB

Commissioned by the Royal Doulton International Collectors Club in a limited edition of 7,500 pieces.

STYLE TWO: HANDLE: QUILL PEN AND INK POT

CHARLES DICKENS

"*Whatever the word 'great' means, Dickens was what it means*".

G. K. Chesterton.

EXCLUSIVELY FOR
COLLECTORS CLUB
LIMITED EDITION OF 7,500

THIS IS N° 963

© 1991 ROYAL DOULTON
MODELLED BY

Designer: William K. Harper
Handle: Quill pen and ink pot, book
"The Old Curiosity Shop"
Colourway: Black and olive green

Backstamp: Doulton / RDICC

Doulton Number	Size	Backstamp	Height	Intro.	Discon.	Current Market Value		
						U.K. £	U.S. $	Can. $
D6901	Small	Doulton/RDICC	4"	1991	Ltd. Ed.	55.00	100.00	125.00

CHELSEA PENSIONER

THE LONDON COLLECTION
ONE OF TEN

Charles II founded the Royal Hospital in Chelsea for "worthy old soldiers broken in the wars". It was built by Christopher Wren and completed in 1692. Each year on Founders Day, the hospital's opening is celebrated by the soldiers in full dress uniform, as worn by the gentleman depicted on this jug.

Royal Doulton®
CHELSEA PENSIONER
D 6817
Modelled by
Stanley James Taylor.
© 1988 ROYAL DOULTON

Designer: Stanley J. Taylor
Handle: Medals of honour
Colourway: Black tricorn trimmed with gold, scarlet tunic with black collar

Backstamp: A. Doulton
For General Issue: 1989
Pre-released in the U.S.A. in 1988 at the following four stores in a limited edition of 1,000 pieces, with 250 jugs per store.

Royal Doulton®
CHELSEA PENSIONER
D 6830
Modelled by
Stanley James Taylor
*Specially Commissioned
from*
Royal Doulton®
To commemorate the First Anniversary of
the opening of The Royal Doulton Room
Joseph Hornes, Pittsburgh, Pennsylvania, U.S.A.
© 1988 ROYAL DOULTON
A LIMITED EDITION OF 250
THIS IS Nº 114

Royal Doulton®
CHELSEA PENSIONER
D 6831
Modelled by
Stanley James Taylor
*Specially Commissioned
from*
Royal Doulton®
To commemorate the First Anniversary of
the opening of The Royal Doulton Room
D. H. Holmes, New Orleans, Louisiana, U.S.A.
© 1988 ROYAL DOULTON
A LIMITED EDITION OF 250
THIS IS Nº 227

Royal Doulton®
CHELSEA PENSIONER
D 6832
Modelled by
Stanley James Taylor
*Specially Commissioned
from*
Royal Doulton®
To commemorate the Third Anniversary of
the opening of The Royal Doulton Room
The Higbee Company, Cleveland, Ohio, U.S.A.
© 1988 ROYAL DOULTON
A LIMITED EDITION OF 250
THIS IS Nº 229

BACKSTAMP B   BACKSTAMP C   BACKSTAMP D

Backstamps: **B. Doulton / Joseph Horne's** "To commemorate the First Anniversary of the opening of the Royal Doulton Room Joseph Horne's, Pittsburgh, Pennsylvania, U.S.A."

C. Doulton / D. H. Holme's "To commemorate the First Anniversary of the opening of the Royal Doulton Room D. H. Holme's, New Orleans, Louisiana, U.S.A."

D. Doulton / Higbee Company "To commemorate the Third Anniversary of the opening of the Royal Doulton Room The Higbee Company, Cleveland, Ohio, U.S.A."

E. Doulton / Strawbridge and Clothier "To commemorate the Second Anniversary of the opening of the Royal Doulton Room Strawbridge and Clothier, Philadelphia, Pennsylvania, U.S.A."

Doulton Number	Size	Backstamp	Height	Intro.	Discon.	Current Market Value U.K. £	U.S. $	Can. $
D6817	Large	Var. A	6 1/2"	1989	1991	60.00	110.00	185.00
D6830	Large	Var. B	6 1/2"	1988	Ltd. Ed.	110.00	135.00	200.00
D6831	Large	Var. C	6 1/2"	1988	Ltd. Ed.	110.00	135.00	200.00
D6832	Large	Var. D	6 1/2"	1988	Ltd. Ed.	110.00	135.00	200.00
D6833	Large	Var. E	6 1/2"	1988	Ltd. Ed.	110.00	135.00	200.00

CHIEF SITTING BULL
GEORGE ARMSTRONG CUSTER

THE ANTAGONISTS (TWO FACED JUG)
ONE OF FOUR

Chief Sitting Bull (1831-1890) as chief of the Sioux Indians spent his life working for the rights of his people to own and control their land. He was shot by Indian Police on a questionable charge of resisting arrest.

George Armstrong Custer (1839-1876) was the youngest general in the U.S. Army. He first saw action in the Civil War and was later stationed in the Dakota Territory during the gold rush on Sioux Land. In 1876, in the interests of the whites, he led an attack against an Indian encampment at Little Big Horn. Sitting Bull and his men outnumbered Custer's regiment and easily defeated them, leaving no survivors.

This jug was issued in a limited edition of 9,500 pieces.

VARIATION No. 1: Colourway: Multi-coloured, Sitting Bull with grey eyes.

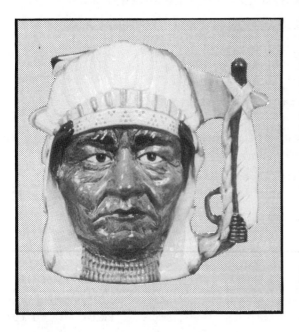 

Designer:	Michael Abberley	**Backstamp:** Doulton
Handle:	Sitting Bull - Tomahawk; Custer - Pistol	
Colourway:	Multi-coloured, Sitting Bull has grey eyes.	

Doulton Number	Size	Variation	Height	Intro.	Discon.	Current Market Value U.K. £	U.S. $	Can. $
D6712	Large	Var. 1	7"	1984	Ltd. Ed.	120.00	175.00	225.00

VARIATION No. 2: Colourway: Multi-coloured, Sitting Bull with brown eyes.

VARIATION No. 2	VARIATION No. 1
BROWN EYES	GREY EYES

Doulton Number	Size	Variation	Height	Intro.	Discon.	Current Market Value U.K. £	U.S. $	Can. $
D6712	Large	Var. 2	7"	1984	1989	120.00	165.00	195.00

CHRISTOPHER COLUMBUS

A trader and explorer, Italian-born Columbus (c.1451-1506) was financed by Spain's Queen Isabella, to find a quicker route to the gold and spices of The Indies. Believing the world was round, he set sail due west, landing in the Americas in 1492. He is popularly credited with "discovering" the New World.

STYLE ONE   *HANDLE: MAP OF NEW WORLD*

Designer: Stanley J. Taylor
Handle: Map of New World
Colourway: Dark blue and white

Backstamp: Doulton

Doulton Number	Size	Backstamp	Height	Intro.	Discon.	Current Market Value U.K. £	U.S. $	Can. $
D6891	Large	Doulton	7"	1991	Current	59.95	155.00	200.00

CHRISTOPHER COLUMBUS

This jug was issued to recognize the 500th Anniversary of Columbus' voyage to America in 1942. It was created exclusivley for the Royal Doulton International Collectors Club and was issued in a limited edition of 7,500. The jug was exhibited in the British Pavillion at Expo '92, Seville, Spain.

STYLE TWO: HANDLE: SHIP SANTA MARIA

Exhibited in the British Pavilion
EXPO '92.
Seville, Spain.

Designer:	Stanley J. Taylor	
Handle:	The ship "Santa Maria"	
Colourway:	Brown, light brown, grey and cream	

Backstamp: Doulton / RDICC
"Christopher Columbus "Admiral of the Oceans"." Exclusively For Collectors Club The Discovery Edition of 7,500.

Doulton Number	Size	Backstamp	Height	Intro.	Discon.	Current Market Value U.K. £	U.S. $	Can. $
D6911	Small	Doulton/RDICC	3 1/2"	1992	Ltd. Ed.	40.00	100.00	125.00

CHURCHILL

Sir Winston Leonard Spencer Churchill (1874-1965) was first lord of the Admiralty and Home Secretary. He was Prime Minister on three occasions. As Wartime Prime Minister he led Britain to victory and captured the spirit of the Allied World with his famous radio broadcasts. He was awarded the Nobel Prize for Literature in 1953.

VARIATION No. 1:   Colourway: Cream with two black handles.
                         Inscription on base.

Designer: Charles Noke
Handle: Plain
Colourway: Cream with two black handles

Backstamp: Doulton

Doulton Number	Size	Variation	Height	Intro.	Discon.	Current Market Value U.K. £	U.S. $	Can. $
D6170	Large	Doulton	6 1/2"	1940	1941	2,500.00	6,000.00	5,000.00

VARIATION No. 2: Different modelling portraying a younger Churchill.
                   Colourway: Very lightly coloured overall with two grey handles.
                   No inscription on base, has green Doulton backstamp.

VARIATION No. 2   VARIATION No. 3

Doulton Number	Size	Variation	Height	Intro.	Discon.	Current Market Value U.K. £	U.S. $	Can. $
D6170	Large	Var.2	6 1/2"	Unknown			Extremely Rare	

VARIATION No. 3: Modelling portrays a young Churchill.
                   Colourway: Fully decorated in natural colours with two dark brown handles.
                   No inscription on base.

Doulton Number	Size	Variation	Height	Intro.	Discon.	Current Market Value U.K. £	U.S. $	Can. $
D6170	Large	Var. 3	6 1/2"	Unknown			Extremely Rare	

CITY GENT

THE LONDON COLLECTION
ONE OF TEN

This archetypical British businessman represents the finery and style of London. Strolling along the street, perhaps on his way to the House of Lords, he's sure to tip his hat to the ladies he passes on the way.

Royal Doulton®
CITY GENT
D 6815
Modelled by
Stanley James Taylor
© 1988 ROYAL DOULTON

Designer: Stanley J. Taylor
Handle: Umbrella handle
Colourway: Black and grey hat,
black coat, white shirt, grey tie

Backstamp: Doulton

Doulton Number	Size	Backstamp	Height	Intro.	Discon.	Current Market Value U.K. £	U.S. $	Can. $
D6815	Large	Doulton	7"	1988	1991	55.00	100.00	130.00

CLARK GABLE

THE CELEBRITY COLLECTION

An Ohio native, Gable (1901-1960) worked in a tire factory and as a lumberjack before he took up acting. He began his career in 1930 and appeared in over seventy films. He won an Academy Award in 1934 for his performance in "It Happened One Night" but is perhaps best remembered as Rhett Butler in "Gone With the Wind."

This jug was issued in the U.S.A. prior to approval of the Gable Estate and had to be withdrawn when permission was not forthcoming. A small number of jugs are known to exist.

Designer: Stanley J. Taylor
Handle: Movie camera entwined in film
Colourway: Brown, light brown suit and tan tie.

Backstamp: Doulton

Doulton Number	Size	Backstamp	Height	Intro.	Discon.	Current Market Value		
						U.K. £	U.S. $	Can. $
D6709	Large	Doulton	7"	1984	1984	2,000.00	3,000.00	3,500.00

THE CLOWN

From the early jesters of the Royal Courts to the present day, clowns have entertained audiences of all ages with their acrobatics, tricks, and humorous satires of human life. At the present time there are three recognised variations of the clown (without hat). They are the red, brown and white haired clowns.

STYLE ONE: *CLOWN WITHOUT HAT*

VARIATION No. 1:   Colourway: **Red hair.**
                         Handle: **Multi-coloured.**

The Clown.
COPR. 1930.
DOULTON & CO. LIMITED.
RⁿNº 28163.
RⁿNº 6207.
RⁿNº 92/30.

Designer: Harry Fenton   **Backstamp:** Doulton
Handle: Multi-coloured
Colourway: Red hair

Doulton Number	Size	Colour	Height	Intro.	Discon.	Current Market Value U.K. £	U.S. $	Can. $
D5610	Large	Red hair	7 1/2"	1937	1942	1,000.00	1,800.00	2,250.00

VARIATION No. 2:   Colourway: **Brown hair.**
                         Handle: **Plain brown.**

Doulton Number	Size	Colour	Height	Intro.	Discon.	Current Market Value U.K. £	U.S. $	Can. $
D5610	Large	Brown hair	7 1/2"	c. 1937	1942	1,000.00	1,800.00	2,250.00

VARIATION No. 3:   Colourway: **White hair.**
                         Handle: **Multi-coloured.**

Doulton Number	Size	Colour	Height	Intro.	Discon.	Current Market Value U.K. £	U.S. $	Can. $
D6322	Large	White hair	7 1/2"	1951	1955	500.00	1,000.00	1,250.00

Note: A black haired example exists on the market, however its authencity as a factory release has not yet been determined.

THE CLOWN

THE CIRCUS
ONE OF FOUR

STYLE TWO: CLOWN WITH HAT

Royal Doulton®

THE CLOWN
D 6834
Modelled by
Stanley James Taylor

© 1988 ROYAL DOULTON

Designer: Stanley J. Taylor
Handle: Gloved hand touching cap
Colourway: Green cap, yellow bow-tie with
black spots, red nose and mouth

Backstamp: Doulton

Doulton Number	Size	Backstamp	Height	Intro.	Discon.	Current Market Value		
						U.K. £	U.S. $	Can. $
D6834	Large	Doulton	6 1/2"	1989	Current	63.00	195.00	250.00

THE COLLECTOR

THE COLLECTING WORLD
ONE OF THREE

The large size, commissioned by Kevin Francis Ceramics Ltd. (KFC) was issued in 1988 in a special edition of 5,000 pieces. The small size was issued in 1991, is a special edition of 1,500 pieces. Again note the Kevin Francis characteristic of the left handed jug.

Designer: Stanley J. Taylor
Handle: A hand holding a Mephistopheles jug
Colourway: Black hat, dark green jacket with tan shirt

Backstamp: Doulton / Kevin Francis

Doulton Number	Size	Backstamp	Height	Intro.	Discon.	Current Market Value U.K. £	U.S. $	Can. $
D6796	Large	Doulton/KFC	7"	1988	Sp. Ed.	75.00	175.00	225.00
D6906	Small	Doulton/KFC	4"	1991	Sp. Ed.	55.00	95.00	110.00

THE COOK AND THE CHESHIRE CAT

ALICE IN WONDERLAND
ONE OF SIX

These are two characters from Lewis Carroll's charming story of "Alice's Adventures in Wonderland". The Cat's fixed, broad smile has become recognized world-wide.

Designer: William K. Harper
Handle: A Cheshire cat
Colourway: White mop-cap trimmed with a blue bow

Backstamp: Doulton

Doulton Number	Size	Backstamp	Height	Intro.	Discon.	Current Market Value		
						U.K. £	U.S. $	Can. $
D6842	Large	Doulton	7"	1990	1991	75.00	125.00	195.00

D'ARTAGNAN

THE "THREE MUSKETEERS", ONE OF FOUR
NOW PART OF THE CHARACTERS FROM LITERATURE, ONE OF ELEVEN

A character in Alexandre Dumas' lively 19th century fiction, D'Artagnan comes to Paris to join the celebrated band of the Three Musketeers and share their adventures.

Designer: Stanley J. Taylor
Handle: An extension of the feathers with a Fleur-de-lis and sword at the base
Colourway: Black hat trimmed with white feathers, white lace collar

Backstamp: Doulton

Doulton Number	Size	Backstamp	Height	Intro.	Discon.	Current Market Value U.K. £	U.S. $	Can. $
D6691	Large	Doulton	7 1/2"	1982	Current	55.00	142.50	160.00
D6764	Small	Doulton	4"	1987	Current	28.95	78.00	90.00
D6765	Miniature	Doulton	2 1/2"	1987	1991	25.00	45.00	60.00

DAVID COPPERFIELD

CHARLES DICKENS COMMEMORATIVE SET
DICKENS TINIES, ONE OF TWELVE

David Copperfield is the orphan protagonist in Dickins' novel "David Copperfield".
Issued to commemorate the 170th Anniversary of the birth of Charles Dickens. There are twelve jugs in this set, each issued with a certificate of authenticity. A mahogany display shelf completes the set. The set was first sold by Lawleys By Post in the U.K. during 1982 to 1988, and in 1985 onward in North America and Australia.

David Copperfield
D. 6680

Designer: Michael Abberley
Handle: Plain
Colourway: Dark blue and black

Backstamp: Doulton

Doulton Number	Size	Backstamp		Height	Intro.	Discon.	Current Market Value		
							U.K. £	U.S. $	Can. $
D6680	Tiny	Doulton	1 1/2"		1982	1989	30.00	45.00	60.00
		Display for 12 Tinies					65.00	45.00	50.00

DAVY CROCKETT AND SANTA ANNA

THE ANTAGONISTS' COLLECTION (TWO-FACED JUG)
ONE OF FOUR

Davy Crockett (1786-1836) was born "on a mountaintop in Tennessee", as the popular song goes. Crockett was a hunter and expert marksman as well as a gregarious drinker.

Antonio Lopez de Santa Anna (1795-1876) was a Mexican General who led troops on many missions into the U.S. He was finally defeated in Texas in 1837 and jailed for a year.

This jug was issued in 1985 in a limited edition of 9,500 pieces.

 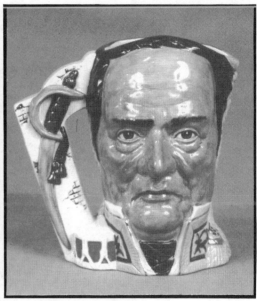

Designer: Michael Abberley
Handle: Crocket: The word "Alamo" and a horn, mission wall
Santa Anna: Sword, Mission wall
Colourway: Yellow and brown

Royal Doulton
'The Antagonists'
Collection
D.6729
The Battle of the Alamo 1836
Davy Crockett/Antonio Lopez de Santa Anna
Hand made and Hand decorated
Designed by Michael Abberley

Michael Abberley
© ROYAL DOULTON (UK) 1984
Worldwide Limited Edition of 9,500
This is Number 293

Backstamp: Doulton

Doulton Number	Size	Backstamp	Height	Intro.	Discon.	Current Market Value		
						U.K. £	U.S. $	Can. $
D6729	Large	Doulton	7"	1985	Ltd. Ed.	75.00	125.00	225.00

DICK TURPIN

Dick Turpin was born in Hempstead, Essex in 1705. The son of an innkeeper, he was an apprentice butcher before taking up the life of a highwayman. Turpin joined forces with fellow highwayman Tom King whom he later accidently shot. King died from his wound but before doing so betrayed Turpin. Dick Turpin was hanged in 1739 at York for the murder of an Epping Forest gamekeeper.

The first style of Dick Turpin has the mask up on the brim of the tricorn, and the handle is a pistol. All of the sizes should have "R.T." inscribed on the pistol grip, however, it may be more obvious on certain jugs due to the casting variations. There is no premium value with or without the "R.T." inscription.

STYLE ONE: HANDLE: A PISTOL

Designer:	Charles Noke / Harry Fenton	Backstamps:	A. Doulton
Handle:	Pistol		B. Doulton / Bentalls,
Colourway:	Brown hat with black mask		"Souvenir From Bentalls 1936"
	up at the front, green coat, white cravat		

Doulton Number	Size	Backstamps	Height	Intro.	Discon.	Current Market Value U.K. £	U.S. $	Can. $
D5485	Large	Doulton	6 1/2"	1935	1960	75.00	150.00	195.00
D5618	Small	Doulton	3 1/2"	1936	1960	45.00	75.00	95.00
D5618	Small	Doulton/Bentalls	3 1/2"	1936	1936	350.00	750.00	850.00
D6128	Miniature	Doulton	2 1/4"	1940	1960	40.00	65.00	85.00

Miscellaneous "Dick Turpin" Items

Doulton Number	Item	Height	Intro.	Discon.	Current Market Value U.K. £	U.S. $	Can. $
D5601	Matchstand/Ashtray	3"	1936	1960	85.00	115.00	150.00

DICK TURPIN

This second style of Dick Turpin has the mask covering the eyes, and the handle depicts a horse's head and neck.

STYLE TWO: HANDLE: NECK AND HEAD OF HORSE

Dick Turpin
D 6528
COPR 1959
DOULTON & CO LIMITED
Rd No 893841
Rd No 39649
Rd No 8313
Rd No 420/59

Designer:	David Biggs
Handle:	Head and neck of a horse
Colourway:	Green tricorn, black mask over the eyes, red jacket

Backstamp: Doulton

Doulton Number	Size	Backstamp	Height	Intro.	Discon.	Current Market Value		
						U.K. £	U.S. $	Can. $
D6528	Large	Doulton	7"	1960	1981	60.00	90.00	135.00
D6535	Small	Doulton	3 3/4"	1960	1981	45.00	50.00	95.00
D6542	Miniature	Doulton	2 1/4"	1960	1981	35.00	45.00	70.00

DICK WHITTINGTON

The first Dick Whittington jug was styled on the character of a poor orphan boy who is employed in a London kitchen, as described in a play dated 1605. He gave his cat to his employer to sell to earn money, but then ran away to escape his evil employer's cook who mistreats him. The Bow Bells rang as he fled and seemed to say "Turn back Whittington, Lord Mayor of London". He obeyed and found that his cat had fetched a huge sum, making him a wealthy man. The Pantomine Dick Whittington and His Cat can be seen at Christmas time at theatres in Great Britain.

Dick Whittington
D 6375
COPR 1952
DOULTON & CO LIMITED
R⁴ N° 868419
R⁴ N° 30500
R⁴ N° 193/52
R⁴ N° 6849

Designer: Geoff Blower
Handle: A stick and handkerchief
Colourway: Dark green cap and robes

Backstamp: Doulton

Doulton Number	Size	Backstamp	Height	Intro.	Discon.	Current Market Value		
						U.K. £	U.S. $	Can. $
D6375	Large	Doulton	6 1/2"	1953	1960	200.00	425.00	425.00

DICK WHITTINGTON, LORD MAYOR OF LONDON

Richard Whittington (1358-1423) in actual fact, made his fortune as a textile dealer. He entered London politics as a councilman and rose to Lord Mayor of London in 1397, an office he held three times.

Commissioned by "The Guild of Specialist China and Glass Retailers" and issued in 1989 in a limited edition of 5,000 pieces.

Designer:	William K. Harper
Handle:	Handle is of a sign-post to London; the "Bow Bells" are above the sign-post, and a sack of gold is at the base.
Colourway:	Blue tricorn hat trimmed with white feathers, blue coat trimmed with white fur, yellow chain of office.

Backstamp: Doulton / Guild

Doulton Number	Size	Backstamp	Height	Intro.	Discon.	Current Market Value		
						U.K. £	U.S. $	Can. $
D6846	Large	Doulton/Guild	7 1/2"	1989	Ltd. Ed. (1991)	60.00	125.00	150.00

DOC HOLLIDAY

THE WILD WEST COLLECTION
ONE OF SIX

The son of a lawyer, John Henry Holliday (1852-1887) worked as a dentist in Baltimore, Maryland. At the age of twenty he learned he had tuberculosis and moved to a warmer climate to prolong his life. He moved west, became adept at both firearms and the Bowie knife, and became known for his wild gambling, brawls and shootouts. He survived the famous gunfight at the O.K. Corral, but died in a sanatorium at age thirty-five.

Designer: Stanley J. Taylor
Handle: Pistol in a holster and dice
Colourway: Black and grey hat, black coat

Backstamp: Doulton

Doulton Number	Size	Backstamp	Height	Intro.	Discon.	Current Market Value U.K. £	U.S. $	Can. $
D6731	Mid	Doulton	5 1/2"	1985	1989	45.00	85.00	110.00

DON QUIXOTE

CHARACTERS FROM LITERATURE
ONE OF ELEVEN

Hero of the novel by Cervantes, a satirical parody of the chivalrous knight, Don Quixote leads a life of adventure, capturing many hearts along the way. "Quixotic", meaning impractical, enthusiastic or honourable finds its origins in this character.

Helmet colour varies from dark grey to light grey with no difference in value.

"Don Quixote".
D 6455
COPR 1956
DOULTON & CO LIMITED
Rᵈ Nº 881509
Rᵈ Nº 35705
Rᵈ Nº 7560
Rᵈ Nº 332'56

Designer: Geoff Blower
Handle: A feather; a shield at the base
Colourway: Blue-grey helmet, dark green robes

Backstamp: Doulton

Doulton Number	Size	Backstamp	Height	Intro.	Discon.	Current Market Value		
						U.K. £	U.S. $	Can. $
D6455	Large	Doulton	7 1/4"	1957	1991	60.00	100.00	145.00
D6460	Small	Doulton	3 1/4"	1957	1991	40.00	60.00	80.00
D6511	Miniature	Doulton	2 1/2"	1960	1991	30.00	45.00	60.00

DRAKE

Sir Francis Drake (1540-1596) was an English navigator and admiral. He was Queen Elizabeth I's right hand against the Spanish, going on many plundering expeditions in the Spanish West Indies. On one of these voyages, between 1577 and 1580, Drake became the first Englishman to sail around the world. As Admiral of the British Navy, he repelled the Spanish Armada sent to invade England.

STYLE ONE: WITHOUT HAT (HATLESS)

VARIATION No. 1:   Colourway: White ruff, red-brown coat
The raised lettering "Sir Francis Drake" on the back of the coat is painted over

REGISTRATION
APPLIED FOR

Designer: Harry Fenton
Handle: Plain
Colourway: White ruff, red-brown coat

Backstamp: Doulton

Doulton Number	Size	Backstamp	Height	Intro.	Discon.	Current Market Value		
						U.K. £	U.S. $	Can. $
D6115	Large	Doulton	5 3/4"	1940	1941	1,500.00	3,000.00	3,500.00

VARIATION No. 2:   Colourway: White ruff, green coat
The raised lettering "Sir Francis Drake" on the
back of the coat is painted white, highlighting the name

"Drake."

R⁴ N⁰ 838085.

Doulton Number	Size	Backstamp	Height	Intro.	Discon.	Current Market Value		
						U.K. £	U.S. $	Can. $
D6115	Large	Doulton	5 3/4"	1940	1941		Extremely Rare	

DRAKE

STYLE TWO: *WITH HAT*

Designer: Harry Fenton   **Backstamp:** Doulton
Handle: Rope
Colourway: Brown hat, green robes, white ruff;
Brown drum at back of handle alongside ruff

Doulton Number	Size	Backstamp	Height	Intro.	Discon.	Current Market Value		
						U.K. £	U.S. $	Can. $
D6115	Large	Doulton	5 3/4"	1940	1960	80.00	160.00	200.00
D6174	Small	Doulton	3 1/4"	1941	1960	50.00	75.00	110.00

DUKE OF WELLINGTON

THE GREAT GENERALS COLLECTION
ONE OF TEN

Arthur Wellesley (1769-1852), First Duke of Wellington, was a British General and Statesman. He led the British forces in the defeat of Napoleon at Waterloo in 1815 and also served as Prime Minister from 1828 to 1830.

This jug was commissioned by UK International Ceramics Ltd., in a special edition. The backstamp states that 5,000 were made but according to UK International Ceramics only 3,500 were made available for sale.

Designer: William K. Harper	**Backstamp:** Doulton / UK Int'l
Handle: Cannon; above a banner "Waterloo"	
Colourway: Blue and gold	

Doulton Number	Size	Backstamp	Height	Intro.	Discon.	Current Market Value U.K. £	U.S. $	Can. $
D6848	Large	Doulton/UK Int'l	7 1/4"	1989	Sp. Ed.	100.00	185.00	250.00

EARL MOUNTBATTEN OF BURMA

HEROIC LEADERS
ONE OF THREE

A British naval and military leader, Louis Francis Albert Victor Nicholas Mountbatten (1900-1979) was the last Viceroy of India. Mountbatten was Governor General of the Dominion of India from 1947 to 1948, relinquishing power to native rule in 1948.

Upon his retirement from the Navy in 1959 he became the principal military adviser to the Ministry of Defence. He was killed when a bomb exploded his fishing boat off the coast of Ireland.

Commissioned by Lawleys By Post. Issued as one of a set of three in 1989 in a limited edition of 9,500 pieces.

STYLE ONE: HANDLE: NAVAL ENSIGN

Royal Doulton®
EARL MOUNTBATTEN OF BURMA
1900-1979
D 6851
Modelled by
Stanley James Taylor
© 1989 ROYAL DOULTON
A LIMITED EDITION OF 9500
THIS IS NO. 1,609

Designer: Stanley J. Taylor
Handle: Naval Ensign
Colourway: White naval uniform trimmed with gold

Backstamp: Doulton

Doulton Number	Size	Backstamp	Height	Intro.	Discon.	Current Market Value		
						U.K. £	U.S. $	Can. $
D6851	Small	Doulton	3 1/4"	1990	Ltd. Ed. (1991)	45.00	125.00	135.00

EARL MOUNTBATTEN OF BURMA

The first large size character jug commissioned by the Royal Doulton International Collectors Club was issued in a limited edition of 5,000 jugs.

STYLE TWO: *HANDLE: ANCHOR AND INTERTWINED ROPE*

Designer: Stanley J. Taylor
Handle: Anchor and intertwined rope
Colourway: Yellow, black and white

Backstamp: Doulton/Royal Doulton Internatinal Collectors Club

Doulton Number	Size	Backstamp	Height	Intro.	Discon.	Current Market Value U.K. £	U.S. $	Can. $
D6944	Large	Doulton/RDICC	7"	1993	Ltd. Ed.	120.00	225.00	250.00

THE ELEPHANT TRAINER

THE CIRCUS
ONE OF FOUR

No circus is complete without the marvellous trained elephants doing their acrobatics. With their trainer (and a few peanuts) they continue to capture hearts of all ages.

Royal Doulton®

THE ELEPHANT TRAINER
D 6841
Modelled by

Stanley James Taylor.

© 1989 ROYAL DOULTON

BACKSTAMP A

Designer: Stanley J. Taylor
Handle: Head of an elephant
Colourway: Orange turban, black coat trimmed
with green and yellow

Backstamps   A. Doulton
General Issue: 1990.
B. Doulton / The Higbee Company "To commemorate the Fourth Anniversary of the opening of The Royal Doulton Room The Higbee Company, Cleveland, Ohio, U.S.A." Commissioned by The Higbee Company, Cleveland, Ohio. Issued in 1989 in a limited edition of 250 pieces.
C. Doulton / Royal Doulton Rooms, USA Strawbridge and Clothier, Hornes, Holmes "To commemorate the anniversary of the opening of the Royal Doulton Rooms in the United States of America".
Issued in a limited edition of 250.

Doulton Number	Size	Backstamp	Height	Intro.	Discon.	Current Market Value		
						U.K. £	U.S. $	Can. $
D6841	Large	A.	7"	1990	Current 1993	63.00	195.00	250.00
D6856	Large	B.	7"	1989	Ltd. Ed.	200.00	195.00	250.00
D6857	Large	C.	7"	1989	Ltd. Ed.	200.00	195.00	250.00

ELF

The Elf miniature character jug was specially commissioned for the U.S. market. He is designed to compliment the miniature Santa Clause (D6900) and Mrs. Clause (D6922). Although commissioned for the U.S. market the jug is also available in other countries through the Royal Doulton International Collectors Club.

Designer: William K. Harper
Handle: Holly Wreath
Colourway: Green

Backstamp: Doulton

Doulton Number	Size	Backstamp	Height	Intro.	Discon.	Current Market Value U.K. £	U.S. $	Can. $
D6942	Miniature	Doulton	2 3/4"	1993	Current	25.00	55.00	60.00

ELVIS PRESLEY

THE CELEBRITY COLLECTION

PROTOTYPE

Elvis Aaron Presley (1935-1977), the "King of Rock 'n Roll", was the most popular artist in the history of American rock music. After his debut in 1955, he appeared in thirty-three films, as well as issuing numerous albums. His home in Graceland is visited by thousands of fans every year. The only example of this jug is in the Henry Doulton Museum. Not issued due to copyright problems. While at least two prototypes are known to exist, none are known to be in private collections.

Designer: Stanley J. Taylor
Handle: Guitar and strap
Colourway: Black hair, white shirt with gold trim

Backstamp: Doulton

Doulton Number	Size	Backstamp	Height	Intro.	Discon.	Current Market Value		
						U.K. £	U.S. $	Can. $
D6730	Large	Doulton	7 1/4"	1987	1987		Unique	

THE ENGINE DRIVER

JOURNEY THROUGH BRITAIN
ONE OF FOUR

Rail travel in Britain has played a large part in the development of the country and remains the most-used method of transportation. In a skilled and important job, the engine driver is responsible for the safe arrival of his freight and passengers.

Each jug in the Journey Through Britain series was given a specially designed backstamp relating to the subject of the jug. The "Engine Driver" backstamp has the wording within the outline of a locomotive engine. Issued through Lawleys By Post in a limited edition of 5,000 pieces.

Designer: Stanley J. Taylor
Handle: A railway signal
Colourway: Black cap and coat, white shirt

Backstamp: Doulton

Doulton Number	Size	Backstamp	Height	Intro.	Discon.	Current Market Value		
						U.K. £	U.S. $	Can. $
D6823	Small	Doulton	4"	1988	Ltd. Ed. (1991)	40.00	125.00	135.00

EVERTON (FOOTBALL CLUB)

THE FOOTBALL SUPPORTERS
ONE OF EIGHT

Royal Doulton®
FOOTBALL SUPPORTER'S
CHARACTER JUG.
D 6926
Modelled by
Stanley James Taylor
© 1992 ROYAL DOULTON
"EVERTON"

Designer: Stanley J. Taylor
Handle: Team coloured scarf
Colourway: Blue and white uniform

Backstamp: Doulton

Doulton Number	Size	Backstamp	Height	Intro.	Discon.	Current Market Value		
						U.K. £	U.S. $	Can. $
D6926	Mid	Doulton	5"	1992	Current	35.00	125.00	95.00

FAGIN

CHARLES DICKENS COMMEMORATIVE SET
DICKENS TINIES, ONE OF TWELVE

Fagin runs the bank of child thieves with a hard hand in Dickens' novel "Oliver Twist".
Issued to commemorate the 170th Anniversary of the birth of Charles Dickens. There are twelve jugs in this set, each issued with a certificate of authenticity. A mahogany display shelf completes the set. The set was first sold by Lawleys By Post in the U.K. during 1982 to 1988, and in 1985 onward in North America and Australia.

Fagin
D.6679

Designer: Robert Tabbenor
Handle: Plain
Colourway: Orange and brown

Backstamp: Doulton

Doulton Number	Size	Backstamp	Height	Intro.	Discon.	Current Market Value U.K. £	U.S. $	Can. $
D6679	Tiny	Doulton	1 1/2"	1982	1989	30.00	45.00	60.00
		Display for 12 Tinies				65.00	45.00	50.00

THE FALCONER

Once called "The Sport of Kings," falconry is the art of training birds of prey for the hunt. The sport began in China more than 3,000 years ago and still enjoys popularity in Europe and North America, even though the addition of firearms to hunting almost brought it to an end in the 18th century.

VARIATION No. 1:   Colourway: Green with black and white striped fur hat, green coat, grey and white falcon.

Designer: Max Henk
Handle: A falcon
Colourway: Green with black and white striped fur hat, green coat, grey and white falcon.

The Falconer
D 6540
COPR 1959
DOULTON & CO LIMITED
Rd No 893846
Rd No 39654
Rd No 8318
Rd No 415/59
Backstamp: Doulton

Doulton Number	Size	Backstamp	Height	Intro.	Discon.	Current Market Value U.K. £	U.S. $	Can. $
D6533	Large	Doulton	7 1/2"	1960	1991	40.00	100.00	125.00
D6540	Small	Doulton	3 3/4"	1960	1991	30.00	60.00	75.00
D6547	Miniature	Doulton	2 3/4"	1960	1991	30.00	40.00	60.00

VARIATION No. 2:   Colourway: Dark green and brown striped fur hat, dark brown coat,
ginger beard, brown falcon.

Backstamp: Doulton/Joseph Horne Company "Celebrating the opening of The Royal Doulton Room,
Hornes, Pittsburgh, Pennsylvania, U.S.A. Specially commissioned from Royal Doulton by the
Joseph Horne Company, Pittsburgh, Pennsylvania, U.S.A. Issued in 1987 in a limited edition of
250 pieces.

Doulton Number	Size	Backstamp	Height	Intro.	Discon.	Current Market Value		
						U.K. £	U.S. $	Can. $
D6798	Large	Doulton/Horne	7 1/2"	1987	Ltd. Ed.	225.00	150.00	190.00

VARIATION No. 3:   Colourway: Black with maroon and white striped fur hat, red-brown coat, brown falcon.

Royal Doulton®

THE FALCONER

D 6800

Modelled by

© 1959 ROYAL DOULTON
NEW COLOURWAY 1987
SPECIAL COMMISSION 1000
PETER JONES COLLECTION
LEEDS AND WAKEFIELD

Backstamp: Doulton/Peter Jones China Ltd "New Colourway 1987 Special Commission 1000 Peter Jones Collection Leeds and Wakefield" Commissioned by Peter Jones China Ltd, Leeds and Wakefield, England. Issued in 1987 in a special edition of 1,000 pieces.

Doulton Number	Size	Backstamp	Height	Intro.	Discon.	Current Market Value U.K. £	U.S. $	Can. $
D6800	Large	Doulton/Jones	7 1/2"	1987	Sp. Ed.	45.00	150.00	175.00

FALSTAFF

CHARACTERS FROM LITERATURE
ONE OF ELEVEN

Sir John Falstaff is a fat, convivial, good-humoured braggart who figures in Shakespeare's "Henry IV" and "The Merry Wives of Windsor".

A trial piece exists in a red and dark green colourway.

VARIATION No. 1:   **Colourway: Rose-pink tunic, black hat trimmed with rose-pink plumes, grey beard.**

Falstaff
D 6287
COPR 1949
DOULTON & CO LIMITED

Designer: Harry Fenton   **Backstamp:** Doulton
Handle: Plain
Colourway: Rose-pink tunic, black hat trimmed with rose-pink plumes, grey beard.

Doulton Number	Size	Backstamp	Height	Intro.	Discon.	Current Market Value U.K. £	U.S. $	Can. $
D6287	Large	Doulton	6"	1950	Current	49.95	142.50	160.00
D6385	Small	Doulton	3 1/2"	1950	Current	25.00	78.00	90.00
D6519	Miniature	Doulton	2 1/2"	1960	1991	25.00	40.00	60.00

VARIATION No. 2:   Colourway: Yellow tunic, black hat trimmed
with yellow plumes, brown beard

Royal Doulton®
FALSTAFF
D 6795
Modelled by

H. FENTON

© 1949 ROYAL DOULTON
NEW COLOURWAY 1987

Backstamp: **Doulton/ U.K. Fairs Ltd.**
Produced Exclusively for U.K. Fairs
Ltd. in a Special Edition of 1500

Doulton Number	Size	Backstamp	Height	Intro.	Discon.	Current Market Value U.K. £	U.S. $	Can. $
D6797	Large	Doulton/ U.K. Fairs	6"	1987	Sp. Ed.	70.00	130.00	150.00

Miscellaneous "Falstaff" Items

Doulton Number	Item	Height	Intro.	Discon.	Current Market Value U.K. £	U.S. $	Can. $
D6385	Table lighter	4 1/2"	1958	1973	110.00	125.00	150.00
D6854	Teapot		1989	1991	65.00	95.00	115.00

FARMER JOHN

The archetypical English farmer, "John" is cheerful and hard-working from his early morning chores until dusk finds him at the local pub with his daily draught of ale.

STYLE ONE: HANDLE "INSIDE" JUG

"Farmer John".

R^d N° 820500.
REG^d IN AUSTRALIA

Coleman's Compliments

BACKSTAMP B

Designer:	Charles Noke		**Backstamps:**	A. **Doulton**
Handle:	Brown handle which is			B. **Doulton / Coleman's**
	set within the neck of the jug			**"Coleman's Compliments"**
Colourway:	Brown			

Doulton Number	Size	Backstamp	Height	Intro.	Discon.	Current Market Value U.K. £	U.S. $	Can. $
D5788	Large	Doulton	6 1/2"	1938	1960	80.00	175.00	225.00
D5788	Large	Doulton/Coleman's	6 1/2"	1938	1938	1,000.00	1,700.00	2,000.00
D5789	Small	Doulton	3 1/4"	1938	1960	55.00	85.00	110.00

FARMER JOHN

STYLE TWO: *HANDLE "OUTSIDE" JUG*

Designer: Charles Noke
Handle: Brown handle which sits at
the top of the neck.
Colourway: Brown

Backstamp: Doulton

Doulton Number	Size	Backstamp	Height	Intro.	Discon.	Current Market Value		
						U.K. £	U.S. $	Can. $
D5788	Large	Doulton	6 1/2"	1938	1960	75.00	150.00	190.00
D5789	Small	Doulton	3 1/4"	1938	1960	45.00	85.00	100.00

Miscellaneous "Farmer John" Items

Doulton Number	Item	Height	Intro.	Discon.	Current Market Value		
					U.K. £	U.S. $	Can. $
D6007	Ash bowl	3"	1939	1960	85.00	125.00	150.00

FAT BOY

Another wonderful Dickens' character, Joe, the Fat Boy was the lazy glutton who worked as servant to Mr. Wardle in "The Pickwick Papers".

Designer: Leslie Harradine / Harry Fenton
Handle: Plain
Colourway: Blue shirt, white scarf

Backstamp: Doulton

Doulton Number	Size	Backstamp	Height	Intro.	Discon.	Current Market Value U.K. £	U.S. $	Can. $
D5840	Mid	Doulton	5"	1938	1948	120.00	200.00	240.00
D5840	Small	Doulton	4"	1948	1960	60.00	125.00	125.00
D6139	Miniature	Doulton	2 1/2"	1940	1960	45.00	75.00	95.00
D6142	Tiny	Doulton	1 1/2"	1940	1960	65.00	125.00	130.00

Miscellaneous "Fat Boy" Items

Doulton Number	Item	Height	Intro.	Discon.	Current Market Value U.K. £	U.S. $	Can. $
M59	Napkin Ring	3 1/2"	1935	1939	200.00	400.00	450.00

FIELD MARSHALL MONTGOMERY

Issued for the 50th Anniversary of the WWII "Montgomery Victory" over Rommel in North Africa during 1942. Issued in a limited edition of 2,500 worldwide.

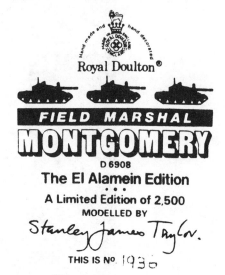

Royal Doulton®

FIELD MARSHAL

MONTGOMERY

D 6908

The El Alamein Edition
• • •
A Limited Edition of 2,500

MODELED BY

Stanley James Taylor.

THIS IS N°. 1936

© 1991 ROYAL DOULTON

Designer:	Stanley J. Taylor
Handle:	Baton, oak leaves, El Alamein
Colourway:	Black beret, khaki uniform, purple and cream baton

Backstamp: Doulton

prDoulton Number	Size	Backstamp	Height	Intro.	Discon.	Current Market Value		
						U.K. £	U.S. $	Can. $
D6908	Large	Doulton	6 1/2"	1992	Ltd. Ed.	80.00	185.00	285.00

THE FIREMAN

Admired as courageous and gallant, the profession of fireman has often been the envy of all youngsters.

Launched exclusively by Griffith Pottery House in 1983 and then released into the general range in 1984. Varieties exist with the nozzle handle ranging from dark orange to light yellow. There is no premium value for these colourway variations

An error jug of the fireman character jug exists. The red background of the helmet badge was not applied during painting, resulting in a white badge. This is a curiosity piece with very little premium value.

STYLE ONE: *HANDLE: NOZZLE OF FIRE HOSE*

Royal Doulton
The Fireman
D.6697
Hand made and Hand decorated
Designed by Jerry D. Griffith
Modelled by Robert Tabbenor
ⓒ ROYAL DOULTON
TABLEWARE LTD 1982

BACKSTAMP C

Designer:	Robert Tabbenor
Handle:	Nozzle of fire hose
Colourway:	Black, brown and red helmet badge

Backstamps:
A. Doulton/"Hand made and Hand decorated", no credits
B. Doulton/"Hand made and Hand decorated, Modelled by Robert Tabbenor"
C. Doulton / "Hand made and Hand decorated, Designed by Jerry D. Griffith". Modelled by Robert Tabbenor

Doulton Number	Size	Backstamp	Height	Intro.	Discon.	Current Market Value		
						U.K. £	U.S. $	Can. $
D6697	Large	A Doulton	7 1/4"	1984	1991	55.00	100.00	145.00
D6697	Large	B Doulton	7 1/4"	1984	1991	55.00	100.00	145.00
D6697	Large	C Doulton	7 1/4"	1983	1991	55.00	100.00	145.00

THE FIREMAN

JOURNEY THROUGH BRITAIN
ONE OF FOUR

As with the other pieces in this series, the wording of the backstamp is contained within a design connected with the subject. This design is a coiled hosepipe. Issued through Lawleys By Post in 1988 in a limited edition of 5,000 pieces.

STYLE TWO: HANDLE: AXE AND FIRE HOSE

Designer: Stanley J. Taylor
Handle: An axe and fire hose
Colourway: Yellow helmet, dark blue jacket

Backstamp: Doulton

Doulton Number	Size	Backstamp	Height	Intro.	Discon.	Current Market Value U.K. £	U.S. $	Can. $
D6839	Small	Doulton/Lawleys	4 1/4"	1989	Ltd. Ed. (1991)	40.00	110.00	135.00

THE FORTUNE TELLER

Fortune telling and other methods of predicting the future have been a part of many cultures throughout history. Astrology uses the position of the stars to provide information on people or events while the Tarot tells fortunes from a deck of seventy-eight cards, each with a different symbolic meaning.

STYLE ONE: HANDLE: SIGNS OF THE ZODIAC

The Fortune Teller
D.6497
COPR 1958
DOULTON & CO LIMITED
Rd No 889568
Rd No 38224
Rd No 8034
Rd No 425/58

Designer: Garry Sharpe
Handle: Zodiac design
Colourway: Green scarf around head, black shawl, purple handle

Backstamp: Doulton

Doulton Number	Size	Backstamp	Height	Intro.	Discon.	Current Market Value U.K. £	U.S. $	Can. $
D6497	Large	Doulton	6 3/4"	1959	1967	275.00	550.00	600.00
D6503	Small	Doulton	3 3/4"	1959	1967	200.00	350.00	400.00
D6523	Miniature	Doulton	2 1/2"	1960	1967	200.00	375.00	375.00

THE FORTUNE TELLER

Beginning in 1991, one special jug was selected as "Character Jug of the Year", produced for one year only and issued with a certificate of authenticity. Each subsequent year will have a Character Jug of the Year. The Fortune Teller is the Character Jug of the Year for 1991.

STYLE TWO: *HANDLE: TAROT CARDS*

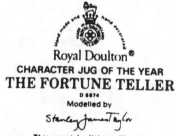

Royal Doulton®
CHARACTER JUG OF THE YEAR
THE FORTUNE TELLER
D 6874
Modelled by

Stanley James Taylor

This special edition will only
be available during the year
1991
© 1990 ROYAL DOULTON

Designer: Stanley J. Taylor
Handle: Bandana and tarot cards
Colourway: Orange polka-dot bandana, light blue shirt

Backstamp: Doulton / "Character Jug of the Year"

Doulton Number	Size	Backstamp	Height	Intro.	Discon.	Current Market Value		
						U.K. £	U.S. $	Can. $
D6874	Large	Jug of the Year	7"	1991	1991	75.00	150.00	180.00

FRIAR TUCK

Fat and jolly and fond of drink, Friar Tuck joined the legendary Robin Hood and his band of rogues as they robbed the rich to feed the poor in rural England. Living in Sherwood Forest, the merry group shared many hair-raising adventures.

Friar Tuck.
COPR.1950.
DOULTON & CO.LIMITED.
R⁴N° 862066.
R⁴N° 25162.
R⁴N° 6206.
R⁴N° 95/50.

Designer: Harry Fenton
Handle: Tree trunk
Colourway: Light and dark brown robes,
green oak leaves

Backstamp: Doulton

Doulton Number	Size	Backstamp	Height	Intro.	Discon.	Current Market Value		
						U.K. £	U.S. $	Can. $
D6321	Large	Doulton	7"	1951	1960	225.00	425.00	400.00

GAOLER

CHARACTERS FROM WILLIAMSBURG
ONE OF SEVEN

During the morally Puritan times of 18th century Virginia, it was not uncommon to land in jail for improprietous language or behaviour. This gentleman held the unpopular yet necessary job of "keeper of the keys" to one's freedom.

Character Jugs from Williamsburg®

Gaoler
D 6 5 7 0
COPR 1962
DOULTON & CO LIMITED
Rd No 906340
Rd No 43447
Rd No 9226
Rd No 284/62

Designer: David Biggs
Handle: Two keys
Colourway: Black tricorn, white shirt and red vest

Backstamp: Doulton

Doulton Number	Size	Backstamp	Height	Intro.	Discon.	Current Market Value		
						U.K. £	U.S. $	Can. $
D6570	Large	Doulton	7"	1963	1983	70.00	110.00	150.00
D6577	Small	Doulton	3 3/4"	1963	1983	45.00	75.00	95.00
D6584	Miniature	Doulton	2 3/4"	1963	1983	35.00	65.00	80.00

THE GARDENER

Engaged in a pastime enjoyed world-wide, this cheerful gent is shown with his spade and some of the fruits of his labour. From carrots to roses, the cultivation of a garden is an immensely rewarding pursuit.

STYLE ONE: HANDLE: A SPADE AND VEGETABLES

VARIATION No. 1: Colourway: Red scarf, red striped shirt, brown hat.

The Gardener
D.6630
ⓒ DOULTON & CO. LIMITED 1972
REGISTRATION APPLIED FOR.

Designer: David Biggs
Handle: A spade with carrots and a marrow at the base
Colourway: Colourway: Red scarf, red striped shirt, brown hat.
Backstamp: Doulton

Doulton Number	Size	Backstamp	Height	Intro.	Discon.	Current Market Value U.K. £	Current Market Value U.S. $	Current Market Value Can. $
D6630	Large	Doulton	7 3/4"	1971	1971	Extremely Rare		

VARIATION No. 2: Colourway: Yellow scarf, white shirt, light brown hat.

Doulton Number	Size	Backstamp	Height	Intro.	Discon.	Current Market Value U.K. £	Current Market Value U.S. $	Current Market Value Can. $
D6630	Large	Doulton	7 3/4"	1973	1981	135.00	200.00	195.00
D6634	Small	Doulton	4"	1973	1981	85.00	80.00	110.00
D6638	Miniature	Doulton	2 3/4"	1973	1981	65.00	70.00	95.00

THE GARDENER

CHARACTERS FROM LIFE
ONE OF SEVEN

STYLE TWO: HANDLE: A RED FLOWERING POTTED PLANT

Designer: Stanley J. Taylor
Handle: A potted plant
Colourway: Beige hat, green sweater and beige shirt
Backstamp: Doulton

Royal Doulton®
THE GARDENER
D 6867
Modelled by

Stanley James Taylor

© 1990 ROYAL DOULTON

VARIATION No. 1: Mould: Younger face with hair in front.

Doulton Number	Size	Variation	Height	Intro.	Discon.	Current Market Value U.K. £	U.S. $	Can. $
D6867	Large	Var. 1	7 1/4"	1990	1991	45.00	100.00	180.00

VARIATION No. 2: Mould: Older face without hair in front.

Doulton Number	Size	Variation	Height	Intro.	Discon.	Current Market Value U.K. £	U.S. $	Can. $
D6868	Small	Var. 2	4"	1990	Current	28.95	60.00	90.00

GENERAL EISENHOWER

THE GREAT GENERALS COLLECTION
ONE OF TEN

This jug was issued by U.K. International Ceramics in a limited edtion of 1,000 to commemorate the 50th Anniversary of the U.S. Army landing in Africa on the 7th and 8th of November, 1942.

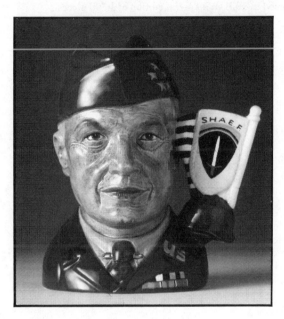

Designer: William K. Harper
Handle: Face: Shield "S.H.A.E.F."
Back: U.S. Flag
Both rest on tin helmet
Colourway: Brown uniform, cream shield,
red and white stars and stripes

Backstamp: Doulton / U.K. International Ceramics

Doulton Number	Size	Backstamp	Height	Intro.	Discon.	Current Market Value		
						U.K. £	U.S. $	Can. $
D6937	Large	Doulton/UK Int'l	7"	1993	Sp. Ed.	195.00	325.00	350.00

GENERAL GORDON

THE GREAT GENERALS COLLECTION
ONE OF TEN

Charles George Gordon (1833-1885) was known as "Chinese Gordon" after he commanded the Chinese forces against Taiping rebels in 1863. As Governor-General of the Sudan, he was instrumental in closing down the slave trade. In 1884 he was ordered to return to rescue Egyptian garrisons there, was beseiged at Khartoum and killed. Commissioned by UK International Ceramics and issued in 1991 in a special edition of 1,500 pieces.

Designer: William K. Harper
Handle: Camel's head and neck with Khartoum ensign
Colourway: Red, blue and gold

Backstamp: Doulton / U.K. International Ceramics

Doulton Number	Size	Backstamp	Height	Intro.	Discon.	Current Market Value		
						U.K. £	U.S. $	Can. $
D6869	Large	Doulton/UK Int'l	7 1/4"	1991	Sp. Ed. (1991)	125.00	275.00	295.00

GENIE

MYSTICAL CHARACTERS
ONE OF THREE

Finding its origins in the Arabic "jinnee", the genie is a sprite with supernatural powers who can change from animal to human form. Popularized through fable and legend, the modern genie is thought to reside in a magic lantern and become the servant of whoever frees it.

Royal Doulton®
THE GENIE
D 6892
Modelled by

Stanley James Taylor

© 1991 ROYAL DOULTON

Designer: Stanley J. Taylor
Handle: Lamp and flame
Colourway: Grey, black, red and yellow

Backstamp: Doulton

Doulton Number	Size	Backstamp	Height	Intro.	Discon.	Current Market Value U.K. £	U.S. $	Can. $
D6892	Large	Doulton	7"	1991	1991	120.00	150.00	250.00

GEORGE HARRISON

THE BEATLES
ONE OF FOUR

One of the original members of the world-famous and legendary rock band, the Beatles, Harrison (b. 1943) was born in Liverpool, England. He played guitar in the band, writing songs occasionally from 1961 to 1970. Since the break-up of the Beatles, Harrison has pursued a solo career in music and film.

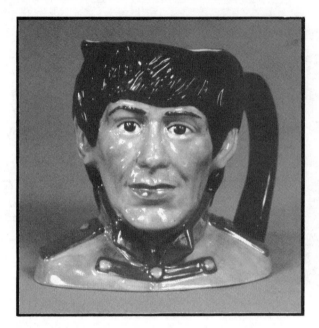

Designer: Stanley J. Taylor   **Backstamp:** Doulton
Handle: Plain
Colourway: Green tunic trimmed with orange collar and epaulettes

Doulton Number	Size	Backstamp	Height	Intro.	Discon.	Current Market Value U.K. £	U.S. $	Can. $
D6727	Mid	Doulton	5 1/2"	1984	1991	50.00	75.00	95.00

GEORGE WASHINGTON

As commander-in-chief of the American States, Washington (1732-1799) led them to victory in the War of Independence. In 1789 he became the first president of the United States, governing for two terms, until 1797. This jug was issued to celebrate the 250th Anniversary of Washington's birth.

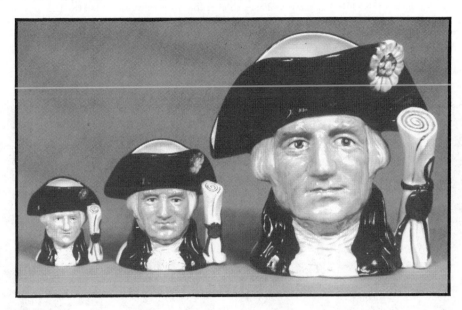

Designer: Stanley J. Taylor
Handle: Declaration of Independence
Colourway: Black hat and coat, beige shirt

Backstamps: A. Doulton.
B. Doulton / George Washington 1732-1799
"FIRST ISSUED IN 1982 TO CELEBRATE THE 250TH ANNIVERSARY OF HIS BIRTH"
C. Doulton / George Washington
"TO COMMEMORATE THE 200th ANNIVERSARY OF THE ELECTION OF THE FIRST PRESIDENT OF THE UNITED STATES OF AMERICA"

© ROYAL DOULTON
TABLEWARE LTD. 1982
D6669

George Washington
1732-1799

First Issued in 1982 to Celebrate
the 250th Anniversary of his Birth

BACKSTAMP B

Doulton Number	Size	Backstamp	Height	Intro.	Discon.	Current Market Value		
						U.K. £	U.S. $	Can. $
D6669	Large	A	7 1/2"	1982	Current	55.00	142.50	145.00
D6669	Large	B	7 1/2"	1989	1989	95.00	150.00	175.00
D6824	Small	A	4"	1989	1991	35.00	55.00	80.00
D6824	Small	B	4"	1989	1989	45.00	65.00	90.00
D6825	Miniature	C	2 1/2"	1989	1991	30.00	60.00	60.00

GEORGE WASHINGTON AND GEORGE III

THE ANTAGONISTS' COLLECTION (TWO FACED JUG)
ONE OF FOUR

George Washington (1732-1799) as commander-in-chief of the American States, led the U.S. to victory in the War of Independence. In 1789 he became the first president of the United States, governing for two terms, until 1797.

George William Frederick (1738-1820) ruled as King George III from 1760 until his death. He led Great Britain in the war against the American States, which he lost in 1776. England did not recognize the American Independence until 1781.

Issued in a limited edition of 9,500 in 1986.

Designer: Michael Abberley
Handle: George Washington:
Declaration of Independence
George III: A cannon
Colourway: Red crown and black hat

Royal Doulton®
**'The Antagonists'
Collection**
D.6749
The Siege of Yorktown 1781
George III/George Washington
Hand made and Hand decorated .
Designed by Michael Abberley

Michael Abberley

© 1985 ROYAL DOULTON (UK)
Worldwide Limited Edition of 9.500
This is Number **3895**

Backstamp: Doulton

Doulton Number	Size	Backstamp	Height	Intro.	Discon.	Current Market Value		
						U.K. £	U.S. $	Can. $
D6749	Large	Doulton	7 1/4"	1986	Ltd. Ed. (1991)	85.00	125.00	155.00

GERONIMO

THE WILD WEST COLLECTION
ONE OF SIX

Geronimo (1829-1909) was the last leader of the Apache Indians while they were still independent of Colonial rule by the white American colonists. He fought many battles to protect their freedom. In 1886 he surrendered to General Nelson Miles and the Apache territory became the state of Arizona. After a prison term in Florida, Geronimo moved west and settled down to become a prosperous farmer, while his exploits became the stuff of legends.

Designer: Stanley J. Taylor
Handle: Indian game pieces
Colourway: Black, red and white

Backstamp: Doulton

Doulton Number	Size	Backstamp	Height	Intro.	Discon.	Current Market Value U.K. £	U.S. $	Can. $
D6733	Mid	Doulton	5 1/2"	1985	1989	65.00	150.00	110.00

GLADIATOR

From about 246 B.C. gladiatorial games were a popular form of entertainment for Roman audiences. The gladiators were most often slaves or prisoners condemned to fight, which they did to the death using sword, spear or trident. The most famous gladiator of the period was Spartacus, a slave, who led an unsuccessful rebellion against Rome. Emperor Honorius banned the brutal games in 404 A.D.

Gladiator
D 6550
COPR 1960
DOULTON & CO LIMITED
Rd No 897939
Rd No 40889
Rd No 8598
Rd No 548A-60

Designer: Max Henk
Handle: A dagger and shield
Colourway: Brown helmet, grey armour

Backstamp: Doulton

Doulton Number	Size	Backstamp	Height	Intro.	Discon.	Current Market Value		
						U.K. £	U.S. $	Can. $
D6650	Large	Doulton	7 3/4"	1961	1967	325.00	700.00	750.00
D6553	Small	Doulton	4 1/4"	1961	1967	225.00	425.00	450.00
D6556	Miniature	Doulton	2 3/4"	1961	1967	225.00	400.00	475.00

GOLFER

An outdoor sport enjoying great popularity in Europe and North America, golf requires the player to shoot a small ball into a hole using the least number of strokes of a wooden or metal club. Usually played to eighteen holes, a typical game of golf can last up to six hours and require a great deal of walking.

The Golfer character jug was modelled in the likeness of W. J. Carey, the former chairman of Doulton U.S.A.

STYLE ONE: *HANDLE: GOLD BAG AND CLUBS*

VARIATION No. 1:   Colourway: Blue cap, brown sweater, brown golf bag

Royal Doulton
GOLFER
D 6623
Modelled by

David B Biggs

© ROYAL DOULTON TABLEWARE
LIMITED 1970

Designer: David Biggs
Handle: A golf bag and clubs
Colourway: Blue cap, brown sweater, brown golf bag

Backstamp: Doulton

Doulton Number	Size	Backstamp	Height	Intro.	Current Market Value Discon.	U.K. £	U.S. $	Can. $
D6623	Large	Doulton	7"	1971	Current	49.95	142.50	160.00
D6756	Small	Doulton	4 1/2"	1987	Current	35.00	50.00	90.00
D6757	Miniature	Doulton	2 1/2"	1987	1991	30.00	50.00	60.00

VARIATION No. 2: Colourway: Dark blue cap, blue striped sweater, light brown golf bag

Backstamp: Doulton / John Sinclair
Commissioned by John Sinclair, Sheffield, England. Issued in 1987 in a limited edition of 1,000 pieces.

Doulton Number	Size	Backstamp	Height	Intro.	Discon.	Current Market Value U.K. £	U.S. $	Can. $
D6787	Large	Doulton/Sinclair	7"	1987	Ltd. Ed.	50.00	125.00	125.00

THE GOLFER / THE MODERN GOLFER

CHARACTERS FROM LIFE
ONE OF SEVEN

In the United States, the Royal Doulton product list carries this jug as "The Modern Golfer".

STYLE TWO: *HANDLE: 18TH HOLE FLAG, BALL, TEE AND GOLF CLUB*

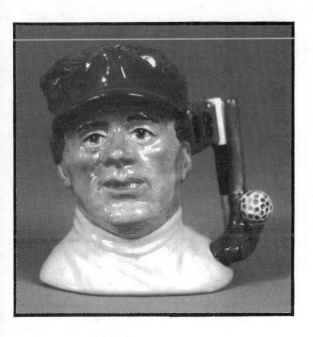

Royal Doulton ®
THE GOLFER
D 6865
Modelled by
Stanley James Taylor.
© 1990 ROYAL DOULTON

Designer: Stanley J. Taylor

Handle: Golf club, eighteenth hole flag, ball and tee

Colourway: Yellow sweater, green sun visor

Backstamp: Doulton

Doulton Number	Size	Backstamp	Height	Intro.	Discon.	Current Market Value		
						U.K. £	U.S. $	Can. $
D6865	Small	Doulton	4"	1990	Current	28.95	78.00	100.00

GONDOLIER

The shallow, long craft the gondolier pilots through Venetian canals must be painted all black, according to ancient law. When not ferrying or serenading lovers on moonlight rides, the gondolier moors his gondola to a brightly striped pole by the waterside.

Gondolier
D 6 5 8 9
COPR 1 9 6 3
DOULTON & CO LIMITED
Rd No 9 1 3 1 3 9
Rd No 4 5 3 5 7
Rd No 9 6 8 2
Rd No 8 1 2 / 6 3

Designer: David Biggs
Handle: Gondola
Colourway: Yellow hat, blue and white t-shirt, maroon and white pole.

Backstamp: Doulton

Doulton Number	Size	Backstamp	Height	Intro.	Discon.	Current Market Value U.K. £	U.S. $	Can. $
D6589	Large	Doulton	8"	1964	1969	300.00	625.00	700.00
D6592	Small	Doulton	4"	1964	1969	200.00	425.00	450.00
D6595	Miniature	Doulton	2 1/2"	1964	1969	200.00	375.00	475.00

GONE AWAY

The very British huntsman looks ready to give the traditional call signalling the loss of the quarry. His prey, the fox, has won this round!

Gone Away
D 6531
COPR 1959
DOULTON & CO LIMITED
Rd No 893844
Rd No 39652
Rd No 8316
Rd No 417/59

Designer: Garry Sharpe
Handle: A fox
Colourway: Red jacket, black cap

Backstamp: Doulton

Doulton Number	Size	Backstamp	Height	Intro.	Discon.	Current Market Value		
						U.K. £	U.S. $	Can. $
D6531	Large	Doulton	7 1/4"	1960	1982	60.00	100.00	155.00
D6538	Small	Doulton	3 3/4	1960	1982	40.00	65.00	90.00
D6545	Miniature	Doulton	2 1/2"	1960	1982	35.00	55.00	80.00

THE GRADUATE (MALE)

Royal Doulton®
THE GRADUATE
D 6916
Modelled by
Stanley James Taylor
© 1991 ROYAL DOULTON

Designer: Stanley J. Taylor
Handle: Diploma
Colourway: Black and white

Backstamp: Doulton

Doulton Number	Size	Backstamp	Height	Intro.	Discon.	Current Market Value		
						U.K. £	U.S. $	Can. $
D6916	Small	Doulton	3 1/2"	1991	Current	28.95	82.50	105.00

GRANNY

PROTOTYPE

This early coloured prototype proved too expensive to produce. Only one copy is known to exist.

STYLE ONE: "TOOTHLESS" GRANNY

Designer: Harry Fenton
Handle: Plain
Colourway: Yellows

Backstamp: Doulton

Doulton Number	Size	Backstamp	Height	Intro.	Discon.	Current Market Value U.K. £	U.S. $	Can. $
D5521	Large	Doulton	6 1/4"	1935	Unknown		Unique	

GRANNY

A delight for children, and often the favourite relative, Granny can always be counted on for a little treat or a big hug.

STYLE ONE: "TOOTHLESS" GRANNY

The wimple on this style does not show between the hat and the hair at the front of the head. There is no tooth showing between the lips.

Granny
D 6384

Designer: Harry Fenton
Handle: Plain
Colourway: Dark green and white

Backstamp: Doulton

Doulton Number	Size	Backstamp	Height	Intro.	Discon.	Current Market Value		
						U.K. £	U.S. $	Can. $
D5521	Large	Doulton	6 1/4"	1935	c. 1945	450.00	1,200.00	1,200.00
D6384	Small	Doulton	3 1/4"	1935	Unknown		Extremely Rare	

GRANNY

STYLE TWO: GRANNY HAS ONE TOOTH SHOWING

The wimple on this style shows in waves under most of the hat.

Designer: Harry Fenton, Large
Max Henk, Small and Miniature
Handle: Pink, blue, green and cream tied yarn
Colourway: Dark grey and white

Backstamp: Doulton

Doulton Number	Size	Backstamp	Height	Intro.	Discon.	Current Market Value		
						U.K. £	U.S. $	Can. $
D5521	Large	Doulton	6 1/4"	1946	1983	65.00	100.00	135.00
D6384	Small	Doulton	3 1/4"	1953	1983	40.00	50.00	90.00
D6520	Miniature	Doulton	2 1/4"	1960	1983	35.00	50.00	80.00

Miscellaneous "Granny" Items

Doulton Number	Item	Height	Intro.	Discon.	Current Market Value		
					U.K. £	U.S. $	Can. $
D —	Lighter	3 1/2"	Unknown			Extremely Rare	

GROUCHO MARX

PROTOTYPE

This design having two of the Marx Brothers peering from behind the cigar was never put into production due to the complicated handle. Only one is known to exist.

Designer: Stanley J. Taylor
Handle: Cigar with two other Marx brothers
Colourway: Plain jacket, spotted bow-tie

Backstamp: Doulton

Doulton Number	Size	Variation	Height	Intro.	Discon.	U.K. £	Current Market Value U.S. $	Can. $
D6710	Large	Prototype	7"		Unknown		Unique	

GROUCHO MARX

THE CELEBRITY COLLECTION
ONE OF FIVE

Julius Marx (1895-1977) was one of four brothers who became hits of American comedy film. The "Marx Brothers" were known for their crazy slapstick antics and hilarious puns. Groucho led the gang, always smoking his trademark cigar.

VARIATION No. 1: Colourway: Plain jacket, spotted bow tie.

Designer:	Stanley J. Taylor	Backstamp: Doulton
Handle:	Cigar	
Colourway:	Plain jacket, spotted bow tie.	

Doulton Number	Size	Variation	Height	Intro.	Discon.	Current Market Value U.K. £	Current Market Value U.S. $	Current Market Value Can. $
D6710	Large	Var. 1	7"	1984	1988	75.00	100.00	155.00

VARIATION No. 2: Colourway: Plaid jacket

Doulton Number	Size	Variation	Height	Intro.	Discon.	Current Market Value U.K. £	Current Market Value U.S. $	Current Market Value Can. $
D6710	Large	Var. 2	7"	Unknown			Extremely Rare	

GUARDSMAN

CHARACTERS FROM WILLIAMSBURG
ONE OF SEVEN

In a new and foreign land, any colony must also be a well protected fortress. Williamsburg, Virginia was no exception and this guardsman was always at the ready to protect the American pioneers against attack.

STYLE ONE: TRICORN HAT WITH PIKE

Character Jugs from Williamsburg®

Guardsman
D 6575
COPR 1962
DOULTON & CO LIMITED
Rd No 906338
Rd No 43445
Rd No 9224
Rd No 286/62

Designer: Max Henk
Handle: Pike
Colourway: Dark blue and yellow hat and jacket

Backstamp: Doulton

Doulton Number	Size	Backstamp	Height	Intro.	Discon.	Current Market Value		
						U.K. £	U.S. $	Can. $
D6568	Large	Doulton	6 3/4"	1963	1983	70.00	120.00	160.00
D6575	Small	Doulton	4 1/4"	1963	1983	50.00	75.00	95.00
D6582	Miniature	Doulton	2 1/2"	1963	1983	40.00	65.00	80.00

THE GUARDSMAN

PROTOTYPE

This was the original design of The Guardsman Jug, a prototype with the Union Jack as the flag.

Designer: Stanley J. Taylor
Handle: A sword draped with the Union Jack
Colourway: Red tunic, black bearskin hat

Backstamp: Doulton

Doulton Number	Size	Variation	Height	Intro.	Discon.	Current Market Value U.K. £	U.S. $	Can. $
D —	Large	Prototype	8"		Unknown	Extremely Rare		

THE GUARDSMAN

THE LONDON COLLECTION
ONE OF TEN

Long a fixture in London, the guardsman is easily identified by his tall bearskin hat and scarlet uniform. Today he still stands outside Buckingham Palace, to protect the Queen. The London Collection, one of ten.

STYLE TWO: *BEARSKIN HAT WITH SWORD*

Designer: Stanley J. Taylor
Handle: Sword with draped brown flag
Colourway: Red tunic, black bearskin hat

Royal Doulton®

THE GUARDSMAN
D 6755
Modelled by
Stanley James Taylor

© 1986 ROYAL DOULTON

Backstamp: Doulton

Doulton Number	Size	Backstamp	Height	Intro.	Discon.	Current Market Value U.K. £	U.S. $	Can. $
D6755	Large	Doulton	8"	1986	Current	49.95	142.50	160.00
D6771	Small	Doulton	4"	1987	Current	25.00	78.00	90.00
D6772	Miniature	Doulton	2 1/2"	1987	1991	35.00	40.00	60.00

GULLIVER

Jonathon Swift, when he published "Gulliver's Travels" under a pseudonym in 1726, intended to satirize society's leading men and institutions. The book was so fascinating however, that even the intended victims didn't realize they were the butt of a joke.

Gulliver the traveller sails to foreign lands, surviving shipwrecks, giants and many odd adventures. Perhaps his best known experience was waking up in the land of Lilliput to find he had been tied up by the miniature people who lived there.

```
Gulliver
D 6560
COPR 1961
DOULTON & CO LIMITED
Rd No 902091
Rd No 42143
Rd No 8926
Rd No R 85/ 61
```

Designer: David Biggs
Handle: Castle tower with two Lilliputians in the turret
Colourway: Dark blue and grey hat, blue jacket, grey handle

Backstamp: Doulton

Doulton Number	Size	Backstamp	Height	Intro.	Discon.	Current Market Value		
						U.K. £	U.S. $	Can. $
D6560	Large	Doulton	7 1/2"	1962	1967	325.00	700.00	750.00
D6563	Small	Doulton	4"	1962	1967	225.00	475.00	550.00
D6566	Miniature	Doulton	2 1/2"	1962	1967	225.00	400.00	500.00

GUNSMITH

PROTOTYPE

This prototype has a different hat, hair style and handle from the issued design. Only one jug known to exist.

Designer: David Biggs
Handle: Stock of a musket and flintlock
Colourway: Black hat, cream shirt,
light brown apron

Backstamp: Doulton

Doulton Number	Size	Backstamp	Height	Intro.	Discon.	Current Market Value U.K. £	U.S. $	Can. $
D —	Large	Doulton	7 1/4"		c. 1963	Unique		

GUNSMITH

CHARACTERS FROM WILLIAMSBURG
ONE OF SEVEN

The production of guns in 18th century America was not an exacting science. It was part metalwork and part chemistry. To have a resident expert within the colony meant that arms could be quickly manufactured or repaired in case of danger.

Designer: David Biggs	**Backstamp:** Doulton
Handle: Stock of a musket	
Colourway: Black hat, cream shirt, light brown apron	

Doulton Number	Size	Backstamp	Height	Intro.	Discon.	Current Market Value		
						U.K. £	U.S. $	Can. $
D6573	Large	Doulton	7 1/4"	1963	1983	70.00	110.00	160.00
D6580	Small	Doulton	3 1/2"	1963	1983	50.00	70.00	95.00
D6587	Miniature	Doulton	2 1/2"	1963	1983	40.00	60.00	80.00

GUY FAWKES

Guy Fawkes (1570-1606), a Yorkshire Catholic, was part of the infamous "Gunpowder Plot," a plan by Catholic rebels to blow up the British Houses of Parliament and King James I on November 5, 1605.

The conspiracy was leaked by a mysterious letter to Lord Monteagle and Guy Fawkes was arrested and hanged. Every year on November 5th, Guy Fawkes day is celebrated with fireworks and the burning of Fawkes in effigy.

VARIATION No. 1: Colourway: Black hat, red band, white collar on black coat

Royal Doulton®
GUY FAWKES
D 6861
Modelled by

William K. Harper

© 1990 ROYAL DOULTON

Designer: William K. Harper
Handle: A lantern above a barrel of gunpowder
Colourway: Black hat, red band, beige collar, black coat.

Backstamp: Doulton

Doulton Number	Size	Backstamp	Height	Intro.	Discon.	Current Market Value U.K. £	U.S. $	Can. $
D6861	Large	Doulton	7"	1990	Current	49.95	142.50	250.00

VARIATION No. 2: Colourway: Black hat, orange band, white collar on black coat

Designer:	William K. Harper	
Handle:	A lantern above a barrel of gunpowder	
Colourway:	Black hat, orange band, white collar, black coat.	

Backstamp: Doulton / Canadian Art and Collectables Show
Pre-release limited to 750 for the 3rd Annual Canadian Doulton Show and Sale in conjuction with the 1990 Canadian Collectables Showcase May 5 & 6, 1990, Durham, Ontario

Doulton Number	Size	Backstamp	Height	Intro.	Discon.	Current Market Value		
						U.K. £	U.S. $	Can. $
D6861	Large	Doulton/Can.	7"	1990	Ltd. Ed.	95.00	150.00	195.00

HAMLET

THE SHAKESPEAREAN COLLECTION
ONE OF SIX

Probably Shakespeare's most famous play, "Hamlet, Prince of Denmark" was first performed between 1599 and 1602. Hamlet became the quintessential tragic hero, driven by conscience and familial obligation to avenge his father's murder.

© ROYAL DOULTON TABLEWARE LIMITED 1982
D 6672

The
Shakespearean
Collection
HAMLET
A series of hand-made, hand-decorated Character Jugs by
Royal Doulton

Designer: Michael Abberley
Handle: A dagger and skull join the feather of the cap
Colourway: Black cap and robes, blond hair and grey feather

Backstamp: Doulton

Doulton Number	Size	Backstamp	Height	Intro.	Discon.	Current Market Value		
						U.K. £	U.S. $	Can. $
D6672	Large	Doulton	7 1/4"	1982	1989	75.00	100.00	145.00

THE HAMPSHIRE CRICKETER

An honourable and gentlemanly game, cricket enjoys great popularity in the United Kingdom. Two teams of eleven compete on an outdoor field with balls, wickets and bats.

Developed and sold by the Hampshire Cricket Club to celebrate the centenary of the Hampshire cricket grounds. Issued in 1985 in a limited edition of 5,000 pieces.

THE HAMPSHIRE CRICKETER
D 6739
Specially Commissioned
from
Royal Doulton
by
© HAMPSHIRE C.C.C. 1985
Celebrating 100 years of
County Cricket at Southampton
Hand Modelled and Hand Decorated
Designed by Harry Sales
Modelled by
WORLDWIDE LIMITED EDITION OF 5,000
THIS IS NUMBER

Designer: Harry Sales
Handle: Cricket bat
Colourway: Navy blue cap, cream sweater with navy and yellow stripes

Backstamp: Doulton / Hampshire Cricket Club

Doulton Number	Size	Backstamp	Height	Intro.	Discon.	Current Market Value		
						U.K. £	U.S. $	Can. $
D6739	Small	Doulton/ Hampshire	5"	1985	Ltd. Ed. (1991)	45.00	90.00	145.00

HENRY V

THE SHAKESPEAREAN COLLECTION
ONE OF SIX

King Henry V (1387-1422) during his reign from 1413 to 1422 renewed the Hundred Years' War against France. At the Battle of Agincourt in 1415, he won one of the most famous victories in English history. Henry married the daughter of King Charles VI of France and by the Treaty of Troyes became heir to the French throne.

The story of his reign and battles was dramatized in a play by William Shakespeare.

VARIATION No. 1:   **Handle:** Embossed
Colourway: Yellow crown with gold, turquoise and red design.

© ROYAL DOULTON TABLEWARE LIMITED 1982
D 6671

The
Shakespearean
Collection
HENRY V
A series of hand-made, hand-decorated Character Jugs by
Royal Doulton

Designer: Robert Tabbenor
Handle: Royal Ensign
Colourway: Yellow crown with gold, turquoise and red design.

Backstamp: Doutlon

Doulton Number	Size	Variation	Height	Intro.	Discon.	Current Market Value U.K. £	U.S. $	Can. $
D6671	Large	Var. 1	7 1/4"	1982	c. 1984	145.00	250.00	275.00

VARIATION No. 2:   Handle: Embossed.
                        Colourway: Yellow crown, some blue colouring, no red or gold.
                                      This jug is actually a factory second, marked and sold as such.
One of the steps used when firing and painting the jugs was
missed. Hundreds are known to exist.

Doulton Number	Size	Variation	Height	Intro.	Discon.	Current Market Value U.K. £	U.S. $	Can. $
D6671	Large	Var. 2	7 1/4"		Unknown	600.00	1,200.00	1,500.00

VARIATION No. 3:   Handle: Decorated with a decal.
                        Colourway: Yellow crown with gold, blue and red design.

Doulton Number	Size	Variation	Height	Intro.	Discon.	Current Market Value U.K. £	U.S. $	Can. $
D6671	Large	Var. 3	7 1/4"	c.1984	1989	75.00	115.00	145.00

HENRY VIII

HENRY VIII AND HIS SIX WIVES
ONE OF EIGHT

Henry VIII (1491-1547) was king of Great Britain from 1509 to 1547 during which time he established the English Navy as one of the most powerful in the world. Henry's infamous private life changed the course of history. Attempting to produce a male heir to the throne, he married six times, was excommunicated by the Pope for divorcing, and ultimately founded the Church of England.

HENRY VIII
D 6642
ⓒ ROYAL DOULTON
TABLEWARE LTD 1975

Designer: Eric Griffiths
Handle: A tower joins the feather in the hat
Colourway: Black and gold hat, white plume, brown and maroon tunic

Backstamp: Doulton

Doulton Number	Size	Backstamp	Height	Intro.	Discon.	Current Market Value		
						U.K. £	U.S. $	Can. $
D6642	Large	Doulton	6 1/2"	1975	Current	49.95	142.50	160.00
D6647	Small	Doulton	3 3/4"	1979	Current	25.00	78.00	90.00
D6648	Miniature	Doulton	2 3/4"	1979	1991	30.00	50.00	60.00

HIGHWAYMAN

This design by Leslie Harradine could very well be interpreted as the forerunner of the Doulton line of character jugs.

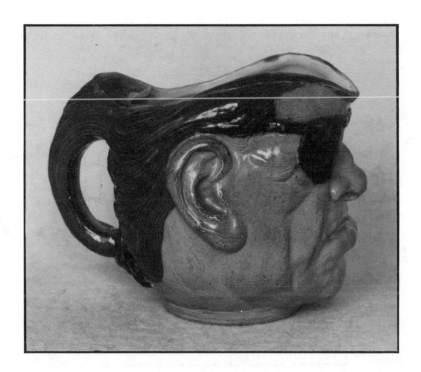

Designer: Leslie Harradine
Handle: Strands of hair
Colourway: Salt-glazed stoneware

Backstamp: Doulton Lambeth

Doulton Number	Size	Variation	Height	Intro.	Discon.	Current Market Value		
						U.K. £	U.S. $	Can. $
D —	Large	Lambeth	Unknown	c. 1912			Extremely rare	

HOME GUARD

HEROES OF THE BLITZ
ONE OF THREE

The early part of WWII saw the young and old join the Home Guard to protect the country from what was perceived at the time as an imminent invasion by the German army. The Home Guard allowed the regular army to be used elsewere. The "Heroes of the Blitz" was available only from Lawleys By Post in a Limited Edtion of 9500.

Designer: Stanley J. Taylor
Handle: Sten gun with hand grenade
Colourway: Khaki uniform and cap

Backstamp: Doulton

Doulton Number	Size	Variation	Height	Intro.	Discon.	Current Market Value U.K. £	U.S. $	Can. $
D6886	Small	Doulton	4"	1991	Ltd. Ed.	60.00	125.00	110.00

HUMPHREY BOGART

THE CELEBRITY COLLECTION

PROTOTYPE

Born in New York city, Humphrey DeForest Bogart began his acting career in 1920 on the stage. Turning to film, he had a prolific career, winning an Academy Award in 1952 for his performance in "The African Queen." His best known role, however, must be that of Rick in "Casablanca". Not issued due to copyright problems. Not known to be in private collections.

Designer: Eric Griffiths	**Backstamp:** Doulton
Handle: Movie camera pointing right	
Colourway: Black hat and brown coat, black bow-tie	

Doulton Number	Size	Variation	Height	Intro.	Discon.	Current Market Value U.K. £	U.S. $	Can. $
D —	Large	Prototype	7"		Unknown		Extremely Rare	

IZAAK WALTON

An English writer, Walton (1593-1683) is best known for his book "The Compleat Angler, or Contemplative Man's Recreation." First published in 1653, this work later became the most famous book written on the sport of fishing in the English language. Styled as a conversation between a fisherman and a hunter, the book breathes serenity and contentment.

TO COMMEMORATE THI
300ᵗᴴ ANNIVERSARY
OF THE
" COMPLEAT ANGLER
1653 - 1953.

IZAAK WALTON.
D. 6404.
COPR.1953.
DOULTON & CO LIMITED
R⁰N⁰ 871560
R⁰N⁰ 31804
R⁰N⁰ 6825
R⁰N⁰ 237/53

BACKSTAMP A

CITY OF
STOKE-ON-TRENT
JUBILEE YEAR
1959-1960
WITH THE COMPLIMENTS OF
LORD MAYOR AND LADY MAYORESS
ALDERMAN HAROLD CLOWES O.B.E. J.P
AND
MISS CHRISTINE CLOWES

BACKSTAMP B

Designer:	Geoff Blower
Handle:	A fishing rod resting on a tree trunk
Colourway:	Brown hat, brown coat, white collar

Backstamps: A. Doulton
B. Doulton / City of Stoke-on-Trent Jubilee Year 1959-1960
"With the compliments of LordMayor and Lady Mayoress
Alderman Harold Clowes, O.B.E., J.P. and Miss Christine Clowes"

Doulton Number	Size	Backstamp	Height	Intro.	Discon.	Current Market Value		
						U.K. £	U.S. $	Can. $
D6404	Large	Doulton	7"	1953	1982	65.00	100.00	135.00
D6404	Large	Doulton/City	7"	1959	1960	475.00	800.00	950.00

JANE SEYMOUR

HENRY VIII AND HIS SIX WIVES
ONE OF EIGHT

While serving as lady-in-waiting to both Catherine of Aragon and Anne Boleyn, Jane Seymour (1509-1537) attracted the attention of Henry VIII. She refused any proposal from the King except marriage, a factor leading to the trial of Anne. Two weeks after Anne Boleyn was beheaded, Jane Seymour became the third wife of Henry VIII, and the only one to bear him a male heir. She died shortly after Edward was born, and is the only wife to be buried at Henry's side.

Designer: Large Size: Michael Abberley
Small & Miniature Size: Peter Gee
Handle: A mandolin
Colourway: Black and gold

Royal Doulton®
JANE SEYMOUR
D 6746
Designed by M Abberley
Modelled by
PeterAGee
© 1978 ROYAL DOULTON (UK)

Backstamp: Doulton

Doulton Number	Size	Backstamp	Height	Intro.	Discon.	Current Market Value U.K. £	U.S. $	Can. $
D6646	Large	Doulton	7 1/4"	1979	1990	60.00	100.00	155.00
D6746	Small	Doulton	4 1/4"	1986	1990	40.00	65.00	90.00
D6747	Miniature	Doulton	2 3/4"	1986	1990	35.00	60.00	65.00

JARGE

The dialect form of "George" to name this fellow indicates he's a typical country bumpkin, with his polka-dot scarf and the piece of straw in his teeth.

"Jarge."

COPR 1949
DOULTON & CO LIMITED.
Rd No 857577.
Rd No 5904.
Rd No 76/49.

Designer: Harry Fenton
Handle: The scarf extends upwards to the cap
Colourway: Green cap, white scarf with red polka-dots

Backstamp: Doulton

Doulton Number	Size	Backstamp	Height	Intro.	Discon.	Current Market Value		
						U.K. £	U.S. $	Can. $
D6288	Large	Doulton	6 1/2"	1950	1960	175.00	350.00	400.00
D6295	Small	Doulton	3 1/2"	1950	1960	100.00	200.00	265.00

JESTER

Taking his name from the Latin "gesta" for "exploits", this character's comic antics entertained the courts of kings and noblemen. In the modern-day clown one can see the evolution of this funny role which maintains its popularity today.

Note: The green and yellow colouring on either side of the hat may be reversed as a preference of the painter. Minor variations of this nature do not command a price differential.

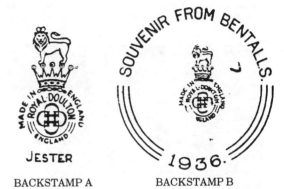

JESTER
BACKSTAMP A   BACKSTAMP B

SHEFFIELD &
ROTHERHAM
BACKSTAMP C

Designer: Charles Noke
Handle: Plain
Colourway: Brown, green and yellow

Backstamps: **A. Doulton**
B. Doulton/Bentalls "Souvenir From Bentalls 1936"
Commissioned by Bentalls as an advertising piece.
C. Doulton / Darley "Souvenir from Darley & Son, Sheffield & Rotherham"

Number	Doulton Size	Backstamp	Height	Intro.	Discon.	U.K. £	Current Market Value U.S. $	Can. $
D5556	Small	Doulton	3 1/8"	1936	1960	65.00	125.00	125.00
D5556	Small	Doulton/Bentalls	3 1/8"	1936	1936	350.00	750.00	850.00
D5556	Small	Doutlon/Darley	3 1/8"	1936	1936	350.00	750.00	850.00

Miscellaneous "Jester" Items

Doulton Number	Item	Height	Intro.	Discon.	U.K. £	Current Market Value U.S. $	Can. $
D6111	Wall Pocket	7 1/4"	1940	1941	950.00	1,700.00	2,000.00

JIMMY DURANTE

THE CELEBRITY COLLECTION
ONE OF FIVE

James Francis Durante (1893-1980) began his entertaining career playing the piano. His comic singing and clowning brought him fame in Vaudeville theatre, night clubs, films, radio and television. Using his own large nose as the object of jokes, Durante earned the long-standing nickname "Schnozzle".

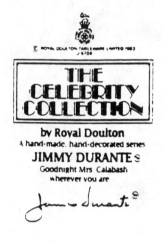

Designer: David Biggs
Handle: A piano keyboard
Colourway: Grey and black cap, yellow jacket and cream shirt

Backstamp: Doulton

Doulton Number	Size	Backstamp	Height	Intro.	Discon.	Current Market Value		
						U.K. £	U.S. $	Can. $
D6708	Large	Doulton	7 1/2"	1985	1988	65.00	100.00	145.00

JOCKEY

Winning or losing a horse race ultimately depends on the skill of the jockey. Master horsemen, these riders are chosen for their small size and lightweight as well as talent. The brightly coloured clothes they wear are the signature shades of the horse's owner.

Small and miniature sized jugs were test piloted but not produced. A small pilot jug is known to exist.

STYLE ONE: GOGGLES RESTING ON HIS CHEST; WINNING POLE

Jockey
D 6625
COPR 1970
DOULTON & CO LIMITED
Rd No 949548
Rd No 57983
Rd No 12388
Rd No 917/70

Designer:	David Biggs
Handle:	The winning pole
Colourway:	Red and yellow striped cap and racing jersey

Backstamp: Doulton

Doulton Number	Size	Backstamp	Height	Intro.	Discon.	Current Market Value U.K. £	U.S. $	Can. $
D6625	Large	Doulton	7 3/4"	1971	1975	250.00	375.00	475.00
D6629	Small	Doulton	4"	1974	1974		Unique	

THE JOCKEY

CHARACTER JUGS FROM LIFE
ONE OF SEVEN

STYLE TWO: *GOGGLES RESTING ON CAP; WINNING POLE AND HORSE HEAD*

Royal Doulton®
THE JOCKEY
D 6877
Modelled by

Stanley James Taylor

© 1990 ROYAL DOULTON

Designer: Stanley J. Taylor
Handle: Head of a horse and the winning pole
Colourway: Beige riding cap, yellow and
black racing jersey

Backstamp: Doulton

Doulton Number	Size	Backstamp	Height	Intro.	Discon.	Current Market Value		
						U.K. £	U.S. $	Can. $
D6877	Small	Doulton	4"	1991	Current	28.95	78.00	100.00

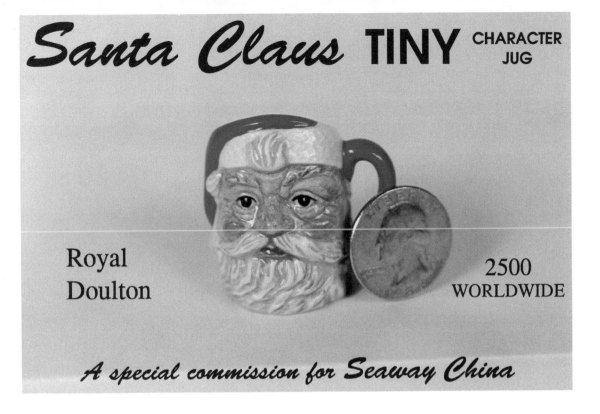

Santa Claus TINY CHARACTER JUG

Royal
Doulton

2500
WORLDWIDE

A special commission for Seaway China

Santa Claus "TINY" Character Jug is a special Worldwide Edition for Seaway China in Marine City, MI. U.S.A. Seaway China is a leading Royal Doulton Specialist. Mail this handy form or order **Toll Free** at 1-800-968-2424. If you prefer, you can use our **Toll Free Fax Order Line** 1-800-968-9005. Be sure to note if you would like our catalogue of all sizes of Royal Doulton Character Jugs.

-------------- CLIP AND MAIL OR COPY AND FAX --------------

Seaway China 102 Broadway
Marine City MI 48039 U.S.A.

Please accept my Order for _____ *Santa Claus* TINY Character Jug(s).
I understand the price for each Jug is **$55**. US. Funds **$70**. Can. Funds
30£ Sterling. (Plus $4 Postage, Handling & Insurance.)
☐ Send me your free list of all Royal Doulton Character Jugs.

Name _____

Address _____ City _____

State _____ Phone ( ) _____

Method of Payment   ☐ Money Order   ☐ Cheque   ☐ Charge my card
    ☐ VISA   ☐ MASTERCARD   ☐ AMEX   ☐ DISCOVER

Card Number _____   Expiry Date _____

| TOLL FREE | **1-800-968-2424** |
| TOLL FREE FAX | **1-800-968-9005** |

Signature _____
All orders will be acknowledged. MI Residents add 4% Sales Tax.
Worldwide orders Phone (313) 765-9000. Fax (313) 765-9005.
Answered 24 hours a day.

ORDER FORM

TOLL FREE FAX

ROYAL DOULTON CHARACTER JUGS

fun to collect....a fun investment!

"Royal Doulton Tinies"

The News is Out - 1993 Santa Claus TINY Added to the collection.
Seaway China offers their Special Commission of 2500 "Santa Claus Tiny".
   Add this special Royal Doulton Tiny to your collection today. Call Seaway today **toll free** 1-800-968-2424 Coast to Coast - Canada and the United States. Have your credit card number ready.

--CLIP AND MAIL OR COPY AND FAX--

From:

_____

_____

_____

PLACE
STAMP
HERE

Seaway China Company

ROYAL DOULTON SPECIALISTS

102 Broadway
Marine City, MI U.S.A.
48039

1-800-968-2424

JOHN BARLEYCORN

John is the personification of barley, the grain source of malt liquor. This Character jug is the first design created by Charles Noke in 1934.

STYLE ONE: *HANDLE "INSIDE" JUG - 1934 TO 1939*

JOHN BARLEYCORN.

BACKSTAMP A

R⁰N⁰782778

Coleman's Compliments

D 5327

BACKSTAMP B

Designer: Charles Noke
Handle: Plain brown
Colourway: Brown rim with light brown body

Backstamps: **A. Doulton**
 B. Doulton / Coleman's "Coleman's Compliments"
  Commissioned by Coleman's as an advertising piece large size
 C. Doulton / Salt River Cement Works "With Compliments From Salt River Cement Works"
  Commissioned by Salt River Cement Works as an advertising piece, large size

Doulton Number	Size	Backstamp	Height	Intro.	Discon.	Current Market Value U.K. £	U.S. $	Can. $
D5327	Large	Doulton	6 1/2"	1934	1939	100.00	160.00	225.00
D5327	Large	Doulton/Coleman's	6 1/2"	1938	1939	500.00	850.00	850.00
D5327	Large	Doulton/Salt River	6 1/2"	Unknown		1,000.00	2,500.00	850.00
D5735	Small	Doulton	3 1/2"	1937	1939	70.00	80.00	120.00

JOHN BARLEYCORN

STYLE TWO: HANDLE "OUTSIDE" JUG - 1939 TO 1960

VARIATION No. 1: Handle: Brown shading.

Designer: Charles Noke
Handle: Plain, brown shading
Colourway: Brown rim with light brown face

Backstamp: Doulton

Doulton Number	Size	Backstamp	Height	Intro.	Discon.	Current Market Value		
						U.K. £	U.S. $	Can. $
D5327	Large	Doulton	6 1/2"	1939	1960	75.00	150.00	195.00
D5735	Small	Doulton	3 1/2"	1939	1960	50.00	75.00	110.00
D6041	Miniature	Doulton	2 1/2"	1939	1960	45.00	75.00	85.00

VARIATION No. 2: **Handle: Black shading.**

Issued 1978 to 1982. Similar design, but a new mould as the original John Barleycorn mould was not available. This special exhibition jug, limited to 7,500, was sold at Royal Doulton special events. Modelled by Michael Abberley.

JOHN BARLEYCORN
D.5327
SPECIAL EXHIBITION REPRODUCTION
LIMITED TO 7,500 PIECES
THIS IS NUMBER 249

Designer: Charles Noke	**Backstamp:** Doulton/"SPECIAL EXHIBITION
Modeller: Michael Abberley	REPRODUCTION LIMITED TO
Handle: Plain, black shading	7,500 PIECES"
Colourway: Brown rim with light brown face	

Doulton Number	Size	Backstamp	Height	Intro.	Discon.	U.K. £	U.S. $	Can. $
						Current Market Value		
D5327	Large	Doulton/Special	6"	1978	Ltd. Ed.	70.00	160.00	200.00

Miscellaneous "John Barleycorn" Items

Doulton Number	Item	Height	Intro.	Discon.	U.K. £	U.S. $	Can. $
					Current Market Value		
D5602	Ashtray	4"	1936	1960	85.00	150.00	175.00

JOHN BARLEYCORN

Commissioned by American Express to form part of a twelve tankard set from various manufacturers. The set was test marketed to their card members.

It is estimated that between 500 and 600 were sold.

STYLE THREE: BLUE HAT WITH BARLEY EARS

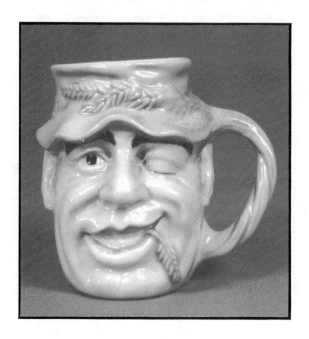

Designer: Stanley J. Taylor
Handle: Twisted barley stock
Colourway: Pale blue cap and light
brown barley ears

Backstamp: Doulton / American Express

Doulton Number	Size	Backstamp	Height	Intro.	Discon.	Current Market Value		
						U.K. £	U.S. $	Can. $
D6780	Mid	Doulton/Amex	5 1/2"	1988	Sp. Ed.	175.00	300.00	425.00

JOHN DOULTON

ROYAL DOULTON INTERNATIONAL COLLECTORS CLUB

John Doulton (1793-1873) served a seven year apprenticeship in the pottery industry as a thrower before fortune smiled on him and he was able to buy into a pottery partnership. He bought a one-third share of a stoneware pot-house in Vauxhall Walk, Lambeth. Doulton and Watts began its life around 1815 in that borough on the banks of the Thames in South London.

To honour John Doulton, The Royal Doulton International Collectors Club, in 1980, made this jug available to all their orginal charter members.

This first style has the time shown on "Big Ben" as 8 o'clock.

STYLE ONE: TIME SHOWN ON BIG BEN IS 8 O'CLOCK

JOHN DOULTON
1793 · 1873
EXCLUSIVELY FOR
COLLECTORS CLUB
ⓒ **ROYAL DOULTON**
TABLEWARE LTD 1980

Designer: Eric Griffith
Handle: The tower of "Big Ben"
Colourway: White cravat, "Big Ben" is grey

Backstamp: Doulton / RDICC

Doulton Number	Size	Backstamp	Height	Intro.	Discon.	Current Market Value U.K. £	U.S. $	Can. $
D6656	Small	Doulton/RDICC	4 1/4"	1980	c. 1982	65.00	125.00	150.00

JOHN DOULTON

ROYAL DOULTON INTERNATIONAL COLLECTORS CLUB

Starting in 1981 each new member joining the Royal Doulton International Collectors Club had the opporunity of purchasing the John Doulton jug, however, the time shown on 'Big Ben' is 2 o'clock.

STYLE TWO: *TIME SHOWN ON "BIG BEN" IS 2 O'CLOCK*

JOHN DOULTON
1793 - 1873
**EXCLUSIVELY FOR
COLLECTORS CLUB**
© ROYAL DOULTON
TABLEWARE LTD 1989

Designer: Eric Griffiths
Handle: The tower of "Big Ben"
Colourway: Yellow cravat, "Big Ben" is light brown

Backstamp: Doulton / RDICC

Doulton Number	Size	Backstamp	Height	Intro.	Discon.	Current Market Value U.K. £	U.S. $	Can. $
D6656	Small	Doulton/RDICC	4 1/4"	1981	Current	25.00	50.00	60.00

JOHN GILPIN

PROTOTYPE

"The Diverting History of John Gilpin" is an 18th century poem by Cowper. Gilpin, a "linen draper bold" and his wife go to Edmonton to celebrate their 20th wedding anniversary. His horse runs out of control on the way, and John careers ten miles beyond Edmonton and back again.

Designer: David Biggs   **Backstamp:** Doulton
Handle: Brown wood sign post "Edmonton"
Colourway: Dark green hat, maroon coat

Doulton Number	Size	Backstamp	Height	Intro.	Discon.	Current Market Value		
						U.K. £	U.S. $	Can. $
D —	Large	Doulton	7"	1968	1968		Extremely Rare Only Two Known	

JOHN LENNON

THE BEATLES
ONE OF FOUR

One of the original members of the famous English rock band, the Beatles, John Winston Lennon (1940-1980) played guitar and wrote songs until the group disbanded in 1970. With his wife Yoko Ono, Lennon pursued a successful solo career until his tragic assassination in 1980.

VARIATION No. 1: Colourway: Turquoise jacket with maroon collar and epaulettes

Royal Doulton
THE BEATLES
John Lennon
D 6725
Modelled by

Stanley James Taylor.

© ROYAL DOULTON TABLEWARE
LIMITED 1984

Designer: Stanley J. Taylor
Handle: Plain
Colourway: Turquoise jacket with
maroon collar and epaulettes

Backstamp: Doulton

Doulton Number	Size	Backstamp	Height	Intro.	Discon.	Current Market Value U.K. £	U.S. $	Can. $
D6725	Mid	Doulton	5 1/2"	1984	1991	55.00	95.00	95.00

VARIATION No. 2: Colourway: Red jacket with yellow collar and epaulettes

Backstamp: Doulton / John Sinclair "NEW COLOURWAY SPECIAL EDITION OF 1000
FOR JOHN SINCLAIR, SHEFFIELD"
Commissioned by John Sinclair, Sheffield. Issued in 1987 in a limited edition of 1,000 pieces.

Doulton Number	Size	Backstamp	Height	Intro.	Discon.	U.K. £	Current Market Value U.S. $	Can. $
D6797	Mid	Doulton/Sinclair	5 1/2"	1987	Ltd. Ed.	95.00	125.00	150.00

JOHN PEEL

John Peel (1776-1854) was a famous English huntsman, known for his enthusiam, skill and hospitality. Fond of drink, he hosted large, popular post-hunt celebrations. Peel has been immortalized in the song "D'ye ken John Peel," written by John Woodcock Graves.

VARIATION No. 1: Colourway: Grey handle

"John Peel."
Rᵈ Nº 809559.

Designer: Harry Fenton
Handle: Riding crop, with hunting horn forming on top of handle
Colourway: Dark grey hat, maroon coat, bark blue bow tie.

Backstamp: Doulton

Doulton Number	Size	Variations	Height	Intro.	Discon.	Current Market Value		
						U.K. £	U.S. $	Can. $
D5612	Large	Var. 1	6 1/2"	1936	1960	85.00	165.00	195.00
D5731	Small	Var. 1	3 1/2"	1937	1960	55.00	80.00	110.00
D6130	Miniature	Var. 1	2 1/4"	1940	1960	45.00	65.00	85.00
D6259	Tiny	Var. 1	1 1/4"	1947	1960	110.00	220.00	225.00

VARIATION No. 2: Colourway: Black and orange handle

Doulton Number	Size	Variations	Height	Intro.	Discon.	Current Market Value		
						U.K. £	U.S. $	Can. $
D5612	Large	Var. 2	6 1/2"	Unknown		75.00	170.00	210.00

JOHN SHORTER

Commissioned by the Character and Toby Jug Collectors Society of Australia, this depiction of Australian retailer Shorter was released in 1991 in a limited edition of 1,500 pieces.

Royal Doulton®
JOHN SHORTER
D.6880
Modelled by

William K. Harper

© 1990 ROYAL DOULTON
Specially commissioned from Royal Doulton
by the Character and Toby Jug Collectors Society
of Australia to commemorate
the 10th anniversary of the Society 1980 – 1990.
ISSUED IN A WORLDWIDE
LIMITED EDITION OF 1,500
THIS IS Nº. **372**

Designer: William K. Harper
Handle: A kangaroo and joey
Colourway: Grey hair, black jacket, maroon and white polka-dot bow-tie

Backstamp: Doulton / CJCSA

Doulton Number	Size	Backstamp	Height	Intro.	Discon.	Current Market Value		
						U.K. £	U.S. $	Can. $
D6880	Small	Doulton/CJCSA	4 1/4"	1991	Ltd. Ed. (1991)	75.00	150.00	145.00

JOHNNY APPLESEED

John Chapman (1774-1845) was an American pioneer who sold and gave saplings and apple seeds to colonizing families. He travelled the Eastern U.S., sowing apple orchards and tending his trees. After his death, Chapman became the hero of many legends.

Johnny Appleseed
D.6372
COPR.1952.
DOULTON & CO.LIMITED
R⁴N⁰ 868196
R⁹N⁰ 98801
R⁰N⁰ 30304
R⁴N⁰ 6647.

Designer:	Harry Fenton	Backstamp: Doulton
Handle:	An apple tree and knapsack	
Colourway:	Maroon and grey cap, brown robes	

Doulton Number	Size	Backstamp	Height	Intro.	Discon.	Current Market Value U.K. £	U.S. $	Can. $
D6372	Large	Doulton	6"	1953	1969	200.00	325.00	495.00

THE JUGGLER

THE CIRCUS
ONE OF FOUR

A favourite performer at the circus, the juggler dazzles audiences as he tosses balls, hoops or flaming wands without missing a beat.

Royal Doulton®

THE JUGGLER
D 6835
Modelled by

Stanley James Taylor

© 1988 ROYAL DOULTON

Designer: Stanley J. Taylor
Handle: Skittles and balls
Colourway: Brown hair, yellow, red and black tunic

Backstamp: Doulton

Doulton Number	Size	Backstamp	Height	Intro.	Discon.	Current Market Value		
						U.K. £	U.S. $	Can. $
D6835	Large	Doulton	6 1/2"	1989	1991	65.00	115.00	140.00

KING ARTHUR AND GUINEVERE

THE STAR CROSSED LOVERS COLLECTION (TWO-FACED JUG)
ONE OF FOUR

Arthur is the legendary 5th century King of Britain, known for his courage and honesty. His twelve knights, with whom he ruled and planned his campaigns, sat at a round table so that none had precedence. His best friend, the knight Lancelot, betrayed him by falling in love with his beautiful wife Guinevere. Arthur died at Camelford in a battle against his usurping nephew Mordred.
Issued in 1989 in a limited edition of 9500.

Designer: Stanley J. Taylor
Handle: King Arthur - Sword
Guinevere - Chalice
Colourway: Blue-grey, yellow and white

Royal Doulton®
THE
STAR-CROSSED **L**OVERS
COLLECTION
King Arthur & Guinevere
D 6836
Modelled by Stanley James Taylor

Stanley James Taylor

Worldwide Limited Edition of 9,500
This is Number **792**
© 1988 Royal Doulton

Backstamp: Doulton

Doulton Number	Size	Backstamp	Height	Intro.	Discon.	Current Market Value		
						U.K. £	U.S. $	Can. $
D6836	Large	Doulton	6 1/2"	1989	Ltd. Ed. (1991)	85.00	135.00	165.00

KING CHARLES I

This jug was issued in a limited edition of 2,500 to commemorate the 350th Anniversary of the English Civil War. It is unusual in the sense that it is the first three-handled character jug ever produced by Doulton. On Charles' left the handle is Oliver Cromwell. On his right, Queen Henrietta. The third handle, at the King's back and not seen in the photo below, is a plume.

Royal Doulton®
KING CHARLES I
D 6917
Modelled by

William K. Harper

© 1992 ROYAL DOULTON
LIMITED EDITION OF 2,500
THIS IS № 1931
To commemorate the 350th
Anniversary of the start of
the English Civil War, 1642

Designer: William K. Harper
Handle: Three Handles (see above)
Colourway: Black, yellow and red

Backstamp: Doulton

Doulton Number	Size	Backstamp	Height	Intro.	Discon.	Current Market Value		
						U.K. £	U.S. $	Can. $
D6917	Large	Doulton	7"	1992	Ltd. Ed. (1993)	199.00	450.00	625.00

KING EDWARD VII

RDICC EXCLUSIVE

In this jug, King Edward is shown wearing a crown and all his finery. The handle is comprised of the traditional Royal Doulton backstamp of the crown and lion. This piece had a limited edition of 2,500 and was issued exclusively for the Royal Doulton International Collectors Club.

King Edward V11

D.6923
EXCLUSIVELY FOR
COLLECTORS CLUB
Limited edition of
2,500

THIS IS NO
1586
MODELLED BY

© 1992 Royal Doulton

Designer: William K. Harper
Handle: Lion and crown of the Doulton backstamp
Colourway: Red, gold, and white

Backstamp: Doulton/RDICC

Doulton Number	Size	Backstamp	Height	Intro.	Discon.	Current Market Value U.K. £	U.S. $	Can. $
D6923	Mid	Doulton/RDICC	5 1/2"	1992	Ltd. Ed.	120.00	250.00	295.00

KING HENRY VIII

This is a two handled jug and strictly speaking should be classified as a loving cup. Issued in 1991 in a limited edition of 1991 to commemorate the 500th anniversary of the birth of Henry VIII.

Designer: William K. Harper	**Backstamp:** Doulton
Handle: Double handle, three wives on either side	
Colourway: White and black with gold trim	

Doulton Number	Size	Backstamp	Height	Intro.	Discon.	Current Market Value		
						U.K. £	U.S. $	Can. $
D6888	Large	Doulton	7"	1991	Ltd. Ed. (1991)	300.00	750.00	695.00

KING PHILIP OF SPAIN

Reigning king of Spain during its most powerful and influential era, Philip (1527-1598) was a strong defender of Catholicism and leader of an anti-reformation movement against Protestant leaders, such as Queen Elizabeth I. He led a rebellion in the Netherlands and waged wars against the Ottoman Empire and England in the name of his cause. His attempted invasion of England in 1588 was repressed in one of the most famous naval battles in history, and his Armada was defeated. Issued by Lawleys By Post in 1988, this jug is one of a pair (with Queen Elizabeth I) produced to celebrate the 400th anniversary of the defeat of the Spanish Armada. Both jugs are limited editions of 9500 pieces.

Designer: William K. Harper
Handle: Galleon sailing on the left
Colourway: Grey, white and brown

Backstamp: Doulton

Doulton Number	Size	Backstamp	Height	Intro.	Discon.	Current Market Value		
						U.K. £	U.S. $	Can. $
D6822	Small	Doulton	4"	1988	Ltd. Ed. (1991)	75.00	100.00	125.00

THE LAWYER

This solicitor is dressed in the old English tradition of lawyers that is carried on today. The actual wig is made of horsehair and complements a stylized white collar and black robes.

The Lawyer
D6498
COPR 1958
DOULTON & CO LIMITED
Rd No 889569
Rd No 38225
Rd No 8035
Rd No 424/58

Royal Doulton

THE LAWYER
D 6504
Modelled by

© ROYAL DOULTON TABLEWARE
LIMITED 1958

Designer: Max Henk
Handle: Green feather quill
Colourway: Grey wig, black robes, white shirt

Backstamp: Doulton

Doulton Number	Size	Backstamp	Height	Intro.	Discon.	Current Market Value U.K. £	U.S. $	Can. $
D6498	Large	Doulton	7"	1959	Current	49.95	142.50	160.00
D6504	Small	Doulton	4"	1959	Current	25.00	78.00	90.00
D6524	Miniature	Doulton	2 1/2"	1960	1991	30.00	40.00	60.00

Miscellaneous "The Lawyer" Items

Doulton Number	Item	Height	Intro.	Discon.	Current Market Value U.K. £	U.S. $	Can. $
D6504	Table Lighter	3 1/2"	1962	1974	120.00	225.00	260.00

LEEDS UNITED (FOOTBALL CLUB)

THE FOOTBALL SUPPORTERS
ONE OF EIGHT

Designer: Stanley J. Taylor   **Backstamp:** Doulton
Handle: Team coloured scarf
Colourway: White, blue and yellow uniform

Doulton Number	Size	Backstamp	Height	Intro.	Discon.	Current Market Value		
						U.K. £	U.S. $	Can. $
D6928	Mid	Doulton	5"	1992	Current	35.00	125.00	95.00

LEN HUTTON

Sir Leonard Hutton played for the Yorkshire County Cricket Club. The ribbon bearing the number 364 which is intertwined around the handle of the jug represents his famous records innings against Australia at the Oval cricket grounds in 1938. A record which still stands today in England. The jug was commissioned by Lawleys By Post and is issued in a limited edition of 9,500. The first jug was presented to Her Royal Highness The Duchess of Kent who is Patron of the Ken HUtton 364 Appeal.

Designer: Stanley J. Taylor
Handle: Cricket bat, stumps and ball
Colourway: White shirt and sweater, black cap

Backstamp: Doulton

Doulton Number	Size	Backstamp	Height	Intro.	Discon.	Current Market Value		
						U.K. £	U.S. $	Can. $
D6945	Mid	Doulton	4"	1993	Ltd. Ed.	49.00	125.00	125.00

LEPRECHAUN

This wizened little elf is a legenday Irish sprite with a mischievous nature. The Irish believed that leprechauns guarded hoards of treasure hidden at the end of rainbows.

BACKSTAMP A

BACKSTAMP C

Designer:	William K. Harper
Handle:	Rainbow with a sack of gold at the base
Colourway:	Green cap, brown coat

Backstamps: A. Doulton
For General Release: Large size - 1991, Small size -1992
B. Doulton/The Site of the Green -
Large size Commissioned by The Site of The Green and issued in 1990 in a special edition of 500 pieces.
C. Doulton/The Site of The Green -
Small size Commissioned by The Site of The Green and issued in 1991 in a special edition of 500 pieces.

Doulton Number	Size	Backstamp	Height	Intro.	Discon.	Current Market Value U.K. £	Current Market Value U.S. $	Current Market Value Can. $
D6847	Large	Doulton	7 1/2"	1991	Current	59.95	195.00	220.00
D6847	Large	Doulton/Site	7 1/2"	1990	Sp. Ed.	95.00	195.00	220.00
D6899	Small	Doulton	4 1/2"	1992	Current	28.95	82.50	90.00
D6899	Small	Doulton/Site	4 1/2"	1991	Sp. Ed.	60.00	85.00	100.00

LITTLE MESTER MUSEUM PIECE

This jug was modelled on the likeness of Grinder Rowland Swindon, a grinder from Sheffield, England. One thousand jugs were bought by the World Student Games to help launch the games in Sheffield. Commissioned by John Sinclair, Sheffield, England. Issued in 1988 in a limited edition of 3,500 pieces.

Royal Doulton®
LITTLE MESTER
MUSEUM PIECE
D 6819
Modelled by
Stanley James Taylor
© 1988 ROYAL DOULTON
SPECIAL EDITION OF 3,500
790

Designer: Stanley J. Taylor
Handle: Bowie knife and grinder
Colourway: Black cap, blue jacket,
white shirt and red scarf

Backstamp: Doulton

Doulton Number	Size	Backstamp	Height	Intro.	Discon.	Current Market Value		
						U.K. £	U.S. $	Can. $
D6819	Large	Doulton	6 3/4"	1988	Sp. Ed. (1991)	75.00	160.00	200.00

LITTLE NELL

CHARLES DICKENS COMMEMORATIVE SET
DICKENS TINIES, ONE OF TWELVE

Little Nell is the ill-fated protagonist in Dickens' "The Old Curiosity Shop".
Issued to commemorate the 170th Anniversary of the birth of Charles Dickens. There are twelve jugs in this set, each issued with a certificate of authenticity. A mahogany display shelf completes the set. The set was first sold by Lawleys By Post in the U.K. during 1982 to 1988, and in 1985 onward in North America and Australia.

Little Nell
D.6681

Designer: Michael Abberley	**Backstamp:** Doulton
Handle: Plain	
Colourway: Yellow and black	

Doulton Number	Size	Backstamp	Height	Intro.	Discon.	Current Market Value U.K. £	U.S. $	Can. $
D6681	Tiny	Doulton	1 1/2"	1982	1989	30.00	45.00	60.00
		Display for 12 Tinies				65.00	45.00	50.00

LIVERPOOL (FOOTBALL CLUB)

THE FOOTBALL SUPPORTERS
ONE OF EIGHT

Royal Doulton®
FOOTBALL SUPPORTER'S
CHARACTER JUG.
D 6930
Modelled by
Stanley James Taylor
© 1992 ROYAL DOULTON
"LIVERPOOL"

Designer: Stanley J. Taylor
Handle: Team coloured scarf
Colourway: Red and white uniform

Backstamp: Doulton

Doulton Number	Size	Backstamp	Height	Intro.	Discon.	Current Market Value		
						U.K. £	U.S. $	Can. $
D6930	Mid	Doulton	5"	1992	Current	35.00	125.00	95.00

LIVERPOOL CENTENARY JUG (BILL SHANKLY)

Issued to commemorate the 100th Anniversary of the Liverpool Football Club in 1992. The jug is a limited edition of 5,500.

LIVERPOOL CENTENARY JUG
D 6914
Specially Commissioned from
Royal Doulton®
by
LIVERPOOL F.C.
In celebration of
the clubs centenary
In 1992
Modelled by *William K. Harper*
© 1991 ROYAL DOULTON
A LIMITED EDITION OF 5,500
THIS IS N⁰ 775

Designer: William K. Harper
Handle: Two footballs and flag
Colourway: Red jersey, white collar, gray hair

Backstamp: Doulton/Liverpool F.C.

Doulton Number	Size	Backstamp	Height	Intro.	Discon.	Current Market Value		
						U.K. £	U.S. $	Can. $
D6914	Small	Doulton/ Liverpool	3 1/2"	1992	Ltd. Ed.	40.00	125.00	125.00

LOBSTER MAN

This hearty fisherman with the weathered face is out at sea in all weather, catching that hard-shelled creature that is such a delicacy.

VARIATION No. 1: Colourway: Dark blue jacket and cap, white fisherman's jersey

LOBSTER MAN
D 6652
COPR 1967
DOULTON & CO LIMITED

Designer: David Biggs
Handle: Lobster
Colourway: Dark blue jacket and cap, white fisherman's jersey

Backstamp: Doulton

Doulton Number	Size	Backstamp	Height	Intro.	Discon.	Current Market Value U.K. £	U.S. $	Can. $
D6617	Large	Var. 1	7 1/2"	1968	1991	55.00	95.00	145.00
D6620	Small	Var. 1	3 3/4"	1968	1991	35.00	55.00	80.00
D6652	Miniature	Var. 1	2 3/4"	1980	1991	30.00	45.00	60.00

VARIATION No. 2: Colourway: Dark blue jacket and cap, blue-grey fisherman's jersey

Doulton Number	Size	Backstamp	Height	Intro.	Discon.	Current Market Value U.K. £	U.S. $	Can. $
D6783	Large	Var. 2	8"	1987	1989	55.00	130.00	150.00

VARIATION No. 3 Colourway: Light Blue Jacket

Doulton Number	Size	Backstamp	Height	Intro.	Discon.	Current Market Value U.K. £	U.S. $	Can. $
D —	Small	Var. 2	3 3/4"	1987	Unknown	Price Not Established		

THE LONDON 'BOBBY'

THE LONDON COLLECTION
ONE OF TEN

The constabulary of London has long been known by its affectionate nickname, "bobbies". Loyal and professional, they are never too busy to give directions to grateful visitors.

VARIATION No. 1: Hat badge embossed and hand painted

Designer: Stanley J. Taylor
Handle: Tower of "Big Ben" and a whistle
Colourway: Black and white badge, see Variations

Backstamp: Doulton

Doulton Number	Size	Variations	Height	Intro.	Discon.	Current Market Value U.K. £	U.S. $	Can. $
D6744	Large	Var. 1	7"	1986	1987	60.00	160.00	195.00
D6762	Small	Var. 1	3 1/2	1987	1987	30.00	75.00	90.00
D6763	Miniature	Var. 1	2 1/2	1987	1987	35.00	50.00	65.00

VARIATION No. 2: Hat badge decal decorated

Doulton Number	Size	Variations	Height	Intro.	Discon.	Current Market Value U.K. £	U.S. $	Can. $
D6744	Large	Var. 2	7 1/2"	1987	Current	49.95	142.50	160.00
D6762	Small	Var. 2	3 1/2"	1987	Current	25.00	78.00	90.00
D6763	Miniature	Var. 2	2 1/2"	1987	1991	30.00	45.00	60.00

LONG JOHN SILVER

CHARACTERS FROM LITERATURE
ONE OF ELEVEN

This scoundrel and pirate from Robert Louis Stevenson's famous adventure tale, "Treasure Island" had a wooden leg and a parrot companion. Together with the boy-hero Jim Hawkins, he set sail in a hair-raising search for buried treasure that has captured the imaginations of readers for over a century.

VARIATION No. 1: Colourway: Maroon shirt, green and grey parrot

Designer: Max Henk
Handle: A Parrot
Colourway: Maroon shirt, green and grey parrot

`Long John Silver`
D.6335
COPR 1951.
DOULTON & CO LIMITED
R⁴N° 864843
R⁴N° 29156
R⁴N° 6404
R⁴N° 112/51

Backstamp: Doulton

Doulton Number	Size	Backstamp	Height	Intro.	Discon.	Current Market Value		
						U.K. £	U.S. $	Can. $
D6335	Large	Doulton	7"	1952	Current	49.95	142.50	160.00
D6386	Small	Doulton	4"	1952	Current	25.00	78.00	90.00
D6512	Miniature	Doulton	2 1/2"	1960	1991	30.00	40.00	60.00

VARIATION No. 2: Colourway: Yellow shirt, yellow-green parrot

"LONG JOHN SILVER"
D 6799
*Specially Commissioned
from*
Royal Doulton®
by
D.H. HOLMES COMPANY LTD
Celebrating the opening of
The Royal Doulton Room
D.H. Holmes, New Orleans, Louisiana, U.S.A.
HAND MODELLED AND HAND DECORATED
A LIMITED EDITION OF 250
THIS IS NO. 91
© 1987 ROYAL DOULTON

Backstamp: Doulton/ D. H. Holmes "Specially Commissioned from Royal Doulton by D. H. Holmes
Company Ltd. Celebrating the opening of The Royal Doulton Room D. H. Holmes, New
Orleans, Louisiana, U.S.A."
Commissioned by D. H. Holmes Company Ltd. Issued in 1987 in a limited edition of 250 pieces

Doulton Number	Size	Backstamp	Height	Intro.	Discon.	Current Market Value		
						U.K. £	U.S. $	Can. $
D6799	Large	Doulton/Holmes	7"	1987	Ltd. Ed.	225.00	275.00	250.00

Miscellaneous "Long John Silver" Items

Doulton Number	Item	Height	Intro.	Discon.	Current Market Value		
					U.K. £	U.S. $	Can. $
D6386	Lighter	3 1/2"	1958	1973	120.00	150.00	175.00
D6853	Teapot	7"	1990	1991	65.00	95.00	125.00

LORD MAYOR OF LONDON

THE LONDON COLLECTION
ONE OF TEN

The newly elected Mayor of the city of London first presents himself to the people on Mayor's Day. Annually, on the second Sunday in November, a procession takes the Mayor to Westminster to receive from the Lord Chancellor assent of the Crown to his election.

Designer: Stanley J. Taylor	**Backstamp:** Doulton
Handle: Sceptre of office	
Colourway: Black plume hat, red cloak and yellow chain of office.	

Doulton Number	Size	Backstamp	Height	Intro.	Discon.	Current Market Value U.K. £	U.S. $	Can. $
D6864	Large	Doulton	7 1/4"	1990	1991	50.00	125.00	150.00

LORD NELSON

Horatio Nelson (1758-1805), a member of the navy since the age of twelve, was made commander-in-chief of his own fleet in 1803. He saw action in the West Indies and Canada but is best remembered for his courage at the battle of Trafalgar. In 1805 his fleet engaged and defeated the French and Spanish navies. Nelson died during the battle.

Designer: Geoff Blower
Handle: Plain
Colourway: Blue tricorn and jacket with gold trim, white cravat

Backstamps: A. Doulton
B. Doulton/Battle of Trafalgar " Commemorating the 150th Anniversary of the Battle of Trafalgar 21st October 1955"
Commissioned for the Admiralty to commemorate the 150th anniversary of Nelson's victory at Trafalgar, October 21st, 1955.
C. Three of the jugs carry an added line to the backstamp, that of "First Lord", "First Sea Lord" and "Secretary," the intention being that these three jugs would be held in perpetuity at the respective offices. However that did not happen when one of the elected official left office that jug went with him only to later appear on the market.

Doulton Number	Size	Backstamp	Height	Intro.	Discon.	Current Market Value		
						U.K. £	U.S. $	Can. $
D6336	Large	A	7"	1952	1969	225.00	450.00	500.00
D6336	Large	B	7"	1955	1955	750.00	1,250.00	1,500.00
D6336	Large	C	7"	1955	1955	Only Three Issued and each with different backstamps		

LOUIS ARMSTRONG

THE CELEBRITY COLLECTION
ONE OF FIVE

Daniel Louis "Satchmo" Armstrong, (1900-1971), evolved from a self-taught cornet player at fourteen to the first internationally famous soloist in jazz music. He was well-known for both his brilliant technique on the trumpet and for his deep throaty singing voice. Appearing in many live shows, Broadway musicals and films, Armstrong's music made a lasting influence on jazz.

© ROYAL DOULTON TABLEWARE LIMITED 1996
D 6707

THE CELEBRITY COLLECTION
by Royal Doulton
A hand-made, hand-decorated series
LOUIS ARMSTRONG ⊖
"Man, if you gotta ask, you'll never know"
(His reply when asked what Jazz was).

Louis Armstrong ⊖

Designer: David Biggs
Handle: Trumpet and handkerchief
Colourway: Brown and pink

Backstamp: Doulton

Doulton Number	Size	Backstamp	Height	Intro.	Discon.	Current Market Value U.K. £	U.S. $	Can. $
D6707	Large	Doulton	7 1/2"	1984	1988	65.00	125.00	160.00

LUMBERJACK

From early colonial times, lumber has been one of Canada's main industries. The cutting of trees and hauling them to rivers for transportation was a dangerous and isolated task. These sturdy men would leave for "the bush" in the fall, and reappear with the logs in the spring thaw. Many legends have grown-up around this way of life.

A small quantity of miniature prototypes are known to exist.

Lumberjack
D 6610
COPR 1966
DOULTON & CO LIMITED
Rd No 924807
Rd No 49146
Rd No 10601
Rd No 53/66

BACKSTAMP A

CANADIAN CENTENNIAL SERIES
1867 - 1967

The Lumberjack
D 6610
COPR 1966
DOULTON & CO LIMITED
Rd No 924807
Rd No 49146
Rd No 10601
Rd No 53/66

BACKSTAMP B

Designer: Max Henk	**Backstamps** A. **Doulton**
Handle: Tree trunk and axe	B. **Doulton / Canadian Centenary**
Colourway: Red cap, green jacket and pink sweater	"Canadian Centennial Series 1867-1967" Available in North America during 1967 only.

Doulton Number	Size	Backstamp	Height	Intro.	Discon.	Current Market Value		
						U.K. £	**U.S. $**	**Can. $**
D6610	Large	Doulton	7 1/4"	1967	1982	60.00	110.00	155.00
D6610	Large	Centenary	7 1/4"	1967	1967	100.00	225.00	275.00
D6613	Small	Doulton	3 1/2"	1967	1982	40.00	65.00	95.00
D —	Miniature	Doulton	2 1/2"	Unknown			Extremely Rare	

The lumberjack is one of three jugs that received a special backstamp in 1967. The other two, the North American Indian and the Trapper, complete the three jug Canadian Centennial Series.

MACBETH

THE SHAKESPEAREAN COLLECTION
ONE OF SIX

First performed in 1606, this Shakespearean tragedy is based on Scottish history. With the help of his wife, Macbeth plots to usurp the throne. Three witches prophesy that he will succeed but that his enemy, Banquo's heirs, will one day rule the Kingdom. In a series of grisly events, their dark predicitons are fulfilled.

STYLE ONE: HANDLE: WITCHES FACING OUTWARD

The faces of the three witches on the outer side of the handle face outward (noses out). Only after the jug was in the initial stages of production did Doulton realize the hazards that might occur in shipping the jug. The possibility of the handle being damaged in packing was great and thus the moulds were quickly modified resulting in the production of style two.

Designer:	Michael Abberley	**Backstamp:** Doulton
Handle:	Three witches facing to the right	
Colourway:	Brown, yellow and green	

Doulton Number	Size	Backstamp	Height	Intro.	Discon.	Current Market Value U.K. £	U.S. $	Can. $
D6667	Large	Doulton	7 1/4"	1981	1981		Extremely Rare	

MACBETH

THE SHAKESPEAREAN COLLECTION
ONE OF SIX

STYLE TWO: *HANDLE: WITCHES FACING INWARD*

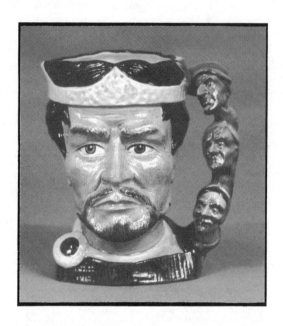

Designer: Michael Abberley
Handle: The faces of the three witches are on
the front of the handle facing forwards.
Colourway: Brown, yellow and grey

Backstamp: Doulton

Doulton Number	Size	Backstamp	Height	Intro.	Discon.	Current Market Value U.K. £	U.S. $	Can. $
D6667	Large	Doulton	7 1/4"	1982	1989	65.00	115.00	145.00

MAD HATTER

ALICE IN WONDERLAND
ONE OF SIX

A guest at a tea party that Alice attends uninvited, the Mad Hatter's watch keeps months rather than hours. The March Hare presides over tea and bread and butter and the dormouse sleeps through the party.

VARIATION No. 1: Colourway: Black hat, dark red bow-tie

Mad Hatter
D 6598
COPR 1970
DOULTON & CO LIMITED
Rd No 917231
Rd No 46577
Rd No 10000
Rd No 592/64

Designer: Max Henk
Handle: A dormouse above a pocket watch
Colourway: Black hat, dark red bow-tie

Backstamp: Doulton

Doulton Number	Size	Variation	Height	Intro.	Discon.	Current Market Value U.K. £	U.S. $	Can. $
D6598	Large	Var. 1	7 1/4"	1965	1983	80.00	140.00	175.00
D6602	Small	Var. 1	3 3/4"	1965	1983	55.00	85.00	95.00
D6606	Miniature	Var. 1	2 1/2"	1965	1983	40.00	70.00	75.00

VARIATION No. 2: Colourway: Black hat, yellow bow-tie

"MAD HATTER"
D.6748
*Specially Commissioned
from*
Royal Doulton®
by
THE HIGBEE COMPANY 1985
Celebrating the opening of
The First Royal Doulton Room
Higbee's, Cleveland, U.S.A.
HAND MODELLED AND HAND DECORATED
A LIMITED EDITION OF 250
THIS IS NO. 224
© 1985 ROYAL DOULTON

BACKSTAMP A

Backstamps: A. Doulton/Higbee's - Large size
Commissioned by the Higbee Company to celebrate the opening of the First Royal Doulton Room.
Issued on October 28th, 1985 in a limited edition of 250 pieces.
B. Doulton/Higbee's - Small size
Commissioned by the Higbee Department Store to celebrate the second anniversary of
the opening of the Royal Doulton Room. Issued in 1987 in a limited edition of 500 pieces.

Doulton Number	Size	Backstamp	Height	Intro.	Discon.	Current Market Value U.K. £	U.S. $	Can. $
D6748	Large	Doulton/Higbee	7"	1985	Ltd. Ed.	400.00	675.00	775.00
D6790	Small	Doulton/Higbee	3 1/4"	1987	Ltd. Ed.	125.00	225.00	250.00

MAE WEST

THE CELEBRITY COLLECTION
ONE OF FIVE

From her screen debut in 1932, Mae West (1892-1980) became an instant hit. She is best known for the tough, sophisticated characters she played who loved luxury and men. The public adored her and her witty quips, the most famous of which appears on the base of the jug: "When I'm good, I'm very good. But when I'm bad, I'm better."

THE CELEBRITY COLLECTION
by Royal Doulton
A hand-made hand-decorated series
MAE WEST
When I'm good I'm very good
But when I'm bad I'm better

BACKSTAMP A

Designer:	Colin M. Davidson
Handle:	Umbrella with a bow tied around the handle
Colourway:	Yellow hair, white feather dress

Backstamps:
A. **Doulton General Issue: 1983.**
B. **Doulton / American Express "Premier Edition for American Express"** This series was first introduced in the U.S.A. as a promotional jug for the American Express Company. Approximately five hundred jugs were given the special backstamp and were available only to the North American market.

Doulton Number	Size	Backstamp	Height	Intro.	Discon.	Current Market Value U.K. £	U.S. $	Can. $
D6688	Large	Doulton	7"	1983	1986	75.00	130.00	165.00
D6688	Large	Doulton/Amex	7"	1983	1983	250.00	500.00	600.00

MANCHESTER UNITED (FOOTBALL CLUB)

THE FOOTBALL SUPPORTERS
ONE OF EIGHT

Royal Doulton®
FOOTBALL SUPPORTER'S
CHARACTER JUG.
D 6924
Modelled by
Stanley James Taylor.
© 1992 ROYAL DOULTON
"MANCHESTER UNITED"

Designer: Stanley J. Taylor
Handle: Team coloured scarf
Colourway: Red, white and black uniform

Backstamp: Doulton

Doulton Number	Size	Backstamp	Height	Intro.	Discon.	Current Market Value		
						U.K. £	U.S. $	Can. $
D6924	Mid	Doulton	5"	1992	Current	35.00	125.00	95.00

MAORI

The Maori, people of Polynesian descent, were the first inhabitants of present-day New Zealand. Beginning as hunters and fishers, the Maori later turned to agriculture. Master woodworkers, they are known for the complicated designs they carved on their houses and canoes. Today their population is about 300,000 or 9% of the whole of New Zealand.

STYLE ONE: *BLUE-GREY HAIR; FRIENDLY EXPRESSION*

Designer: Unknown   **Backstamp:** Doulton
   Handle: Plain with plaque of Maori
Colourway: Brown and grey

Doulton Number	Size	Backstamp	Height	Intro.	Discon.	U.K. £	Current Market Value U.S. $	Can. $
D6080	Large	Doulton	7"	1939	1939		Extremely Rare	

MAORI

STYLE TWO: DARK HAIR, TWO WHITE TIPPED FEATHERS
IN HAIR; SERIOUS EXPRESSION

Designer: Unknown
Handle: Plain with plaque of Maori
Colourway: Brown and grey

Backstamp: Doulton

Doulton Number	Size	Backstamp	Height	Intro.	Discon.	Current Market Value		
						U.K. £	U.S. $	Can. $
D6080	Large	Doulton	7"	1939	1939		Extremely Rare	

THE MARCH HARE

ALICE IN WONDERLAND
ONE OF SIX

At the March Hare's home in Wonderland it is always 6 o'clock and time for tea. Not having a moment to tidy up in between, he and his friends the Mad Hatter and the dormouse sit at a table laid for a great number and change seats as they dirty the dishes. Alice makes herself unpopular by asking what they do when they arrive back at the beginning.

Royal Doulton®

THE MARCH HARE
D 6776
Modelled by

William K. Harper

© 1988 ROYAL DOULTON

Designer: William K. Harper
Handle: One of the hare's ears
Colourway: Green hat, yellow bow-tie
with blue spots

Backstamp: Doulton

Doulton Number	Size	Backstamp	Height	Intro.	Discon.	Current Market Value		
						U.K. £	U.S. $	Can. $
D6776	Large	Doulton	6"	1989	1991	75.00	140.00	175.00

MARILYN MONROE

THE CELEBRITY COLLECTION

PROTOTYPE

Norma Jean Baker (1926-1962) was born in Los Angeles, California. As Marilyn Munroe, she made her screen debut in 1948. Her beauty and charisma established her as an international sex symbol but despite a successful career and universal acclaim her private life was tragic. She committed suicide with an overdose of sleeping pills at the age of 36.

The are only two of these jugs known to exist. One is in the Doulton Museum, Stoke-on-Trent. The other came to auction in 1992 in Toronto and fetched $17,500.00. Not issued due to copyright problems.

Designer: Eric Griffith
Handle: A cine-camera encircled by a roll of film
Colourway: Yellow, white and grey

Backstamp: Doulton

Doulton Number	Size	Variation	Height	Intro.	Discon.	Current Market Value		
						U.K. £	U.S. $	Can. $
D6719	Large	Prototype	7 1/4"	1983	1983	Auction, Toronto, 1992, $17,500		

MARK TWAIN

Born Samuel Langhorne Clemens (1835-1910), Twain was an American writer and humourist, best loved for his classic adventure stories, "Tom Sawyer," (1876), and "The Adventures of Huckleberry Finn," (1884), which told of life in his native Mississippi.

The small jug was modelled for "The Queen's Table", Royal Doulton's Exhibit at the United Kingdom Showcase at Walt Disney's Epcot Centre in Orlando, Florida. The jug was sold exclusively to Epcot tourists visiting the exhibition during 1982.

Designer: Eric Griffiths
Handle: Quill and ink-pot
Colourway: Black coat and bow-tie, grey hair

Royal Doulton
MARK TWAIN
D 6654
Modelled by

© ROYAL DOULTON TABLEWARE
LIMITED 1979

Backstamp: Doulton

| Doulton Number | Size | Backstamp | Height | Intro. | Discon. | Current Market Value | | |
						U.K. £	U.S. $	Can. $
D6654	Large	Doulton	7 1/2"	1980	1990	50.00	110.00	145.00
D6694	Small	Doulton	4"	1983	1990	40.00	70.00	80.00
D6758	Miniature	Doulton	2 1/2"	1986	1990	35.00	90.00	60.00

MARRIAGE DAY

Large and small size jugs:
> Upright: Smiling face, "Marriage Day" inscribed at the top of the jug (forehead).
> Upsidedown: Frowning face: "After Marriage" inscribed at the base of the jug (chin)

Miniature size:
> Upright: Frowning face: "After Marriage" inscribed at the top (forehead)
> Upsidedown: Smiling face: "Marriage Day" insribed around base (chin)

The possibility exists that another variety of the miniature jug may exist with the "Marriage Day" smiling face upright.

Designer: Harry Simeon
Handle: Plain
Colourway: **Large and small size:**
> Upright: Blue cap withwhite frill
> Upsidedown: Brown cap with white frill

Backstamp: Doulton Lambeth

> **Miniature Size:**
> Upright: Blue cap with white frill
> Upsidedown: Brown cap with white frill

Doulton Number	Size	Backstamp	Height	Intro.	Discon.	Current Market Value		
						U.K. £	U.S. $	Ca500.00n. $
D —	Large	Doulton Lambeth	4 3/4"	Unknown		250.00	375.00	500.00
D —	Small	Doulton Lambeth	3 1/2"	Unknown		175.00	265.00	350.00
D —	Miniature	Doulton Lambeth	2"	Unknown		125.00	175.00	250.00

THE MASTER / EQUESTRIAN

This piece was released in the U.K. as "The Master", and in North America as "The Equestrian".

Designer: Stanley J. Taylor
Handle: Horse head
Colourway: Dark blue, red and white

Backstamp: Doulton

Doulton Number	Size	Backstamp	Height	Intro.	Discon.	Current Market Value		
						U.K. £	U.S. $	Can. $
D6898	Small	Doulton	4"	1991	Current	28.95	78.00	110.00

McCALLUM

PROTOTYPE

This jug carries the Burslem Lion and Crown backstamp with the number "— 0 —" signifying 1927. The jug has been a controversial one but the backstamp dating might lead one to believe that it may be a trial piece for the 1930 issues.

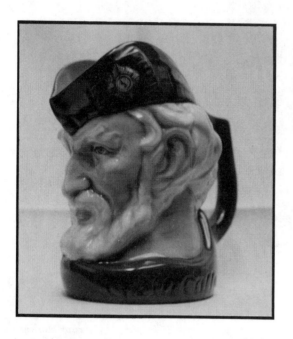

Designer: McCallum
Handle: Plain
Colourway: White hair with pale green and pink
highlights; Black with red and green Glengarry;
green base

Backstamp: Doulton

Doulton Number	Size	Variation	Height	Intro.	Discon.	Current Market Value U.K. £	U.S. $	Can. $
D ---	Large	Prototype	7"	1927			Unique,	

McCALLUM

Produced as a promotional item for the D & J McCallum Distillery, Scotland, this jug exists in three different colour varieties, all in very limited quantities. This jug was also produced by other manufacturers from an almost identical design. The colourways, size, etc. are extremely close to the jug produced by Doulton. The best method of telling the difference is the backstamp.

VARIATION No. 1: Kingsware. Colourway: Light and dark browns.
Approximately 1,000 to 1,500 pieces were thought to have been made.

Designer: McCallum		**Backstamp:** Doulton
Handle: Plain		
Colourway: Light and dark browns.		

Doulton Number	Size	Variation	Height	Intro.	Discon.	Current Market Value U.K. £	U.S. $	Can. $
D ---	Large	Kingsware glaze	7"	1930	Unknown	500.00	2,500.00	2,500.00

VARIATION No. 2: **Colourway: Ivory glaze.**
 Approximately 1,000 pieces

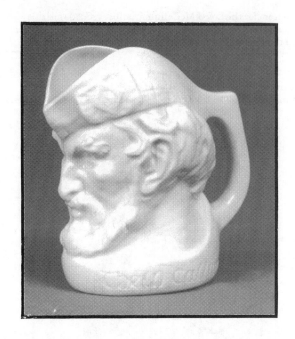

Doulton Number	Size	Variation	Height	Intro.	Discon.	Current Market Value U.K. £	U.S. $	Can. $
D ---	Large	Ivory glaze	7"	1930	Unknown	600.00	2,000.00	2,000.00

VARIATION No. 3: **Colourway: Treacle body with green hat, collar and handle.**

Doulton Number	Size	Variation	Height	Intro.	Discon.	Current Market Value U.K. £	U.S. $	Can. $
D ---	Large	Treacle glaze	7"	1930	Unknown	Extremely Rare		

MEPHISTOPHELES

First found in 16th century German legend, Mephistopheles became best-known in Johann von Goethe's drama, "Faust" (1808). He is portrayed as an evil spirit or devil to whom Faust sells his soul in return for services.

BACKSTAMP A

Designer: Charles Noke
Harry Fenton
Handle: Plain
Colourway: Red and brown
Backstamps: A. Doulton / With verse
B. Doulton / Without verse

Doulton Number	Size	Backstamp	Height	Intro.	Discon.	Current Market Value U.K. £	U.S. $	Can. $
D5757	Large	With Verse	7"	1937	1948	850.00	2,100.00	2,200.00
D5757	Large	Without Verse	7"	1937	1948	800.00	2,000.00	2,000.00
D5758	Small	With Verse	3 3/4"	1937	1948	450.00	1,200.00	1,300.00
D5758	Small	Without Verse	3 3/4"	1937	1948	400.00	1,100.00	1,200.00

MERLIN

CHARACTERS FROM LITERATURE
ONE OF ELEVEN

In the legend of King Arthur of Camelot, Merlin appears as wizard and aide to the King. He is credited with the creation of the famous Round Table.

Designer: Garry Sharpe
Handle: An owl
Colourway: Black, grey and brown

Merlin
D 6543
COPR 1959
DOULTON & CO LIMITED
Rd No 893842
Rd No 39650
Rd No 8314
Rd No 41/959

Backstamp: Doulton

Doulton Number	Size	Backstamp	Height	Intro.	Discon.	Current Market Value		
						U.K. £	U.S. $	Can. $
D6529	Large	Doulton	7 1/4"	1960	Current	49.95	142.50	160.00
D6536	Small	Doulton	3 3/4"	1960	Current	25.00	78.00	90.00
D6543	Miniature	Doulton	2 3/4"	1960	1991	30.00	40.00	60.00

MICHAEL DOULTON

This jug was manufactured in an edition of 9,500 pieces. It was made available for sale only at retail locations where and when Micheal Doulton was present.

Royal Doulton®
D 6808
MICHAEL DOULTON
Modelled by

© 1988 ROYAL DOULTON

Designer: William K. Harper
Handle: Flag bearing the Royal Doulton logo
Colourway: Black, brown and blue

Backstamp: Doulton

Doulton Number	Size	Backstamp	Height	Intro.	Discon.	Current Market Value		
						U.K. £	U.S. $	Can. $
D6808	Small	Doulton	4 1/4"	1988	1989	30.00	80.00	65.00

THE MIKADO

"Mikado", is the ancient title for the emperor of Japan. The Japanese ruling dynasty is considered to be one of the oldest in the world, with legend dating the reign of the Mikado Jimmu to 660 B.C. Believed by many to have descended from the all-powerful Sun Goddess, the same family line has been traced through one hundred and twenty-four reigns. The "Mikado" is popularly known through the Gilbert and Sullivan operetta (1885) of the same name.

The Mikado.
D.6501
COPR 1958
DOULTON & CO LIMITED
Rd No 889572
Rd No 38228
Rd No 8038
Rd No 421,58

Designer: Max Henk
Handle: A Fan
Colourway: Black and turquoise hat, green and white robes

Backstamp: Doulton

Doulton Number	Size	Backstamp	Height	Intro.	Discon.	Current Market Value		
						U.K. £	U.S. $	Can. $
D6501	Large	Doulton	6 1/2"	1959	1969	275.00	600.00	700.00
D6507	Small	Doulton	3 3/4"	1959	1969	200.00	325.00	425.00
D6525	Miniature	Doulton	2 1/2"	1960	1969	175.00	375.00	400.00

MINE HOST

The forerunner of today's English publican, this cheerful man would hang a pine bough on the door of his home to let travellers known that "refreshments" were available. As the handle shows, these often ran to a good pint of strong ale!

Mine Host
D.6513
COPR 1957
DOULTON & CO LIMITED
Rd No 888230
Rd No 37212
Rd No 7854
Rd No 389/57

Designer: Max Henk
Handle: Evergreen bough and barrel
Colourway: Black tricorn, red coat, white
bow-tie with gold spots

Backstamp: Doulton

Doulton Number	Size	Backstamp	Height	Intro.	Discon.	Current Market Value U.K. £	U.S. $	Can. $
D6468	Large	Doulton	7"	1958	1982	65.00	100.00	155.00
D6470	Small	Doulton	3 1/2"	1958	1982	40.00	60.00	95.00
D6513	Miniature	Doulton	2 1/2"	1960	1982	35.00	55.00	75.00

MONTY

Bernard Law Montgomery (1887-1976), later First Viscount Montgomery of Alamein, was always referred to familiarly as "Monty". The highlights of his long and distinguished military career included the first Allied victory of WWII in North Africa, in 1942, and the acceptance of the German surrender at Luneburg Heath in 1945. He was Deputy Supreme Commander of the Allied Powers in Europe from 1951 to 1958.

In 1954 a minor colourway change occurred when the yellow highlighting on the cap badge ceased.

Monty
D 6202

Designer: Harry Fenton
Handle: Plain
Colourway: Brown beret, khaki uniform

Backstamp: Doulton

Doulton Number	Size	Backstamp	Height	Intro.	Discon.	Current Market Value		
						U.K. £	U.S. $	Can. $
D6202	Large	Doulton	5 3/4"	1946	1954	100.00	150.00	165.00
D6202	Large	Doulton	5 3/4"	1954	1991	60.00	95.00	145.00

MR. BUMBLE

CHARLES DICKENS COMMEMORATIVE SET
DICKENS TINIES, ONE OF TWELVE

Mr. Bumble runs a local parish workhouse for orphans in Dickens' "Oliver Twist". The boy Oliver escapes from this dismal life and runs away to London.

Issued to commemorate the 170th Anniversary of the birth of Charles Dickens. There are twelve jugs in this set, each issued with a certificate of authenticity. A mahogany display shelf completes the set. The set was first sold by Lawleys By Post in the U.K. during 1982 to 1988, and in 1985 onward in North America and Australia.

Mr Bumble
D 6686

Designer:	Robert Tabbenor
Handle:	Plain
Colourway:	Yellow, dark blue and green

Backstamp: Doulton

Doulton Number	Size	Backstamp	Height	Intro.	Discon.	Current Market Value		
						U.K. £	U.S. $	Can. $
D6686	Tiny	Doulton	1 1/2"	1982	1989	30.00	45.00	60.00
		Display for 12 Tinies				65.00	45.00	50.00

MR PECKSNIFF

VARIATION No. 1: Ivory

Designer: Leslie Harradine
Handle: Plain
Colourway: Ivory

Backstamp: Doulton Burslem
Impressed Lion & Crown

Doulton Number	Size	Backstamp	Height	Intro.	Discon.	Current Market Value		
						U.K. £	U.S. $	Can. $
D ---	Large	Doulton Burslem	7"	c.1912	Unknown	250.00	375.00	500.00

VARIATION No.2: Treacle Glaze

Designer: Leslie Harradine
Model: 15354
Handle: Plain
Colourway: Treacle glaze

Backstamp: Doulton Burslem
Impressed Lion & Crown

Doulton Number	Size	Backstamp	Height	Intro.	Discon.	Current Market Value		
						U.K. £	U.S. $	Can. $
D —	Large	Doulton Burslem	7"	c.1912	Unknown	250.00	375.00	500.00

MR. MICAWBER

Wilkins Micawber, in Charles Dickens' classic, is David Copperfield's landlord and friend. A sanguine idler, Micawber unmasks Uriah Heep as a villian and is rewarded with passage to Australia where he settles happily in a prominent neighbourhood.

"Micawber."
R⁴Nº 822825.
REGᵈ IN AUSTRALIA

Designer: Leslie Harradine / Harry Fenton
Handle: Plain
Colourway: Black hat, green coat and blue polka-dot bow-tie

Backstamp: Doulton

Doulton Number	Size	Backstamp	Height	Intro.	Discon.	Current Market Value U.K. £	U.S. $	Can. $
D5843	Mid	Doulton	5 1/2"	1938	1948	120.00	200.00	225.00
D5843	Small	Doulton	3 1/4"	1948	1960	50.00	110.00	125.00
D6138	Miniature	Doulton	2 1/4"	1940	1960	40.00	60.00	75.00
D6143	Tiny	Doulton	1 1/4"	1940	1960	60.00	115.00	135.00

Miscellaneous "Mr. Micawber" Items

Doulton Number	Item	Height	Intro.	Discon.	Current Market Value U.K. £	U.S. $	Can. $
D5843	Table Lighter	3 1/2"	1958	1959	165.00	225.00	250.00
D6050	Bust	2 1/4"	1939	1960	65.00	100.00	95.00
HN1615	Bookend	4"	1934	c. 1939	1,000.00	1,750.00	1,750.00
M58	Napkin Ring	3 1/2"	c. 1935	1939	200.00	400.00	400.00

MR. PICKWICK

Founder and chairman of the Pickwick Club, this gentleman is the elegant and genial hero of Charles Dickens' "The Posthumous Papers of the Pickwick Club", first published in 1837.

Designer: Leslie Harradine / Harry Fenton
Handle: Plain
Colourway: Green hat, brown coat, red bow-tie

Backstamp: Doulton

Doulton Number	Size	Backstamp	Height	Intro.	Discon.	Current Market Value		
						U.K. £	U.S. $	Can. $
D6060	Large	Doulton	7"	1940	1960	100.00	165.00	195.00
D5839	Mid	Doulton	4 1/4"	1938	1948	120.00	185.00	240.00
D5839	Small	Doulton	3 1/2"	1948	1960	55.00	80.00	110.00
D6254	Miniature	Doulton	2 1/4"	1947	1960	40.00	60.00	90.00
D6260	Tiny	Doulton	1 1/4"	1947	1960	100.00	240.00	275.00

Miscellaneous "Mr. Pickwick" Items

Doulton Number	Item	Height	Intro.	Discon.	Current Market Value		
					U.K. £	U.S. $	Can. $
D5839	Table Lighter	3 1/2"	1958	1961	135.00	260.00	250.00
D6049	Bust	3 1/2"	1939	1960	65.00	100.00	95.00
HN1623	Bookend	4"	1934	c. 1939	450.00	1,750.00	1,750.00
M57	Napkin Ring	3 1/2"	c. 1935	c. 1939	225.00	450.00	400.00

MR. QUAKER

These jugs were made as an advertising piece for the internal use of Quaker Oats Limited and a few were sold to members of the Royal Doulton International Collectors Club. They were issued with a certificate signed by Sir Richard Bailey, CBE and Michael Doulton.

Commissioned by Quaker Oats Limited. Issued in 1985 in a limited edition of 3,500 pieces.

Designer: Harry Sales
Handle: A sheaf of wheat
Colourway: Black, white and yellow

Backstamp: Doulton / Quaker Oats Ltd

Doulton Number	Size	Backstamp	Height	Intro.	Discon.	Current Market Value		
						U.K. £	U.S. $	Can. $
D6738	Large	Doulton/Quaker	7 1/2"	1985	Ltd. Ed.	225.00	500.00	600.00

MRS. BARDELL

CHARLES DICKENS COMMEMORATIVE SET
DICKENS TINIES, ONE OF TWELVE.

In Dickens' "The Pickwick Papers", Mrs. Bardell sues Mr. Pickwick for breach of promise.
Issued to commemorate the 170th Anniversary of the birth of Charles Dickens. There are twelve jugs in this set, each issued with a certificate of authenticity. A mahogany display shelf completes the set. The set was first sold by Lawleys By Post in the U.K. during 1982 to 1988, and in 1985 onward in North America and Australia.

Mrs Bardell
D 6687

Designer: Robert Tabbenor
Handle: Plain
Colourway: Yellow and green

Backstamp: Doulton

Doulton Number	Size	Backstamp		Height	Intro.	Discon.	Current Market Value U.K. £	U.S. $	Can. $
D6687	Tiny	Doulton		1 1/2"	1982	1989	30.00	45.00	60.00
		Display for 12 Tinies					65.00	45.00	50.00

MRS. CLAUS

Commissioned for the North American market, Mrs. Claus has her handle to the left so she can be paired with her husband Santa Claus (D6900) whose handle points in the opposite direction.

Royal Doulton®
MRS. CLAUS
D 6922
© 1992 ROYAL DOULTON

Designer: Stanley J. Taylor
Handle: Holly wreath
Colourway: Red, Cream and green

Backstamp: Doulton

Doulton Number	Size	Backstamp	Height	Intro.	Discon.	Current Market Value		
						U.K. £	U.S. $	Can. $
D6922	Miniature	Doulton	2 3/8"	1992	Sp. Ltd.	45.00	50.00	85.00

NAPOLEON

Issued in a limited edition of 2,000 pieces. Each jug bears a special backstamp and comes with a certificate of authenticity.

Designer: Stanley J. Taylor	**Backstamp:** Doulton
Handle: An Eagle	
Colourway: Black and gold	

Doulton Number	Size	Backstamp	Height	Intro.	Discon.	Current Market Value		
						U.K. £	U.S. $	Can. $
D6941	Large	Doulton	7"	1993	Ltd. Ed.	79.95	225.00	325.00

NAPOLEON BONAPARTE

*Photograph
Not Available
At Press Time*

Designer: Unknown
Handle: Plain
Colourway: Saltglaze

Backstamp: Doulton Watts

Doulton Number	Size	Backstamp	Height	Intro.	Discon.	Current Market Value		
						U.K. £	U.S. $	Can. $
D ---	Large	Doulton	7 1/2"	1821	1830	300.00	450.00	600.00
D ---	Small	Doulton	3 1/2"	1821	1830	250.00	375.00	500.00

NAPOLEON AND JOSEPHINE

STAR-CROSSED LOVERS (TWO FACED JUG)
ONE OF FOUR

Napoleon (1769-1821), "Le petit Caporal," standing only 5'2", was a military genius who amassed an empire that covered most of western and central Europe.

Josephine (1763-1814), the daughter of a French planter from Martinique, West Indies, first married Vicomte de Beauharnais at the age of seventeen. The Vicomte was killed during the Reign of Terror in the French Revolution and Josephine was imprisoned and nearly guillotined. As a member of fashionable society in Paris, she met Napoleon and married him in 1796. Unable to produce a child to satisfy the need for an heir, Napoleon divorced Josephine in 1809 to marry a younger woman.

Issued in 1986 in a limited edition of 9,500 pieces.

Designer: Michael Abberley
Handle: Napoleon: French Flag
Josephine: A fan and mirror
Colourway: Black, white, yellow and brown
Backstamp: Doulton

Royal Doulton®
THE
STAR-CROSSED LOVERS
COLLECTION
Napoleon & Josephine
D 6750
Modelled by Michael Abberley .
Michael Abberley
Worldwide Limited Edition of 9,500
This is Number 1976
© 1985 Royal Doulton (UK)

Doulton Number	Size	Backstamp	Height	Intro.	Discon.	Current Market Value		
						U.K. £	U.S. $	Can. $
D6750	Large	Doulton	7"	1986	Ltd. Ed. (1991)	75.00	150.00	195.00

NEPTUNE

In Roman mythology, Neptune is the god of the sea. According to legend Neptune married the sea nymph Amphitrite and together they had a son named Triton who was half man and half fish.

Neptune
D 6552
COPR 1960
DOULTON & CO LIMITED
Rd No 897937
Rd No 40887
Rd No 8596
Rd No 547/60

Designer: Max Henk   **Backstamp:** Doulton
Handle: Trident and fish
Colourway: Blue, grey and green

Doulton Number	Size	Backstamp	Height	Intro.	Discon.	Current Market Value U.K. £	U.S. $	Can. $
D6548	Large	Doulton	6 1/2"	1961	1991	60.00	100.00	145.00
D6552	Small	Doulton	3 3/4"	1961	1991	40.00	55.00	80.00
D6555	Miniature	Doulton	2 1/2"	1961	1991	30.00	50.00	60.00

NIGHT WATCHMAN

CHARACTER JUGS FROM WILLIAMSBURG
ONE OF SEVEN

When the sun sets and his colleague the guardsman's duty is over, the night watchman takes charge. Throughout the long "graveyard shift" he admits late travellers and looks out for any threat to the Williamsburg, Virginia, fortress.

Backstamp: Doulton

Designer: Max Henk
Handle: Lantern
Colourway: Black-purple tricorn and cloak

Doulton Number	Size	Backstamp	Height	Intro.	Discon.	Current Market Value		
						U.K. £	U.S. $	Can. $
D6569	Large	Doulton	7"	1963	1983	65.00	110.00	145.00
D6576	Small	Doulton	3 1/2"	1963	1983	45.00	75.00	95.00
D6583	Miniature	Doulton	2 1/2"	1963	1983	35.00	70.00	80.00

NORTH AMERICAN INDIAN

The misnomer "Indian" can be attributed to Christopher Columbus' landing in what he thought was the West Indies. The original inhabitants of North America, these people occupied most of the continent with various and unique cultures. Early white settlers, in the selfish pursuit of land and riches, massacred and subdued so many of these First Peoples that today much of their way of life has been forever destroyed.

VARIATION No. 1: Colourway: Red, white and black feathers, yellow and white band, green robes.

North American Indian
D 6614
COPR 1966
DOULTON & CO LIMITED
Rd No 924806
Rd No 49145
Rd No 10602
Rd No 54/66

BACKSTAMP A

CANADIAN CENTENNIAL SERIES
1867 – 1967

North American Indian
D 6611
COPR 1966
DOULTON & CO LIMITED
Rd No 924806
Rd No 49145
Rd No 10602
Rd No 54/66

BACKSTAMP B

OKOBOJI
75 ANNIVERSARY
1973

North American Indian
D6611
COPR 1966
DOULTON & CO LIMITED
Rd No 924806
Rd No 49145
Rd No 10602
Rd No 54/66

BACKSTAMP C

Designer: Max Henk
Handle: A totem pole
Colourway: Red, white and black feathers, yellow and white band, green robes.
Handle: Dark brown

Backstamps: A. Doulton
  B. Doulton / Canadian Centenary "Canadian Centennial Series 1867-1967"
    Available only in North America during 1967 the club members at the 1973
  C. Doulton / "Okoboji 75 Anniversary 1973" Issued for the 75th Anniversary of the
    Okoboji trap shooting club. 180 jugs were presented to annual "Pow-Wow".

Doulton Number	Size	Backstamp	Height	Intro.	Discon.	Current Market Value U.K. £	Current Market Value U.S. $	Current Market Value Can. $
D6611	Large	A	7 3/4"	1967	1991	55.00	100.00	145.00
D6611	Large	B	7 3/4"	1967	1967	100.00	300.00	300.00
D6611	Large	C	7 3/4"	1973	1973	425.00	750.00	850.00
D6614	Small	A	4 1/4"	1967	1991	40.00	60.00	80.00
D6665	Miniature	A	2 3/4"	1981	1991	30.00	45.00	60.00

VARIATION No. 2:   Colourway: Yellow, blue, white and black feathers,
green and white band, orange robes.
                       Handle: Light brown.

Royal Doulton®

NORTH AMERICAN INDIAN

D 6786

Modelled by

© 1966 ROYAL DOULTON
NEW COLOURWAY 1987
SPECIAL EDITION OF 1000
FOR JOHN SINCLAIR SHEFFIELD

Backstamp: **Doulton / John Sinclair**
Commissioned by John Sinclair, Sheffield, England. Issued in 1987 in a special edition of 1,000 pieces

Doulton Number	Size	Backstamp	Height	Intro.	Discon.	Current Market Value		
						U.K. £	U.S. $	Can. $
D6786	Large	Doulton/Sinclair	7 1/2"	1987	Sp. Ed.	50.00	100.00	195.00

The North American Indian is one of three jugs which received a special backstamp in 1967. The other two, The Lumberjack and The Trapper form a three jug Canadian Centennial Series.

OLD CHARLEY

"10 o'clock and all's well" was the familiar call of the "Charlies", watchmen who originated in the reign of Charles II and named after him. They enjoyed a history of almost two hundred years duration before finally being replaced in the early 1800s by an early version of the present-day policeman.

VARIATION No. 1: Colourway: Brown hat, dark green coat, blue polka-dot bow-tie.

Old Charley
D5420
DOULTON & CO LIMITED

BACKSTAMP A

BACKSTAMP B   BACKSTAMP C

Designer: Charles Noke	**Backstamps:** A. Doulton
Handle: Plain	B. Doulton/Bentalls "Souvenir from Bentalls Jubilee Year 1935" Bentalls Ltd, a London Department Store.
Colourway: Brown hat, dark green coat, blue polka-dot bow-tie.	C. Doulton/Bentalls "Souvenir from Bentalls 1936"

Doulton Number	Size	Backstamp	Height	Intro.	Discon.	Current Market Value U.K. £	U.S. $	Can. $
D5420	Large	Doulton	5 1/2"	1934	1983	60.00	100.00	125.00
D5527	Small	Doulton	3 1/4"	1935	1983	30.00	60.00	95.00
D5527	Small	Bentalls B	3 1/4"	1935	1935	350.00	600.00	750.00
D5527	Small	Bentalls C	3 1/4"	1936	1936	350.00	600.00	750.00
D6046	Miniature	Doulton	2 1/4"	1939	1983	25.00	50.00	70.00
D6144	Tiny	Doulton	1 1/4"	1940	1960	60.00	100.00	135.00

VARIATION No. 2: Colourway: Black hat, maroon coat, black polka-dot bow-tie.

BACKSTAMP B

Backstamps: **A. Doulton / Higbee "Specially Commissioned from Royal Doulton by The Higbee Company To Commemorate the First Anniversary of the Opening of the First Royal Doulton Room Higbee's, Cleveland, Ohio, U.S.A."**
Commissioned by the Higbee Department Store to celebrate the first anniversary of the opening of the Higbee Doulton Shop in 1985. Issued in 1986 in a limited edition of 250 pieces.

B. Doulton / Higbee "Specially Commissioned from Royal Doulton by The Higbee Company To Commemorate the Second Anniversary of the Opening of the First Royal Doulton Room Higbee's, Cleveland, Ohio, U.S.A."
Commissioned by the Higbee Department Store to celebrate the second anniversary of the opening of the Royal Doulton Room. Issued in a limited edition of 500 pieces.

Doulton Number	Size	Backstamp	Height	Intro.	Discon.	Current Market Value U.K. £	U.S. $	Can. $
D6761	Large	A Higbee	5 1/2"	1986	1986	325.00	300.00	375.00
D6791	Small	B Higbee	3 1/4"	1987	1987	125.00	160.00	200.00

Miscellaneous "Old Charley" Items

Doulton Number	Item	Height	Intro.	Discon.	Current Market Value U.K. £	U.S. $	Can. $
D5227	Table Lighter	3 1/2"	1959	1973	125.00	150.00	180.00
D5844	Tobacco Jar	5 1/2"	1937	1960	650.00	1,500.00	1,750.00
D5858	Musical Jug	5 1/2"	1938	1939	300.00	750.00	850.00
D5599	Ashtray	2 3/4	1936	1960	85.00	115.00	150.00
D5925	Ash Bowl	3"	1939	1960	85.00	125.00	150.00
D6012	Sugar Bowl	2 1/2"	1939	1960	375.00	750.00	800.00
D6017	Teapot	7"	1939	1960	650.00	1,750.00	1,750.00
D6110	Wall Pocket	7 1/4"	1940	1960	950.00	2,000.00	2,000.00
D6152	Toothpick Holder	2 1/4"	1940	1960	350.00	1,500.00	700.00

Note: Tune played on musical jug is "Here's a Health Unto His Majesty."

OLD KING COLE

"Old King Cole was a Merry Old Soul", the ever-popular nursery rhyme, inspired the design of this cheerful and benevolent ruler.

The collar frill was remodelled around 1939 and variation two can be found with both deep and shallow white ruff modellings.

VARIATION No. 1: Colourway: Yellow crown, frills in the white ruff are deep and pronounced.

Designer: Harry Fenton
Handle: Plain
Colourway: Yellow crown, frills in the white ruff are deep and pronounced.

Backstamp: Doulton

Doulton Number	Size	Variations	Height	Intro.	Discon.	Current Market Value U.K. £	U.S. $	Can. $
D6036	Large	Var. 1	5 3/4"	1938	1939	1,000.00	4,000.00	4,000.00
D6037	Small	Var. 1	3 1/2"	1938	1939	900.00	2,500.00	2,500.00

VARIATION No. 2: Colourway: Brown crown.

Backstamps: A. Doulton
B. Doulton / Royal Doulton International Collectors Club

Doulton Number	Size	Backstamp	Height	Intro.	Discon.	Current Market Value U.K. £	U.S. $	Can. $
D6036	Large	A	5 3/4"	1939	1960	135.00	300.00	275.00
D6037	Small	A	3 1/2"	1939	1960	90.00	125.00	195.00
D6871	Tiny	B	1 1/2"	1990	1990	55.00	125.00	95.00

Miscellaneous "Old King Cole" Items
Musical Jug

Doulton Number	Variation	Height	Intro.	Discon.	Current Market Value U.K. £	U.S. $	Can. $
D —	Yellow Crown	7 1/2"	1939	1939	1,500.00	2,500.00	2,500.00
D6014	Brown Crown	7 1/2"	1939	1939	750.00	1,250.00	1,500.00

Note: Tune played on musical jug "Old King Cole was a Merry Old Soul."

OLD SALT

With their weather-hardened faces and bottomless repertoire of stories, these retired seamen never tire of explaining just where they saw that mermaid.

When the miniature jug was launched in 1984 it originally had a hollow crook in the mermaid's arm. Later that year, because of production problems, the arm was moulded to the body. The first version of this miniature has attained near "pilot" status and commands a large premium over the general issue.

VARIATION No. 1:   Colourway: Dark blue fisherman's jersey.
Handle: Mermaid has blue tail.

Old Salt
D 6551
COPR 1960
DOULTON & CO LIMITED
Rd No 898030
Rd No 40938
Rd No 8616
Rd No 572/60

Designer: Gary Sharpe , Large and Small
Peter Gee, Miniature
Handle: A mermaid
Colourway: Dark blue fisherman's jersey.

Backstamp: Doulton

Doulton Number	Size	Variation	Height	Intro.	Discon.	Current Market Value U.K. £	U.S. $	Can. $
D6551	Large	Var. 1	7 1/2"	1961	Current	49.95	142.50	160.00
D6554	Small	Var. 1	4"	1961	Current	28.95	78.00	90.00
D6557	Miniature	Open arm	2 1/2"	1984	1984	600.00	1,500.00	1,500.00
D6557	Miniature	Closed arm	2 1/2"	1984	1991	20.00	40.00	60.00

VARIATION No. 2: Colourway: Light and dark blue fisherman's jersey.
Handle: Mermaid has yellow and black tail.

Doulton Number	Size	Variation	Height	Intro.	Discon.	Current Market Value		
						U.K. £	U.S. $	Can. $
D6782	Large	Var. 2	8"	1987	1990	60.00	125.00	150.00

Miscellaneous "Old Salt" Items

Doulton Number	Item	Height	Intro.	Discon.	Current Market Value		
					U.K. £	U.S. $	Can. $
D6818	Teapot	6 1/4"	1989	1989	100.00	200.00	395.00

OLIVER TWIST

CHARLES DICKENS COMMEMORATIVE SET
DICKENS TINIES, ONE OF TWELVE

The hero of Dickens' novel of Victoria, London, Oliver is an orphan who runs away from a workhouse to the city, only to be forced into thieving for the wicked Fagin.

Issued to commemorate the 170th Anniversary of the birth of Charles Dickens. There are twelve jugs in this set, each issued with a certificate of authenticity. A mahogany display shelf completes the set. The set was first sold by Lawleys By Post in the U.K. during 1982 to 1988, and in 1985 onward in North America and Australia.

Backstamp: Doulton

Designer: Robert Tabbenor
Handle: Plain
Colourway: Dark and light blue

Doulton Number	Size	Backstamp		Height	Intro.	Discon.	Current Market Value		
							U.K. £	U.S. $	Can. $
D6677	Tiny	Doulton		1 1/2"	1982	1989	30.00	45.00	60.00
		Display for 12 Tinies					65.00	45.00	50.00

OTHELLO

THE SHAKESPEAREAN COLLECTION
ONE OF SIX

In Shakespeare's tragic play, (1604), Othello is a successful soldier to the Venetian state who marries the attractive Desdemona. His subordinate Iago, out of spite and jealousy, convinces Othello that Desdemona has been unfaithful. Outraged, Othello kills her then commits suicide from grief.

© ROYAL DOULTON TABLEWARE LIMITED 1982
D 6673

The
Shakespearean
Collection
OTHELLO
A series of hand-made, hand-decorated Character Jugs by
Royal Doulton

Designer: Michael Abberley
Handle: A figure of Iago
Colourway: Yellow turban, green, yellow and white robes

Backstamp: Doulton

Doulton Number	Size	Backstamp	Height	Intro.	Discon.	Current Market Value U.K. £	U.S. $	Can. $
D6673	Large	Doulton	7 1/4"	1982	1989	75.00	115.00	145.00

PADDY

Paddy, a colloquial term for an Irishman, is derived from St. Patrick, the country's patron saint. Annually, on the 17th of March, a holiday is celebrated in his honour. This gent is dressed for the occasion in traditional green.

"Paddy."

Designer: Harry Fenton
Handle: Plain
Colourway: Brown hat, green coat, yellow and red scarf

Backstamp: Doulton

Doulton Number	Size	Backstamp	Height	Intro.	Discon.	Current Market Value U.K. £	U.S. $	Can. $
D5753	Large	Doulton	6"	1937	1960	75.00	160.00	145.00
D5768	Small	Doulton	3 1/4"	1937	1960	45.00	75.00	95.00
D6042	Miniature	Doulton	2 1/4"	1939	1960	40.00	55.00	70.00
D6145	Tiny	Doulton	1 1/4"	1940	1960	60.00	110.00	135.00

Miscellaneous "Paddy" Items

Doulton Number	Item	Backstamp	Height	Intro.	Discon.	Current Market Value U.K. £	U.S. $	Can. $
D5845	Tobacco Jar	Doulton	5 1/2"	1939	1942	650.00	1,250.00	1,500.00
D5845	Tobacco Jar	Salt River	5 1/2"	1939	1942	1,500.00	2,750.00	2,750.00
D5845	Tobacco Jar	Coleman's	5 1/2"	1939	1942	1,000.00	1,700.00	2,000.00
D5887	Musical Jug	Doulton	7"	1938	c. 1939	250.00	675.00	850.00
D5926	Ash bowl	Doulton	3"	1938	1960	85.00	110.00	135.00
D6151	Toothpick Holder	Doulton	2 1/4"	1940	1941	350.00	650.00	700.00

Note: Tune played on musical jug is "An Irish Jig."

PARSON BROWN

Typical of the country clergy found in England, Parson Brown would live in a home supplied by his church. In rural areas, the parsonage was often the cultural as well as spiritual centre of a village. A Parson Brown jug with a silver rim exists, made in 1937.

BACKSTAMP C

SHEFFIELD & ROTHERHAM

BACKSTAMP D

Designer: Charles Noke
Handle: Plain
Colourway: Dark grey
Backstamps: A. Doulton Commissioned by Bentalls to celebrate Bentalls Jubilee Year 1935"
 B. Doulton / Bentalls "Souvenir from the silver jubilee of King George VI
 C. Doulton / Bentalls "Souvenir from Bentalls 1936."
 D. Doulton / Darley "Souvenir from Darley & Son Sheffield & Rotherham"

Doulton Number	Size	Backstamp	Height	Intro.	Discon.	Current Market Value U.K. £	U.S. $	Can. $
D5486	Large	Doulton	6 1/2"	1935	1960	75.00	150.00	195.00
D5529	Small	Doulton	3 1/4"	1935	1960	45.00	70.00	110.00
D5529	Small	Bentalls / '35	3 1/24"	1935	1935	350.00	650.00	750.00
D5529	Small	Bentalls / '36	3 1/4"	1936	1936	350.00	650.00	750.00
D5529	Small	Doulton/Darley	3 1/4"	1936	1936	350.00	650.00	750.00

Miscellaneous "Parson Brown" Items

Doulton Number	Size	Backstamp	Height	Intro.	Discon.	Current Market Value U.K. £	U.S. $	Can. $
D5600	Ash Tray	Doulton	3 1/2"	1936	1960	85.00	110.00	130.00
D6008	Ash Bowl	Doulton	3"	1939	1960	85.00	110.00	130.00

PAUL McCARTNEY

THE BEATLES
ONE OF FOUR

Singer/songwriter for the Beatles until 1970, McCartney (b. 1942) went on to form his own successful band "Wings," who played together from 1971-1981. He remains active in the music field, writing and playing with various artists and on his own.
Issued only in Great Britain for copyright reasons.

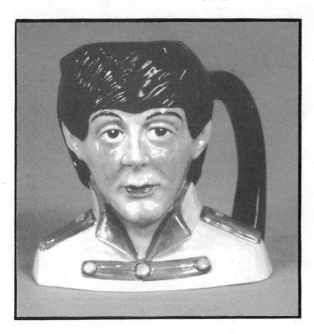

Designer: Stanley J. Taylor
Handle: Plain
Colourway: Yellow tunic trimmed with blue collar and epaulettes

Backstamp: Doulton

Doulton Number	Size	Backstamp	Height	Intro.	Discon.	Current Market Value		
						U.K. £	U.S. $	Can. $
D6724	Mid	Doulton	5 1/2"	1984	1991	55.00	95.00	95.00

PEARLY BOY

Pearly Boy is a coster or costermonger, who sells fruits and vegetables from a barrow in the streets of London. When he is dressed in his finest, pearl buttons or "pearlies" sewn to his clothes, he is known as Pearly Boy. 'Arry is Pearly Boy without his buttons. Please see 'Arry on page 109.

VARIATION No. 1: Colourway: Brown hat with blue peak, blue coat, pearl coloured buttons.

```
" 'arry. "
COPR.1946.
DOULTON & CO LIMITED.
R∂No 847679.
R∂No 23908.
R∂No 133/46
R∂No 5194.
```

Designer: Harry Fenton   **Backstamp:** Doulton
Handle: Plain
Colourway: Brown hat with blue peak, blue coat, white buttons.

Doulton Number	Size	Variation	Height	Intro.	Discon.	U.K. £	U.S. $	Can. $
						Current Market Value		
D —	Large	Var. 1	6 1/2"	1947	Unknown	3,000.00	4,500.00	5,500.00
D —	Small	Var. 1	3 1/2"	1947	Unknown	2,500.00	2,500.00	3,000.00
D —	Miniature	Var. 1	2 1/2"	1947	Unknown	Extremely Rare		

VARIATION No. 2: Colourway: Brown hat, brown coat, pearl coloured buttons.

Doulton Number	Size	Variation	Height	Intro.	Discon.	Current Market Value		
						U.K. £	U.S. $	Can. $
D —	Large	Var. 2	6 1/2"	1947	Unknown	3,000.00	2,500.00	3,000.00
D —	Small	Var. 2	3 1/2"	1947	Unknown	2,500.00	1,750.00	2,250.00
D —	Miniature	Var. 2	2 1/2"	1947	Unknown		Extremely Rare	

VARIATION No. 3: Colourway: Brown hat, brown coat and brown buttons.

Backstamp: Doulton

Doulton Number	Size	Variation	Height	Intro.	Discon.	Current Market Value		
						U.K. £	U.S. $	Can. $
D —	Large	Var. 3	6 1/2"	1947	1947	800.00	2,000.00	2,500.00
D —	Small	Var. 3	3 1/2"	1947	1947	400.00	900.00	1,500.00
D —	Miniature	Var. 3	2 1/2"	1947	1947	300.00	650.00	950.00

VARIATION No. 4: Colourway: Beige hat, brown coat, pearl coloured buttons.

Backstamp: Doulton

Doulton Number	Size	Variation	Height	Intro.	Discon.	Current Market Value		
						U.K. £	U.S. $	Can. $
D —	Large	Var. 4	6 1/2"	1947	Unknown	975.00	2,000.00	2,250.00
D —	Small	Var. 4	3 1/2"	1947	Unknown	700.00	900.00	1,150.00
D —	Miniature	Var. 4	2 1/2"	1947	Unknown	475.00	650.00	800.00

PEARLY GIRL

Pearly Girl is Pearly Boy's female counterpart. She was a costermonger who sold her produce in the streets of London. Pearly Girl is 'Arriet dressed in her finest. Please see 'Arriet on page 108.

VARIATION No. 1: Colourway: Blue jacket, lime green feather, maroon hat and button

'arriet.'

COPR. 1946.
DOULTON & CO LIMITE.
R.N? 847682.
R.N? 23909.
R.N? 132/46.
R.N? 5195.

Designer: Harry Fenton
Handle: Hat feather
Colourway: Blue jacket, lime green feather, maroon hat and button

Backstamp: Doulton

Doulton Number	Size	Variation	Height	Intro.	Discon.	Current Market Value U.K. £	U.S. $	Can. $
D —	Large	Var. 1	6 1/2"	1946	Unknown	3,000.00	5,000.00	5,000.00
D —	Small	Var. 1	3 1/4"	1946	Unknown	2,250.00	3,000.00	3,750.00
D----	Miniature	Var. 1	2 1/2"	1946	Unknown	3,250.00	4,500.00	5,000.00

VARIATION No. 2: Colourway: Dark brown jacket, lime green feather, pink hat and button

Doulton Number	Size	Variation	Height	Intro.	Discon.	Current Market Value U.K. £	U.S. $	Can. $
D —	Large	Var. 2	6 1/2"	1946	Unknown		Extremely Rare	
D —	Small	Var. 2	3 1/4"	1946	Unknown		Extremely Rare	

PEARLY KING

THE LONDON COLLECTION
ONE OF TEN

The Pearly King is the head spokesman of the street market costers of London. Over a hundred years ago his chief mandate was a go-between for the costers and the London police. Today, with this need diminishing, the "Pearlies" have turned their energy to raising money for charity. With the elaborate pearl button designs sewn on their clothes they can bee seen at all the main functions held throughout the year.

Designer: Stanley J. Taylor
Handle: The "Bow Bells" and pearl buttons
Colourway: Black cap and jacket with silver
buttons, yellow scarf with red polka dots

Royal Doulton®
PEARLY KING
D 6760
Modelled by
Stanley James Taylor.
© 1986 ROYAL DOULTON

Backstamp: Doulton

Doulton Number	Size	Backstamp	Height	Intro.	Discon.	Current Market Value		
						U.K. £	U.S. $	Can. $
D6760	Large	Doulton	6 3/4"	1987	1991	65.00	130.00	145.00
D6844	Small	Doulton	3 1/2"	1987	1991	35.00	60.00	80.00

PEARLY QUEEN

THE LONDON COLLECTION
ONE OF TEN

The Pearly Queen, like the Pearly King, is the chief spokesperson for the street market costers of London. The office is both hereditary and elected.

Designer: Stanley J. Taylor
Handle: The "Bow Bells" with pink and blue feathers
Colourway: Black coat with silver buttons, black hat with white, pink and blue feathers

Royal Doulton®
PEARLY QUEEN
D 6759
Modelled by
Stanley James Taylor
© 1986 ROYAL DOULTON

Backstamp: Doulton

Doulton Number	Size	Backstamp	Height	Intro.	Discon.	Current Market Value U.K. £	U.S. $	Can. $
D6759	Large	Doulton	7"	1987	1991	65.00	130.00	145.00
D6843	Small	Doulton	3 1/2"	1987	1991	35.00	60.00	80.00

THE PENDLE WITCH

This jug was the first and only jug issued in the proposed series Myths, Fantasies and Legends. Commissioned and distributed by Kevin Francis Ceramics (KFC). Issued in 1989 in a special edition of 5,000 pieces.

Original Design and Concept by Alison Faulds of My Fair Lady

Royal Doulton®
THE PENDLE WITCH
D 6826
Modelled by
Stanley James Taylor
A Special Edition of 5000
Produced by Royal Doulton
for Kevin Francis Ceramics
© 1988 ROYAL DOULTON
AND KEVIN FRANCIS CERAMICS

Designer: Stanley J. Taylor
Handle: A Hound
Colourway: Grey hair, black dress

Backstamp: Doulton / Kevin Francis

Doulton Number	Size	Backstamp	Height	Intro.	Discon.	Current Market Value		
						U.K. £	U.S. $	Can. $
D6826	Large	Doulton/KFC	7 1/4"	1989	Sp. Ed.	75.00	150.00	195.00

PIED PIPER

PROTOTYPE

STYLE ONE: HANDLE: ONE WHITE RAT / FLUTE

Designer: Geoff Blower
Handle: White rat at the top of a dark brown flute.
Colourway: Light brown hat, blond hair

Backstamp: Doulton

Doulton Number	Size	Variation	Height	Intro.	Discon.	Current Market Value U.K. £	U.S. $	Can. $
D6403	Large	Prototype	7"		Unknown		Unique	

PIED PIPER

In German legend, the town of Hamelin was infested with rats. A stranger came to town and told the mayor he would solve the problem for a sum of money. He walked through town playing a flute and the rats followed him to the Weser river where they drowned.

When the mayor refused to pay him, the Pied Piper again played his flute, and this time the village children followed him into a cave, never to be seen again.

STYLE TWO: HANDLE: THREE BROWN RATS / FLUTE

Pied Piper
D 6403
COPR 1953
DOULTON & CO LIMITED

Designer: Geoff Blower
Handle: Three brown rats atop a flute
Colourway: Green cap, maroon and yellow tunic

Backstamp: Doulton

Doulton Number	Size	Backstamp	Height	Intro.	Discon.	Current Market Value U.K. £	U.S. $	Can. $
D6403	Large	Doulton	7"	1954	1981	75.00	110.00	155.00
D6462	Small	Doulton	3 3/4"	1957	1981	45.00	75.00	90.00
D6514	Miniature	Doulton	2 5/8"	1960	1981	40.00	65.00	80.00

PIERRE ELLIOT TRUDEAU

PROTOTYPE

Joseph Philippe Pierre Yves Elliott Trudeau (b. 1919), is a French Canadian from the province of Quebec. A lawyer, he entered national politics in 1965 and became Minister of Justice and Attorney General in 1967. After the retirement of Prime Minister Lester Pearson, Trudeau was elected leader of the Liberal Party in 1968 and then Prime Minister. He served as Prime Minister from 1968 to 1979 and from 1980 to 1984.

Doulton was unable to obtain permission to issue this jug.

Designer: Unknown
Handle: The Canadian Maple Leaf flag
Colourway: Black and Grey

Backstamp: Doulton

Doulton Number	Size	Variation	Height	Intro.	Discon.	U.K. £	U.S. $	Can. $
D —	Large	Prototype	7"		Unknown		Unique	

PILGRIM FATHER

PROTOTYPE

Designer: David Biggs
Handle: The Mayflower
Colourway: Black suit, white collar, brown and white ship

Backstamp: Doulton

Doulton Number	Size	Variation	Height	Intro.	Discon.	Current Market Value		
						U.K. £	U.S. $	Can. $
D —	Large	Doulton	8 1/4"	1969	1969		Unique	

THE PIPER

Issued in a limited edition of 2500. (Gordon Highlanders)

Royal Doulton®
THE PIPER
D 6918
Modelled by

Stanley James Taylor

© 1992 ROYAL DOULTON
LIMITED EDITION OF 2,500
THIS IS No. 425

Designer: Stanley J. Taylor
Handle: Bag pipes
Colourway: Black, red, white and yellow

Backstamp: Doulton

Doulton Number	Size	Variation	Height	Intro.	Discon.	Current Market Value		
						U.K. £	U.S. $	Can. $
D6918	Large	Doulton	8 1/4""	1992	Ltd. Ed.	150.00	300.00	500.00

THE POACHER

In England poaching, or illegal hunting and fishing, was at one time punishable by death. Although no longer a capital offence, anyone caught committing this crime can expect a heavy fine.

VARIATION No. 1: Colourway: Green coat, red scarf, light brown hat.

"The Poacher"
D 6429
COPR 1954
DOULTON & CO LIMITED
Rd No 875201
Rd No 33325
Rd No 7095
Rd No 321/54

Designer: Max Henk   **Backstamp:** Doulton
Handle: A Salmon
Colourway: Green coat, red scarf, light brown hat

Doulton Number	Size	Variation	Height	Intro.	Discon.	U.K. £	U.S. $	Can. $
						Current Market Value		
D6429	Large	Var. 1	7"	1955	Current	49.95	142.50	160.00
D6464	Small	Var. 1	4"	1957	Current	25.00	78.00	90.00
D6515	Miniature	Var. 1	2 1/2"	1960	1991	20.00	40.00	60.00

VARIATION No 2: Colourway: Maroon coat, yellow striped scarf, black hat.

Royal Doulton®
THE POACHER
D 6781
Modelled by

© 1954 ROYAL DOULTON
NEW COLOURWAY 1987

Doulton Number	Size	Variation	Height	Intro.	Discon.	Current Market Value		
						U.K. £	U.S. $	Can. $
D6781	Large	Var. 2	7"	1987	1989	50.00	100.00	125.00

Miscellaneous "The Poacher" Items

Doulton Number	Item	Backstamps	Height	Intro.	Discon.	Current Market Value		
						U.K. £	U.S. $	Can. $
D6464	Table Lighter	Doulton	4 3/4"	c. 1960	1973	120.00	125.00	175.00

THE POLICEMAN

JOURNEY THROUGH BRITAIN
ONE OF FOUR

The task of ensuring a government's law is carried out has been performed with varying degrees of violence throughout history. Happily, one can say that the English policeman is loyal and impartial, the exemplar of his field.

Commissioned by Lawleys By Post and issued in 1989 in a limited edition of 5,000 pieces. The Doulton backstamp is set within the design of a policeman's badge.

Designer:	Stanley J. Taylor	**Backstamp:** Doulton
Handle:	Handcuffs and truncheon	
Colourway:	Black and white	

Doulton Number	Size	Backstamp	Height	Intro.	Discon.	Current Market Value U.K. £	U.S. $	Can. $
D6852	Small	Douton	4"	1989	Ltd. Ed. (1991)	40.00	100.00	135.00

PORTHOS

THE "THREE MUSKETEERS", ONE OF FOUR.
NOW PART OF THE CHARACTERS FROM LITERATURE, ONE OF ELEVEN.

One of the much-loved three musketeers, Porthos roamed Europe with his merry band in search of adventure in the 1844 novel by Alexandre Dumas.

VARIATION No. 1: Colourway: Black hat, red cloak, black hair and moustache.

Porthos
D 6440
COPR 1955
DOULTON & CO LIMITED
BACKSTAMP A

Porthos
(One of the "Three Musketeers")
D 6453
COPR 1955
DOULTON & CO LIMITED
Rd No 877526
Rd No 34107
Rd No 7246
Rd No 291/55

BACKSTAMP B

Designer: Max Henk	**Backstamps: A. Doulton**
Handle: A sword	**B. Doulton / One of the "Three**
Colourway: Black hat, red cloak, black hair and moustache.	**Musketeers"** The wording "One of the Three Musketeers" was included in the early backstamp to enlighten the unknowledgeable that "Porthos" was one of the famous Musketeers.

Doulton Number	Size	Backstamp	Height	Intro.	Discon.	Current Market Value U.K. £	U.S. $	Can. $
D6440	Large	Doulton	7 1/4"	1956	1991	60.00	95.00	145.00
D6440	Large	Doulton/One	7 1/4"	1956	1970	60.00	95.00	145.00
D6453	Small	Doulton	4"	1956	1991	35.00	50.00	80.00
D6453	Small	Doulton/One	4"	1956	1970	35.00	50.00	80.00
D6516	Miniature	Doulton	2 3/4"	1960	1991	30.00	40.00	60.00
D6516	Miniature	Doulton/One	2 1/2"	1960	1970	30.00	40.00	60.00

VARIATION No. 2 Colourway: Maroon hat, blue cloak, ginger hair and moustache.

Royal Doulton®
PORTHOS
D 6828
Modelled by

© 1955 ROYAL DOULTON
NEW COLOURWAY 1988
SPECIAL COMMISSION 1000
PETER JONES CHINA
LEEDS AND WAKEFIELD

Backstamp: **Doulton / Peter Jones China Ltd.**
Commissioned by Peter Jones China Ltd., Sheffield, England.
Issued in 1988 in a limited edition of 1,000 pieces.

Doulton Number	Size	Backstamp	Height	Intro.	Discon.	Current Market Value		
						U.K. £	U.S. $	Can. $
D6828	Large	Doulton/Jones	7 1/4"	1988	1988	50.00	125.00	175.00

Miscellaneous "Porthos" Items

Doulton Number	Item	Height	Intro.	Discon.	Current Market Value		
					U.K. £	U.S. $	Can. $
D6453	Table Lighter	3 1/2"	1958	Unknown	300.00	750.00	750.00

THE POSTMAN

JOURNEY THROUGH BRITAIN
ONE OF FOUR

Even in this age of instant communication through telephone and facsimile machines, the postman continues to play an integral role in society, keeping even the most isolated places in touch with the world.

Commissioned by Lawleys By Post and issued in 1988 in a limited edition of 5,000 pieces. The Doulton backstamp is set within the design of a postage stamp.

Designer: Stanley J. Taylor
Handle: A pillar box
Colourway: Black jacket and cap, white shirt and red pillar box

Backstamp: Doulton

Doulton Number	Size	Backstamp	Height	Intro.	Discon.	Current Market Value U.K. £	U.S. $	Can. $
D6801	Small	Doulton	4"	1988	Ltd. Ed.	120.00	125.00	225.00

PUNCH AND JUDY MAN

Coming to England in the 17th century by way of Italy and France "commedia del 'arte", the Punch and Judy puppet show retains its initial popularity today. Often performed by street musicians, the show features Punch, the hunchbacked boastful husband who beats his shrew-like wife Judy.

The colours on Punch's bat are occasionally reversed with no effect on the market value.

Designer: David Biggs
Handle: Punch
Colourway: Brown hat, green coat, yellow scarf

Backstamp: Doulton

Doulton Number	Size	Backstamp	Height	Intro.	Discon.	Current Market Value U.K. £	U.S. $	Can. $
D6590	Large	Doulton	7"	1964	1969	300.00	675.00	695.00
D6593	Small	Doulton	3 1/2"	1964	1969	225.00	450.00	475.00
D6596	Miniature	Doulton	2 1/2"	1964	1969	200.00	400.00	425.00

QUEEN ELIZABETH I

Daughter of Anne Boleyn, second wife of Henry VIII, Elizabeth (1533-1603) enjoyed a 45 year reign. The "Virgin Queen" never married and, without heirs, was in constant danger of usurption. Her biggest threat, after Mary Queen of Scots, was King Philip of Spain. With the leadership of Sir Francis Drake, her Royal Navy defeated the Spanish Armada and Philip's attempted invasion of England. Issued by Lawleys in 1988, this jug is one of a pair (with King Phillip of Spain) that was produced to celebrate the 400th anniversary of the defeat of the Spanish Armada in 1588. Both jugs were limited editions of 9,500 pieces.

Designer: William K. Harper
Handle: Warship sailing on the right
Colourway: Grey, dark red and white

Backstamp: Doulton

Doulton Number	Size	Backstamp	Height	Intro.	Discon.	Current Market Value U.K. £	U.S. $	Can. $
D6821	Small	Doulton	4"	1988	Ltd. Ed.	75.00	100.00	125.00

QUEEN VICTORIA

Alexandrina Victoria (1819-1901) succeeded her uncle, William IV, to the throne on her eighteenth birthday in 1837. Reigning until her death in 1901, she had a longer rule than any other British monarch. The marriages of her nine children allied the English royal house with those of Russia, Germany, Greece, Denmark and Romania and helped her reign become known as one of the most peaceful in English history.

VARIATION No. 1: Colourway: Dark blue & yellow crown, beige and pink veils.

BACKSTAMP A

Designer: Stanley J. Taylor
Handle: Yellow sceptre
Colourway: Dark blue & yellow crown, beige and pink veils, yellow jewel in sceptre

Backstamps: A. Doulton
B. Special Limited Edition of 1500
- **Small size** Commissioned by Pascoe & Co. in a limited edition of 1500

BACKSTAMP B

Doulton Number	Size	Backstamp	Height	Intro.	Discon.	Current Market Value		
						U.K. £	U.S. $	Can. $
D6816	Large	Doulton	7 1/4"	1989	1991	55.00	130.00	180.00
D6913	Small	Doulton	3 1/2"	1992	Sp. Ed.	45.00	100.00	115.00

VARIATION No. 2:   Colourway: Purple and yellow crown, grey veil with
white frills, red jewel in sceptre.

Backstamp: **Guild of Specialist China & Glass Retailers, Peter Jones**
"The Guild of Specialist China & Glass Retailers"
Commissioned by the Guild of Specialist China and Glass Retailers in
1988 and issued in a special edition of 3,000 pieces.

Doulton Number	Size	Backstamp	Height	Intro.	Discon.	Current Market Value		
						U.K. £	U.S. $	Can. $
D6788	Large	Doulton / Guild	7 1/4"	1988	Sp. Ed.	50.00	125.00	125.00

RANGERS (FOOTBALL CLUB)

THE FOOTBALL SUPPORTERS
ONE OF EIGHT

Royal Doulton®
FOOTBALL SUPPORTER'S
CHARACTER JUG.
D 6929
Modelled by
Stanley James Taylor
© 1992 ROYAL DOULTON
"RANGERS"

Designer: Stanley J. Taylor
Handle: Team coloured scarf
Colourway: Blue, white and red uniform

Backstamp: Doulton

Doulton Number	Size	Backstamp	Height	Intro.	Discon.	Current Market Value U.K. £	U.S. $	Can. $
D6929	Mid	Doulton	5"	1992	Current	35.00	125.00	95.00

THE RED QUEEN

ALICE IN WONDERLAND
ONE OF SIX

Alice's adventures in Wonderland are, in part, built around a pack of cards. The Queen of Hearts shows her suit on the blade of an axe and her cry of "Off with his head" has become famous. In "Through the Looking Glass" the theme is linked to a chess game and the Red Queen in a chess piece.

Issued in 1987 as the first in the series.

Designer: William K. Harper
Handle: An axe
Colourway: Yellow, red and blue

Royal Doulton®
THE RED QUEEN
D 6777
Modelled by

William K. Harper

© 1987 ROYAL DOULTON

Backstamp: Doulton

Doulton Number	Size	Backstamp	Height	Intro.	Discon.	Current Market Value U.K. £	U.S. $	Can. $
D6777	Large	Doulton	7 1/4"	1987	1991	60.00	110.00	180.00
D6859	Small	Doulton	3"	1990	1991	40.00	65.00	90.00
D6860	Miniature	Doulton	2"	1990	1991	35.00	60.00	60.00

REGENCY BEAU

The Regency of the Prince of Wales lasted from 1811 to 1820 with the Prince becoming George IV in 1820. The Regency Period, however, is a term loosely applied to the years from 1805 to 1830 when classical mythology and Greek and Roman authors were better known than their English counterparts, contemporary and historical.
The period was a time of excess in clothes and appearance.

Regency Beau
D 6559
COPR 1961
DOULTON & CO LIMITED
Rd No 902090
Rd No 42142
Rd No 8925
Rd No R 84/6 ·

Designer: David Biggs
Handle: Cane and handkerchief
Colourway: Green coat, green and yellow hat

Backstamp: Doulton

Doulton Number	Size	Backstamp	Height	Intro.	Discon.	Current Market Value U.K. £	U.S. $	Can. $
D6559	Large	Doutlon	7 1/4"	1962	1967	500.00	850.00	900.00
D6562	Small	Doulton	4 1/4"	1962	1967	325.00	650.00	650.00
D6565	Miniature	Doulton	2 3/4"	1962	1967	400.00	700.00	750.00

THE RINGMASTER

THE CIRCUS
ONE OF FOUR

Much the same as a theatre director, the master-of-ceremonies of the circus is responsible for the quality of his show. Usually operating from the centre of the ring, he ensures that all of the acts proceed safely and smoothly.

Royal Doulton®
THE RING MASTER
D 6863
Modelled by

© 1990 ROYAL DOULTON

BACKSTAMP A

The Maple Leaf Edition

BACKSTAMP B

Designer: Stanley J. Taylor
Handle: Horse's head and plume
Colourway: Black top hat with a light blue ribbon, red jacket, black lapel, green plume atop horses head.

Backstamps: A. Doulton For General Release: 1991.
B. Doulton / The Maple Leaf Edition "The International Royal Doulton Collectors Weekend 1990 Toronto, Ontario, Canada. The Maple Leaf Edition." Commissioned to Commemorate The International Royal Doulton Collectors Weekend, September 14, 15 & 16th, 1990. The design incorporates a red maple leaf in honour of the 25th anniversary of Canada's Maple Leaf Flag. Issued with a certificate of authenticity. Pre-released in 1990 in a special edition of 750 pieces.

Doulton Number	Size	Backstamp	Height	Intro.	Discon.	Current Market Value		
						U.K. £	U.S. $	Can. $
D6863	Large	Doulton	7 1/2"	1991	Current *1993*	63.00	142.50	250.00
D6863	Large	Doulton/Maple	7 1/2"	1990	Sp. Ed.	145.00	125.00	300.00

RINGO STARR

THE BEATLES
ONE OF FOUR

Richard Starkey (b. 1940) was the drummer for the Beatles until they disbanded in 1970. Shyer than his three cohorts, Ringo neither wrote nor sang, beyond one or two notable exceptions.

Royal Doulton
THE BEATLES
Ringo Starr
D 6726
Modelled by

Stanley James Taylor.

© ROYAL DOULTON TABLEWARE
LIMITED 1984

Designer: Stanley J. Taylor
Handle: Plain
Colourway: Black tunic trimmed with yellow collar and epaulettes

Backstamp: Doulton

Doulton Number	Size	Backstamp	Height	Intro.	Discon.	Current Market Value		
						U.K. £	U.S. $	Can. $
D6726	Mid	Doulton	5 1/2"	1984	1991	55.00	95.00	95.00

RIP VAN WINKLE

CHARACTERS FROM LITERATURE
ONE OF ELEVEN

In 1820, the American writer Washington Irving wrote the story of Rip Van Winkle, based on legends he'd heard from Dutch settlers. Rip, while walking in the Catskill mountains of New England, drinks a fairy potion and falls asleep for twenty years. He wakes to find the world unrecognizable.

VARIATION No. 1: Colourway: **Grey-blue cap, brown robes, figure resting against tree dressed in blue**

" Rip Van Winkle "
D.6438.
COPR.1954.
DOULTON & CO.LIMITED.
R⁰N⁰ 874255.
R⁰N⁰ 32854.
R⁰N⁰ 7022.
R⁰N⁰ 193/54.

Designer: Geoff Blower
Handle: A man resting against the trunk of a tree; a blackbird sits atop the tree
Colourway: Grey-blue cap, brown robes, figure resting against tree dressed in blue

Backstamp: Doulton

Number	Doulton Size	Backstamp	Height	Intro.	Discon.	Current Market Value		
						U.K. £	U.S. $	Can. $
D6438	Large	Doulton	6 1/2"	1955	Current	49.95	142.50	160.00
D6463	Small	Doulton	4"	1957	Current	25.00	78.00	90.00
D6517	Miniature	Doulton	2 1/2"	1960	1991	30.00	40.00	50.00

VARIATION No. 2: Colourway: Black cap, green robes, figure resting against tree dressed in black.

Royal Doulton®
RIP VAN WINKLE
D 6785
Modelled by

© 1954 ROYAL DOULTON
NEW COLOURWAY 1987
SPECIAL EDITION OF 1000
FOR JOHN SINCLAIR SHEFFIELD

Backstamp: Doulton / John Sinclair
Commissioned by John Sinclair, Sheffield, England. Issued in 1987 in a special edition of 1,000 pieces.

Doulton Number	Size	Backstamp	Height	Intro.	Discon.	Current Market Value U.K. £	U.S. $	Can. $
D6785	Large	Doulton/Sinclair	7"	1987	Sp. Ed.	50.00	110.00	195.00

Miscellaneous "Rip Van Winkle" Items

Doulton Number	Item	Height	Intro.	Discon.	Current Market Value U.K. £	U.S. $	Can. $
D6463	Table Lighter	3 1/2"	1958	Unknown	400.00	750.00	750.00

ROBIN HOOD

A legendary figure from the reign of Richard I in the 12th century, Robin Hood and his group of benevolent bandits are credited with many adventures while robbing the rich to help the poor of England.

STYLE ONE: *HAT WITH NO FEATHER, HANDLE: PLAIN*

Robin Hood

COPR.1946.
DOULTON & CO LIMITED.
RᵈNº 847681.
RᵈNº 23906.
RᵈNº 134/46.
RᵈNº 5192.

Designer: Harry Fenton
Handle: Two feathers
Colourway: Brown hat, green robes

Backstamp: Doulton

Doulton Number	Size	Backstamp	Height	Intro.	Discon.	Current Market Value		
						U.K. £	U.S. $	Can. $
D6205	Large	Doulton	6 1/4"	1947	1960	85.00	160.00	195.00
D6234	Small	Doulton	3 1/4"	1947	1960	45.00	80.00	110.00
D6252	Miniature	Doulton	2 1/4"	1947	1960	40.00	60.00	85.00

ROBIN HOOD

CHARACTERS FROM LITERATURE
ONE OF ELEVEN

STYLE TWO: *HAT WITH FEATHER,*
HANDLE: BOW, QUIVER AND ARROWS

Robin Hood
D 6527
COPR 1959
DOULTON & CO LIMITED
Rd No 893840
Rd No 39648
Rd No 8312
Rd No 421/59

Royal Doulton
ROBIN HOOD
D 6541
© ROYAL DOULTON
TABLEWARE LTD 1959

Designer: Max Henk
Handle: Bow and quiver of arrows
Colourway: Brown hat with white feather on one side
and oak leaves and acorns on the other,
green robes

Backstamp: Doulton

Doulton Number	Size	Backstamp	Height	Intro.	Discon.	Current Market Value		
						U.K. £	U.S. $	Can. $
D6527	Large	Doulton	7 1/2"	1960	1992	49.00	100.00	150.00
D6534	Small	Doulton	4"	1960	1992	30.00	55.00	80.00
D6541	Miniature	Doulton	2 3/4"	1960	1991	30.00	40.00	60.00

ROBIN HOOD

PROTOTYPE

*Photograph
Not Available
At Press Time*

Designer: Eric Griffiths   **Backstamp:** Doulton
Handle: Plain
Colourway: Black, brown and green

Doulton Number	Size	Backstamp	Height	Intro.	Discon.	Current Market Value		
						U.K. £	U.S. $	Can. $
D —	Large	Doulton	6 1/2"	1987	1987		Unique	

ROBINSON CRUSOE

In 1719, Daniel Defoe wrote a novel based on the experiences of Alexander Selkirk who was marooned on a deserted Pacific island for five years. The book became a huge success and has been printed in many editions and languages.

Robinson Crusoe
D 6532
COPR 1959
DOULTON & CO LIMITED
Rd No 893845
Rd No 39653
Rd No 8317
Rd No 416/59

Designer: Max Henk
Handle: The man Friday peers from behind a palm tree
Colourway: Brown and green

Backstamp: Doulton

Doulton Number	Size	Backstamp	Height	Intro.	Discon.	Current Market Value U.K. £	U.S. $	Can. $
D6532	Large	Doulton	7 1/2"	1960	1982	60.00	115.00	155.00
D6539	Small	Doulton	4"	1960	1982	40.00	65.00	80.00
D6546	Miniature	Doulton	2 3/4"	1960	1982	35.00	50.00	70.00

ROMEO

PROTOTYPE

STYLE ONE: HANDLE: A PHIAL OF POISON SPILLS OVER A DAGGER BELOW

Designer: David Biggs   **Backstamp:** Doulton
 Handle: A phial of poison spills over
                 a dagger below
Colourway: Brown and white

Doulton Number	Size	Variation	Height	Intro.	Discon.	Current Market Value		
						U.K. £	U.S. $	Can. $
D6670	Large	Prototype	7"	1981	1981		Extremely Rare	

ROMEO

THE SHAKESPEAREAN COLLECTION
ONE OF SIX

The hero of Shakespeare's 1596 romantic play, Romeo falls in love with Juliet, the daughter of a Verona family feuding with his own. The lives of these two clandestine lovers end tragically and, with bitter irony, cause the reconciliation of the two families.

STYLE TWO: HANDLE: A DAGGER SUPERIMPOSED ON THE COLUMN SUPPORTING A BALCONY

© ROYAL DOULTON TABLEWARE LIMITED 1982
D 6670

The
Shakespearean
Collection
ROMEO
A series of hand-made, hand-decorated Character Jugs by
Royal Doulton

Designer: David Biggs
Handle: A dagger superimposed on the
column supporting a balcony
Colourway: Brown and white

Backstamp: Doulton

Doulton Number	Size	Backstamp	Height	Intro.	Discon.	Current Market Value		
						U.K. £	U.S. $	Can. $
D6670	Large	Doulton	7 1/2"	1983	1989	65.00	110.00	145.00

RONALD REAGAN

PROTOTYPE

STYLE ONE: THE "STARS AND STRIPES",
WITH GREEN CORD AND NO CAP

*Photograph
Not Available
At Press Time*

Designer: Eric Griffiths
Handle: The "Stars and Stripes"
with green cord, no cap
Colourway: Blue grey suit, dark blue tie

Backstamp: Doulton

Doulton Number	Size	Backstamp	Height	Intro.	Discon.	Current Market Value		
						U.K. £	U.S. $	Can. $
D6718	Large	Doulton	7 3/4"	1984	1984		Unique	

RONALD REAGAN

Ronald Wilson Reagan (b. 1911) began as an Iowa sports announcer for a radio station. In 1937 he began acting, a profession that was to last thirty years and span fifty films, including the "Bonzo" series. In 1966, Reagan was elected governor of California, and his political career began. After losing the Republican Presidential nomination twice, he was elected President of the United States and he served two terms in office from 1980-1988.

This jug was commissioned for the Republican National Committee. Originally to be issued in a limited edition of 5,000 pieces, the jug did not sell well and only 2,000 pieces were said to have been produced.

Issued with a certificate and photograph of President Reagan in a decorative folio.

STYLE TWO: THE "STARS AND STRIPES", WITH YELLOW CORD AND GOLD CAP

THE PRESIDENT'S SIGNATURE EDITION
1984 PRESIDENTIAL ELECTION

Royal Doulton
Worldwide Limited Edition of 5000
This is number 1166.
© Royal Doulton Tableware Ltd 1984

Designer: Eric Griffiths
Handle: The "Stars and Stripes" with yellow cord, gold cap
Colourway: Dark blue suit, white shirt with purple striped tie.

Backstamp: Doulton / Reagan

Doulton Number	Size	Backstamp	Height	Intro.	Discon.	Current Market Value		
						U.K. £	U.S. $	Can. $
D6718	Large	Doulton/Reagan	7 3/4"	1984	Ltd. Ed.	225.00	400.00	600.00

THE SAILOR

THE ARMED FORCES
ONE OF THREE

The sailor would be a member of the navy, operating the various carriers, fighters and submarines in the military arsenal.

STYLE ONE: *WITHOUT "R.C.N." ON BINOCULARS*

Designer: William K. Harper   **Backstamp:** Doulton
Handle: Binoculars
Colourway: White Royal Navy cap, light brown
coat and white sweater

Doulton Number	Size	Backstamp	Height	Intro.	Discon.	Current Market Value U.K. £	U.S. $	Can. $
D6875	Small	Doulton	4 1/2"	1991	1991	28.95	78.00	100.00

THE SAILOR

THE CANADIANS
ONE OF THREE

Commissioned by The British Toby in a limited edition of 250 pieces. Sold originally as a set for $465.00 Canadian Dollars.

STYLE TWO: WITH "R.C.N." ON BINOCULARS

Designer: William K. Harper
Handle: R.C.N. Binoculars
Colourway: White Royal Canadian Navy cap, dark brown coat and white sweater

Backstamp: Doulton/The British Toby

Doulton Number	Size	Backstamp	Height	Intro.	Discon.	Current Market Value		
						U.K. £	U.S. $	Can. $
D6904	Small	Doulton/British	4 1/2"	1991	Ltd. Ed.	120.00	140.00	165.00

SAIREY GAMP

In Charles Dickins' 1843 novel "Martin Chizzlewit" Sairey Gamp is a gossiping, gin-drinking midwife and sick-nurse. Her ubiquitous old cotton umbrella has given rise to the colloquialism "gamp," for particulary untidy specimens.

Please note misnumbered large size jugs exist and carry the number D5528 which is the number allocated to the small size jug. This does not add any premium to the price of the jug.

VARIATION No. 1:   **Colourway:**   **Black hair with light green band, dark green coat, yellow and burgundy bow**
                     Handle: **Green umbrella**

BACKSTAMP B

SHEFFIELD & ROTHERHAM
BACKSTAMP C

Designer: Leslie Harradine / Harry Fenton
Handle: A green umbrella with brown handle
Colourway: Black hair with light green band, dark green coat, yellow and burgundy bow
Backstamp: A. Doulton
B. Doulton / Bentalls "Souvenir From Bentalls Jubilee Year 1935"
Commissioned by Bentalls to commemorate the silver jubilee in 1935 of King George V.
C. Doulton / Darley "Souvenir from Darley & Son Sheffield & Rotherham"

Doulton Number	Size	Backstamp	Height	Intro.	Discon.	Current Market Value		
						U.K. £	U.S. $	Can. $
D5451	Large	Doulton	6 1/4"	1935	1986	50.00	100.00	125.00
D5528	Small	Doulton	3 1/8"	1935	1986	30.00	55.00	75.00
D5528	Small	Doulton/Bentalls	3 1/8"	1935	1935	350.00	600.00	700.00
D5528	Small	Doulton/Darley	3 1/8"	1936	1936	350.00	600.00	700.00
D6045	Miniature	Doulton	2 1/8"	1939	1986	20.00	50.00	60.00
D6146	Tiny	Doulton	1 1/4"	1940	1960	60.00	100.00	135.00

VARIATION No. 2: Colourway: Yellow band on hat, yellow bow, maroon umbrella

"SAIREY GAMP"
D.6770
*Specially Commissioned
from*
Royal Doulton®
by
STRAWBRIDGE & CLOTHIER
Celebrating the opening of
The Royal Doulton Room
Strawbridge & Clothier, Philadelphia, U.S.
HAND MODELLED AND HAND DECORATED
A LIMITED EDITION OF 250
THIS IS NO. 39
© 1986 ROYAL DOULTON

Backstamps: A. Strawbridge and Clothier "Celebrating the opening of The Royal Doulton Room at Strawbridge and Clothier, Philadelphia, U.S.A."
Commissioned by Strawbridge and Clothier, Philadelphia. Issued in 1986 in a limited edition of 250 pieces.
B. Strawbridge and Clothier "Made for the First Anniversary of the Royal Doulton Room at Strawbridge and Clothier"
Commissioned by Strawbridge and Clothier in 1987 and issued in a limited edition of 500 pieces.

Doulton Number	Size	Variations	Height	Intro.	Discon.	Current Market Value U.K. £	U.S. $	Can. $
D6770	Large	Var. 2A	6 1/4"	1986	Ltd. Ed.	225.00	200.00	250.00
D6789	Small	Var. 2B	3"	1987	Ltd. Ed.	135.00	150.00	175.00

Miscellaneous "Sairey Gamp" Items

Doulton Number	Item	Height	Intro.	Discon.	Current Market Value U.K. £	U.S. $	Can. $
D6009	Ash Bowl	3"	1939	1960	85.00	135.00	150.00
D6011	Sugar Bowl	2 1/2"	1939	1942	375.00	750.00	857.00
D6015	Teapot	7"	1939	1942	750.00	1,250.00	1,500.00
D6047	Bust	2 1/4"	1939	1960	65.00	100.00	125.00
D6150	Toothpick Holder	2 3/4"	1940	1942	225.00	450.00	500.00
HN1625	Bookend	3 1/2"	1934	1939	1,000.00	2,000.00	2,000.00
M62	Napkin Ring	3 1/2"	c. 1935	1939	225.00	450.00	550.00

SAM JOHNSON

A celebrated poet, essayist and lexicographer, Dr. Johnson (1709-1784) published his "Dictionary" in 1755. This document was the first systematic study of the English language. His "Literary Club" met regularly at a London pub and included such famous figures as David Garrick, Oliver Goldsmith and Edmund Burke.

"Sam Johnson."

COPR.1949.
DOULTON & CO.LIMITED.
Rd No 857579
Rd No 5906.
Rd No 77/49

Designer: Harry Fenton
Handle: Plain
Colourway: Dark brown hat, light brown, maroon and white robes

Backstamp: Doulton

Doulton Number	Size	Backstamp	Height	Intro.	Discon.	Current Market Value		
						U.K. £	U.S. $	Can. $
D6289	Large	Doulton	6 1/4"	1950	1960	185.00	375.00	425.00
D6296	Small	Doulton	3 1/4"	1950	1960	120.00	225.00	275.00

SAM WELLER

In the 1837 Charles Dickens' novel "The Pickwick Papers," Sam was a "Boots" employed at the White Hart Inn. He becomes the faithful aide and valet to Mr. Pickwick and eventually marries Napkins' housemaid.
This character jug is unusual in that its modelling changes dramatically between the large and smaller versions.

"Sam Weller
R⁴Nº 822824
Regᴰ IN AUSTRALIA

Designer: Leslie Harradine / Harry Fenton
Handle: Plain
Colourway: Dark brown hat, light brown coat, red kerchief with white spots

Backstamp: Doulton

Doulton Number	Size	Backstamp	Height	Intro.	Discon.	Current Market Value U.K. £	U.S. $	Can. $
D6064	Large	Doulton	6 1/2"	1940	1960	80.00	150.00	195.00
D5841	Mid	Doulton	4 1/2"	1938	1948	120.00	200.00	200.00
D5841	Small	Doulton	3 1/4"	1948	1960	50.00	90.00	110.00
D6140	Miniature	Doulton	2 1/4"	1940	1960	35.00	60.00	85.00
D6147	Tiny	Doulton	1 1/4"	1940	1960	55.00	110.00	135.00

Miscellaneous "Sam Weller" Items

Doulton Number	Item	Height	Intro.	Discon.	Current Market Value U.K. £	U.S. $	Can. $
D6052	Bust	2 1/2"	1939	1960	65.00	100.00	125.00
M61	Napkin Ring	3 1/2"	c. 1939	1939	200.00	450.00	550.00

SAMSON AND DELILAH

THE STAR-CROSSED LOVERS COLLECTION (TWO-FACED JUG)
ONE OF FOUR

Samson was an Israelite judge from Biblical times, famous for his strength. Delilah, a Philistine woman, was paid to find the secret of Samson's strength so that her people could overthrow their Israelite enemies. Samson fell in love with Delilah and told her that his strength lay in his hair. She shaved his head while he slept and the Philistines captured and blinded him. Samson avenged himself when his hair grew back by pulling down a Philistine temple, killing himself and many of his enemies.

Issued in 1988 in a limited edition of 9,500 pieces but not yet sold out.

Designer: Stanley J. Taylor
Handle: Samson: Jawbone of an ass
Delilah: A broken column
Colourway: Brown, black and cream

Royal Doulton®
THE
STAR-CROSSED LOVERS
COLLECTION
Samson & Delilah
D 6787
Modelled by Stanley James Taylor

Stanley James Taylor

Worldwide Limited Edition of 9,500
This is Number 1053
© 1987 Royal Doulton

Backstamp: Doulton

Doulton Number	Size	Backstamp	Height	Intro.	Discon.	Current Market Value		
						U.K. £	U.S. $	Can. $
D6787	Large	Doulton	7"	1988	Ltd. Ed. (1991)	75.00	130.00	165.00

SANCHO PANÇA

This amiable peasant is employed as the squire to Don Quixote in Cervantes' 17th century novel. Accompanying Quixote on many adventures, his down-to-earth common sense acts as a foil to his master's romantic musing.

Sancho Panca
(A Servant to Don Quixote)
D 6461
COPR 1956
DOULTON & CO LIMITED
Rd No 881510
Rd No 35706
Rd No 7561
Rd No 332/56

BACKSTAMP B

Designer: Geoff Blower
Handle: Light brown donkey
Colourway: Black hat with a white feather, black coat with a white collar

Backstamps: A. Doulton
B. Doulton / Sancho Panca ("A Servant to Don Quixote")
Produced from 1957 to the early 1970's, with no cedilla.
C. Doulton / Sancho Pança
The spelling of the name Pança with the cedilla makes the "c" sibilant, giving a soft "s" sound in pronunciation. Early versions of the backstamp included the cedilla, but it was dropped in the late fifties. The incised name shows that the cedilla was included in the modelling.

Doulton Number	Size	Backstamp	Height	Intro.	Discon.	Current Market Value U.K. £	U.S. $	Can. $
D6456	Large	Doulton	6 1/2"	1957	1983	60.00	120.00	150.00
D6456	Large	"A Servant"	6 1/2"	1957	1970	60.00	120.00	150.00
D6456	Large	Cedilla	6 1/2	1957	1959	60.00	120.00	150.00
D6461	Small	Doulton	3 1/4"	1957	1983	40.00	65.00	80.00
D6461	Small	"A Servant"	3 1/4"	1957	1970	40.00	65.00	80.00
D6461	Small	Cedilla	3 1/4"	1957	1959	40.00	65.00	80.00
D6518	Miniature	Doulton	2 1/2"	1960	1983	35.00	55.00	60.00
D6518	Miniature	"A Servant"	2 1/2"	1960	1970	35.00	55.00	60.00

Note: The dates for the discontinuance of the backstamp varieties are only approximate.

SANTA CLAUS

A figure who needs no introduction, the Santa Claus jug was introduced in 1981 and was the first to undergo annual design changes. Featuring different well-known Christmas themes, the handle has changed several times since 1981.

STYLE ONE: *HANDLE: A DOLL AND DRUM*

Designer: Michael Abberley
Handle: A doll stands on a drum
Colourway: Red, white and light brown

Backstamp: Doulton

Doulton Number	Size	Backstamp	Height	Intro.	Discon.	Current Market Value U.K. £	U.S. $	Can. $
D6668	Large	Doulton	7 1/2"	1981	1981	70.00	120.00	160.00

SANTA CLAUS

STYLE TWO: HANDLE: THE HEAD OF A REINDEER

ⓒ **ROYAL DOULTON**
TABLEWARE LTD 1982

Santa Claus
D.6675

Designer: Michael Abberley   **Backstamp:** Doulton
  Handle: The head of a reindeer
Colourway: Red, white and brown

Doulton Number	Size	Backstamp	Height	Intro.	Discon.	Current Market Value U.K. £	U.S. $	Can. $
D6675	Large	Doulton	7 1/4"	1982	1982	60.00	135.00	160.00

SANTA CLAUS

STYLE THREE: *HANDLE: A SACK OF TOYS*

© ROYAL DOULTON
TABLEWARE LTD. 1983

Santa Claus
D 6690

Designer: Michael Abberley
Handle: A sack of toys
Colourway: Red, white and light brown

Backstamp: Doulton

Doulton Number	Size	Backstamp	Height	Intro.	Discon.	Current Market Value		
						U.K. £	U.S. $	Can. $
D6690	Large	Doulton	7 1/2"	1983	1983	80.00	140.00	175.00

SANTA CLAUS

STYLE FOUR: *HANDLE: PLAIN RED*

Royal Doulton
SANTA CLAUS
D6704
Modelled by

© ROYAL DOULTON TABLEWARE
LIMITED 1983

BACKSTAMP A

SANTA CLAUS
D 6950

BACKSTAMP B

Designer: Michael Abberley
Handle: Plain
Colourway: Red and white

Backstamps: A. **Doulton**
B. **Doulton/Seaway China**
Commissioned by SEAWAY CHINA
Marine City MI U.S.A.

Doulton Number	Size	Backstamp	Height	Intro.	Discon.	Current Market Value U.K. £	U.S. $	Can. $
D6704	Large	Doulton	7 1/2"	1984	Current	55.00	142.50	160.00
D6705	Small	Doulton	3 1/4"	1984	Current	25.00	78.00	90.00
D6706	Miniature	Doulton	2 1/2"	1984	1991	15.00	40.00	50.00
D6950	Tiny	Doulton/Seaway	1 1/4"	1993	Spec. Ed.	55.00	70.00	30.00

SANTA CLAUS

STYLE FIVE: HANDLE: A HOLLY WREATH

Designer: Michael Abberley
Handle: A holly wreath
Colourway: Red, white and green

Backstamps: A. **Doulton** - Miniature
Issued in a limited edition
of 5,000 Christmas 1991
B. **Doulton / Home Shopping**-Large
Commissioned by "Home
Shopping Network", Florida
Issued in a special edition of 5,000

Doulton Number	Size	Backstamp	Height	Intro.	Discon.	Current Market Value U.K. £	U.S. $	Can. $
D6794	Large	Doulton/Home	7"	1988	Sp. Ed.	150.00	300.00	350.00
D6900	Miniature	Doulton	2 1/2"	1991	Ltd. Ed. (1991)	35.00	50.00	85.00

SANTA CLAUS

STYLE SIX: HANDLE: A CANDY CANE

VARIATION No. 1: Handle: Candy cane with red and white stripes.

Designer: Michael Abberley	**Backstamp:**	**Doulton/Cable Value**
Handle: Candy cane with red and white stripes.		Commissioned by the "Cable Value
Colourway: Red and white		Network". Issued in a special edition
		of 1,000

Doulton Number	Size	Backstamp	Height	Intro.	Discon.	Current Market Value U.K. £	Current Market Value U.S. $	Current Market Value Can. $
D6793	Large	Doulton/Cable	7 1/2"	1988	Sp. Ed.	250.00	650.00	500.00

VARIATION No. 2: Handle: Candy cane with red, white and green stripes

Backstamp: Doulton/American Collectors Society
Commissioned by the "American Collectors Society". Issued in 1989 in a special edition of 1,000 pieces.

Doulton Number	Size	Backstamp	Height	Intro.	Discon.	Current Market Value		
						U.K. £	U.S. $	Can. $
D6840	Large	Doulton/ American	7 1/2"	1989	Sp. Ed.	145.00	350.00	300.00

SCARAMOUCHE

In the 17th century "commedia dell'arte", Scaramouche appears as a boastful, foolish character, dressed in the old Spanish style. He was first featured on his own in the Edward Ravenscroft comedy produced in 1677.

STYLE ONE   HANDLE: A GUITAR WITH THE TWO MASKS OF COMEDY AND TRAGEDY

Scaramouche
D 6558
COPR 1961
DOULTON & CO LIMITED
Rd No 902089
Rd No 42141
Rd No 8924
Rd No R83/61

Designer: Max Henk
Handle: A guitar
Colourway: Blue-black, brown and green

Backstamp: Doulton

Doulton Number	Size	Backstamp	Height	Intro.	Discon.	Current Market Value		
						U.K. £	U.S. $	Can. $
D6558	Large	Doulton	7"	1962	1967	425.00	750.00	700.00
D6561	Small	Doulton	3 1/4"	1962	1967	275.00	475.00	550.00
D6564	Miniature	Doulton	2 1/2"	1962	1967	275.00	450.00	450.00

SCARAMOUCHE

CHARACTERS FROM LITERATURE
ONE OF ELEVEN

STYLE TWO: HANDLE: A CURTAIN WITH THE TWO MASKS
OF COMEDY AND TRAGEDY

VARIATION No. 1:   Colourway: **Yellow hat, turquoise tunic and white ruff, light brown hair.**
Handle: **Lavender**

Royal Doulton®

SCARAMOUCHE
D 6814
Modelled by

Stanley James Taylor.

© 1987 ROYAL DOULTON
NEW COLOURWAY 1988

Designer: Stanley J. Taylor
Handle: The masks of tragedy and comedy
rest against a curtain
Colourway: Yellow hat, turquoise tunic, white ruff,
light brown hair and lavender handle.

Backstamp: Doulton

Doulton Number	Size	Variations	Height	Intro.	Discon.	Current Market Value U.K. £	U.S. $	Can. $
D6814	Large	Var. 1	6 3/4"	1988	1991	55.00	95.00	120.00

VARIATION No. 2: Colourway: Black hat, green tunic and white ruff, dark brown hair; yellow handle

Designer:	Stanley J. Taylor
Handle:	The masks of tragedy and comedy rest against a curtain
Colourway:	Black hat, green tunic, white ruff, dark brown hair and yellow handle

Backstamp: **Doulton/Guild**
Commissioned by the Guild of Specialist China & Glass Retailers in 1987 and issued in a special edition of 1,500 pieces.

Doulton Number	Size	Variations	Height	Intro.	Discon.	Current Market Value U.K. £	Current Market Value U.S. $	Current Market Value Can. $
D6774	Large	Var. 2	6 3/4"	1987	Sp. Ed.	75.00	225.00	300.00

SCARLET PIMPERNEL

PROTOTYPE

In the 1905 novel by the Hungarian Baroness Orczy, the Scarlet Pimpernel was a group of Englishmen dedicated to the rescue of victims of the Reign of Terror in Paris. Sir Percy Blakeney, the group's leader, bests his opponents by clever wit and courage while disguising his identity from his friends back in England.

Designer: Geoff Blower
Handle: Characters in assorted disguises
Colourway: Black, white and blue

Backstamp: Doulton

Doulton Number	Size	Backstamp	Height	Intro.	Discon.	Current Market Value U.K. £	U.S. $	Can. $
D —	Large	Doulton	7"		Unknown		Unique	

SCROOGE

CHARLES DICKENS COMMEMORATIVE SET
DICKENS TINIES, ONE OF TWELVE.

    In Dickens' famous novel, "A Christmas Carol", Scrooge is a loveless, miserly businessman who changes his ways after being visited by the three ghosts on Christmas Eve.

    Issued to commemorate the 170th Anniversary of the birth of Charles Dickens. There are twelve jugs in this set, each issued with a certificate of authenticity. A mahogany display shelf completes the set. The set was first sold by Lawleys By Post in the U.K. during 1982 to 1988, and in 1985 onward in North America and Australia.

Scrooge
D. 6683

Designer: Michael Abberley
Handle: Plain
Colourway: Yellow and brown

Backstamp: Doulton

Doulton Number	Size	Backstamp	Height	Intro.	Discon.	Current Market Value U.K. £	U.S. $	Can. $
D6683	Tiny	Doulton	1 1/2"	1982	1989	30.00	45.00	60.00
		Display for 12 Tinies				65.00	45.00	50.00

SHAKESPEARE

Royal Doulton
SHAKESPEARE
D 6938
Modelled by

© 1993 ROYAL DOULTON

Designer:	William K. Harper
Handle:	Inkwell and books
Colourway:	Black coat, yellow collar, light brown hair and beard, burgundy books, grey inkwell and quill

Backstamp: Doulton

Doulton Number	Size	Backstamp	Height	Intro.	Discon.	Current Market Value U.K. £	U.S. $	Can. $
D6938	Small	Doulton	3 1/2"	1993	Current	70.00	99.00	110.00

SIMON THE CELLARER

Simon was the subject of a 19th century English folksong. The keys on the handle are those to his cellar full of great wines and ales. He was always good for standing a drink for his friends.

BACKSTAMP B

Designer: Charles Noke / Harry Fenton
Handle: A bunch of keys
Colourway: Maroon hat, white ruff

Backstamps: A. **Doulton**
B. **Doulton/Bentalls**
   "Souvenir from Bentalls 1936."

Doulton Number	Size	Backstamp	Height	Intro.	Discon.	Current Market Value		
						U.K. £	U.S. $	Can. $
D5504	Large	Doulton	6 1/2"	1935	1960	80.00	150.00	195.00
D5616	Small	Doulton	3 1/2"	1936	1960	45.00	75.00	110.00
D5616	Small	Doulton/Bentalls	3 1/2"	1936	1936	250.00	650.00	650.00

SIMPLE SIMON

The subject of this jug dates back to a 17th century nursery rhyme of Simon and a "pieman" he meets. The real identity of this character has been lost.

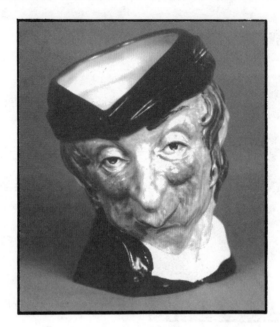

Designer: Geoff Blower   **Backstamp:** Doulton
Handle: Plain
Colourway: Green, brown and white

Doulton Number	Size	Backstamp	Height	Intro.	Discon.	Current Market Value U.K. £	U.S. $	Can. $
D6374	Large	Doulton	7"	1953	1960	225.00	550.00	650.00

SIR FRANCIS DRAKE

This version of the Drake jug was produced to celebrate the 400th anniversary of the defeat of the Spanish Armada in 1588. Commissioned by the Guild of Specialist China and Glass Retailers, this jug was issued in 1988 in a special edition of 6,000 pieces.

Designer: Peter Gee
Handle: The Golden Hind's bow and sails
Colourway: Black and white

Backstamp: Doulton / Guild

Doulton Number	Size	Backstamp	Height	Intro.	Discon.	Current Market Value		
						U.K. £	U.S. $	Can. $
D6805	Large	Doulton/Guild	7"	1988	Sp. Ed.	60.00	150.00	175.00

SIR HENRY DOULTON

ROYAL DOULTON INTERNATIONAL COLLECTORS CLUB

In the mid 1830's Henry (1820-1897) joined his father's firm just in time to capitalize on the expanding market that was developing in London for modern sanitation products. The manufacture of stoneware sewer and water pipes led Doulton and Company, as they were known after 1854, to become a large and flourishing concern. John Doulton retired around this time leaving Doulton and Company in the hands of his son Henry. In the 1860's, with decorative wares expanding, Henry Doulton was persuaded to hire students from the Lambeth School of Art as designers and decorators of the new ornamental wares his company was introducing. Their outstanding artist-signed creations heralded the beginning of the studio art pottery movement.

SIR HENRY DOULTON
1820 - 1897
EXCLUSIVELY FOR
COLLECTORS CLUB
© ROYAL DOULTON
TABLEWARE LTD 1983
MODELLED BY

Designer: Eric Griffiths
Handle: A Doulton art pottery vase
Colourway: Black coat, yellow cravat, grey hair, brown and blue vase

Backstamp: Doulton / RDICC

Doulton Number	Size	Backstamp	Height	Intro.	Discon.	Current Market Value U.K. £	U.S. $	Can. $
D6703	Small	RDICC	4 1/2"	1984	1984	85.00	125.00	155.00

SIR HENRY DOULTON / MICHAEL DOULTON

This two-faced jug was a special edition jug issued to mark the personal appearances at retail locations of Michael Doulton. This piece is one of the few two-faced jugs made in the small size.

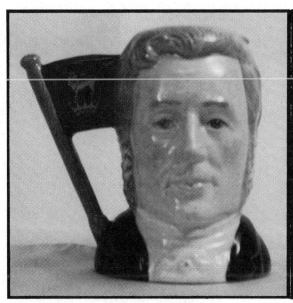 

Designer: William K. Harper
Handle: Flag bearing the lion and crown backstamp of Royal Doulton
Colourway: **Henry:** Grey hair, yellow cravat
Michael: Brown hair, dark blue suit, white shirt, light blue tie
Backstamp: Doulton

Royal Doulton®
Sir Henry Doulton
━━━━◆━━━━
Michael Doulton
D 6921
This small-size Character Jug, modelled by William K. Harper, is a special edition issued to mark personal appearances by Michael Doulton.

© 1992 ROYAL DOULTON

Doulton Number	Size	Backstamp	Height	Intro.	Discon.	Current Market Value		
						U.K. £	U.S. $	Can. $
D6921	Small	Doulton	4 1/2"	1992	1992	50.00	100.00	135.00

SIR THOMAS MORE

HENRY AND HIS SIX WIVES
ONE OF EIGHT

Thomas More (1478-1535) entered the service of King Henry VIII in 1518 as royal councillor. He was knighted and became Lord Chancellor after the dismissal of Cardinal Wolsey in 1529. Henry at this time was embroiled in a battle with Rome over his decision to divorce Catherine of Aragon. Unable to support his King, More resigned.

In 1534 More was arrested for high treason when he refused to swear an Oath of Supremacy, stating that Henry VIII ranked above all foreign leaders, including the Pope. He was beheaded in 1535 and canonized by the Catholic Church 400 years later in 1935.

Royal Doulton®
SIR THOMAS MORE
D 6792
Modelled by
Stanley James Taylor
© 1987 ROYAL DOULTON

Designer:	Stanley J. Taylor
Handle:	A window arch and a bible
Colourway:	Dark green hat, brown fur trim collar, gold chain of office.

Backstamp: Doulton

Doulton Number	Size	Backstamp	Height	Intro.	Discon.	Current Market Value U.K. £	U.S. $	Can. $
D6792	Large	Doulton	6 3/4"	1988	1991	55.00	100.00	145.00

SIR WINSTON CHURCHILL

HEROIC LEADERS
ONE OF THREE

This Churchill jug is a new design, commissioned by Lawleys By Post. Issued in 1989 as a set of three, and limited to 9,500 pieces.

Royal Doulton®
SIR WINSTON CHURCHILL
1874-1965
D 6849
Modelled by
Stanley James Taylor
© 1989 ROYAL DOULTON
A LIMITED EDITION OF 9500
THIS IS NO. 1609

Designer: Stanley J. Taylor
Handle: The Union Jack flag
Colourway: Black, grey and white

Backstamp: Doulton

Doulton Number	Size	Backstamp	Height	Intro.	Discon.	Current Market Value U.K. £	U.S. $	Can. $
D6849	Small	Doulton	3 1/4"	1989	Ltd. Ed.	75.00	115.00	135.00

THE SLEUTH

The unsuccessful doctor, Arthur Conan Doyle, (1859-1930), published the first of his widely popular detective stories in 1887. The amateur sleuth Sherlock Holmes shared rooms on Baker Street and many adventures with his friend and foil Dr. Watson.

VARIATION No. 1: Colourway: Black deerstalker hat, brown cloak

The Sleuth
D 6631
©DOULTON & CO LIMITED 1972
REGISTRATION APPLIED FOR

Designer: Alan Moore   **Backstamp:** Doulton
Handle: A pipe and magnifying glass
Colourway: Dark green deerstalker hat, brown cloak

Doulton Number	Size	Backstamp	Height	Intro.	Discon.	Current Market Value		
						U.K. £	U.S. $	Can. $
D6631	Large	Doulton	7"	1973	Current	49.95	142.50	160.00
D6635	Small	Doulton	3 1/4"	1973	Current	28.95	78.00	90.00
D6639	Miniature	Doulton	2 3/4"	1973	1991	30.00	40.00	60.00

VARIATION No 2:   Colourway: Brown deerstalker hat, red cloak

Backstamp: Doulton/Lawleys "This Limited Edition of 5,000 Commemorates
The Centenary of the Publication of the First Sherlock Holmes story
"A Study In Scarlet"
Commissioned by Lawleys By Post to celebrate 100 years since the publication of the first Sherlock
Holmes story "A Study in Scarlet". Issued in 1987 in a limited edition of 5,000 pieces.

Doulton Number	Size	Backstamp	Height	Intro.	Discon.	Current Market Value		
						U.K. £	U.S. $	Can. $
D6773	Small	Lawleys	3 1/4"	1987	Ltd. Ed.	45.00	95.00	125.00

SMUGGLER

The practice of smuggling has been around since the first trade embargo was introduced. The illegal, dangerous but often lucrative business of smuggling is still a universal occupation for many. The detailing on the barrel of the small size jug is often less distinguishable.

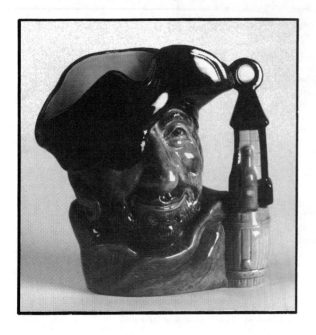

Smuggler
D6616
COPR. 1967
DOULTON & CO. LIMITED
Rd No 932050
Rd No 51328
Rd No 11138
Rd No 630/67

Designer: David Biggs
Handle: Lantern above a barrel
Colourway: Green hat, red scarf

Backstamp: Doulton

Doulton Number	Size	Backstamp	Height	Intro.	Discon.	Current Market Value		
						U.K. £	U.S. $	Can. $
D6616	Large	Doulton	7 1/4"	1968	1981	75.00	115.00	145.00
D6619	Small	Doulton	3 1/4"	1968	1981	40.00	65.00	80.00

SMUTS

A South African attorney, militaryman and politician, Jan Christiaan Smuts (1870-1950) enjoyed a long and distinguished career. Serving as a member of the British War Cabinet in WWI, Smuts was one of the authors of the Covenent of the League of Nations. In 1945, after again serving the Allies in WWII, Smuts is credited with writing the preamble to the Charter of the United Nations.

In South Africa, he served as Attorney General and Minister of Defence, becoming Prime Minister in 1919 and again in 1939.

Designer:	Harry Fenton	**Backstamp:**	Doulton
Handle:	Springbok		
Colourway:	Light brown		

Doulton Number	Size	Backstamp	Height	Intro.	Discon.	Current Market Value		
						U.K. £	U.S. $	Can. $
D6198	Large	Doulton	6 1/2"	1946	1948	750.00	1,500.00	1,750.00

THE SNAKE CHARMER

The traditional and mysterious figure of the snake charmer has enthralled both children and adults for many years. In this piece, issued in a limited edition of 2,500, the snake charmer's venomous cobra coming out of its basket comprises the handle.

Royal Doulton®

THE SNAKE CHARMER

D 6912

Modelled by

Stanley James Taylor.

© 1991 ROYAL DOULTON

A SPECIALLY COMMISSIONED
LIMITED EDITION OF 2,500

THIS IS NO. *833*

Designer: Stanley J. Taylor
Handle: Cobra, basket and pipe
Colourway: Yellow turban with blue-pink jewel, burgundy-yellow robes

Backstamp: Doulton

Doulton Number	Size	Backstamp	Height	Intro.	Discon.	Current Market Value		
						U.K. £	U.S. $	Can. $
D6912	Large	Doulton	7"	1992	Ltd. Ed.	125.00	210.00	250.00

THE SNOOKER PLAYER

CHARACTERS FROM LIFE
ONE OF SEVEN

Snooker is a variety of pool and like billiards requires great accuracy. The speed and angle at which one hits a ball with the cue must be carefully calculated before each shot.

Royal Doulton®
THE SNOOKER PLAYER
D 6879
Modelled by

Stanley James Taylor

© 1990 ROYAL DOULTON

Designer:	Stanley J. Taylor
Handle:	Cue with chalk, red and black cue balls
Colourway:	Black hair, white shirt, black bow-tie and vest

Backstamp: Doulton

Doulton Number	Size	Backstamp	Height	Intro.	Discon.	Current Market Value U.K. £	U.S. $	Can. $
D6879	Small	Doulton	4"	1991	Current	28.95	78.00	100.00

THE SOLDIER

THE ARMED FORCES
ONE OF THREE

In the Armed Forces, the soldier is a member of the Army, which fights the ground battles during a war. In general, the term has come to signify anyone having a military career.

STYLE ONE: WITH "DESERT RAT" PATCH ON CANTEEN

Royal Doulton®
THE SOLDIER
D 6876
Modelled by

William K. Harper

© 1990 ROYAL DOULTON

Designer:	William K. Harper	
Handle:	Bayonet and water canteen	
Colourway:	Army steel helmet with netting, khaki tunic	

Backstamp: Doulton

Doulton Number	Size	Backstamp	Height	Intro.	Discon.	Current Market Value U.K. £	U.S. $	Can. $
D6876	Small	Doulton	4 1/2"	1991	Current	28.95	78.00	100.00

THE SOLDIER

THE CANADIANS
ONE OF THREE

Commissioned by The British Toby in a limited edition of 250 pieces. Originally sold in a set for $465.00 Canadian Dollars.

STYLE TWO: *WITH "RED" PATCH ON CANTEEN*

Designer:	William K. Harper
Handle:	Bayonet and water canteen with red patch
Colourway:	Army steel helmet with netting, khaki tunic

Backstamp: Doulton / The British Toby

Doulton Number	Size	Backstamp	Height	Intro.	Discon.	Current Market Value		
						U.K. £	U.S. $	Can. $
D6905	Small	Doulton / British Toby	4 1/2"	1991	Ltd. Ed.	120.00	140.00	165.00

ST. GEORGE

The patron saint of England since the 13th century, George is the hero of a legend which describes him as a chivalrous knight who single-handedly slays a huge dragon, saving the princess Melisande.

St George
D 6618
COPR 1967
DOULTON & CO LIMITED
Rd No 932048
Rd No 51330
Rd No 11140
Rd No 628/67

Designer: Max Henk
Handle: A dragon
Colourway: Grey helmet, turquoise armour

Backstamp: Doulton

Doulton Number	Size	Backstamp	Height	Intro.	Discon.	Current Market Value U.K. £	U.S. $	Can. $
D6618	Large	Doulton	7 1/2"	1968	1975	120.00	275.00	275.00
D6621	Small	Doulton	3 3/4"	1968	1975	75.00	175.00	140.00

TAM O'SHANTER

In a poem by Robert Burns, written in 1791, Tam O'Shanter is a drunken farmer who happens upon witches who pursue him and his horse. He escapes, but his horse doesn't quite make it - one witch pulls its tail off.

The Scottish woollen cap called a tam is reputedly named after this poem's hero.

Tam o'Shanter
D 6632
© DOULTON & CO. LIMITED 1972
REGISTRATION APPLIED FOR

Designer: Max Henk
Handle: Witch holding horse's tail above a mug of ale
Colourway: Dark blue tam, green cloak

Backstamp: Doulton

Doulton Number	Size	Backstamp	Height	Intro.	Discon.	Current Market Value U.K. £	U.S. $	Can. $
D6632	Large	Doulton	7"	1973	1980	75.00	120.00	155.00
D6636	Small	Doulton	3 1/4"	1973	1980	45.00	70.00	90.00
D6640	Miniature	Doulton	2 1/2"	1973	1980	40.00	60.00	75.00

TERRY FOX

Canadian Terrance Stanley Fox (1958-1981) was a student and athlete until diagnosed with osteogenic sarcoma, a rare form of bone cancer. While recovering from the amputation of most of one leg, Fox conceived of the idea of a "Marathon of Hope", a run across Canada to raise money for cancer research. He began on April 12, 1980 but had to abort his run on September 1st, after being diagnosed with lung cancer. He raised over $24 million and became a source of inspiration for millions of people. Only three jugs were produced. One was given to his family, one was put up for auction at the International Royal Doulton Collectors Weekend, September 14-16, 1990 which realized $32,000 for charity and the third resides in the Sir Henry Doulton Gallery.

Designer: William K. Harper
Handle: Fox's artificial leg
Colourway: Brown and white

Backstamp: Doulton

Doulton Number	Size	Backstamp	Height	Intro.	Discon.	Current Market Value		
						U.K. £	U.S. $	Can. $
D6881	Large	Doulton	7"	1990	Ltd. Ed.	Extremely Rare, Only 3 Known One Sold at Auction, Toronto, 1990, for $32,000.00		

TOBY GILLETTE

Jimmy Saville's British television show, "Jim'll Fix It," invites public requests and received one from Toby Gillette to have a character jug created in his likeness.

In 1984, three were produced; one was given to Toby Gillette, one remains in the Sir Henry Doulton Gallery, and the third was auctioned by Sotheby's with the proceeds ($30,000) going to one of the charities Jimmy Saville supported.

In 1986, Toby Gillette sold his own jug at a Sotheby's auction.

Royal Doulton
TOBY GILLETTE
D6717
Modelled by

Eric Griffiths

© ROYAL DOULTON TABLEWARE
LIMITED 1983
WORLDWIDE
LIMITED EDITION OF 3
This is No. 1

Designer: Eric Griffiths
Handle: Plain
Colourway: Brown

Backstamp: Doulton

Doulton Number	Size	Backstamp	Height	Intro.	Discon.	Current Market Value U.K. £	U.S. $	Can. $
D6717	Large	Doulton	7"	1984	Ltd. Ed.	Extremely Rare, Only 3 Known		

TOBY PHILPOTS

A "thirsty old soul" in an 18th century drinking song, Toby is thought by some to be the source of the traditional British Toby jug, in which a character sits astride a barrel of ale. Popular opinion suggests his name is a derivation of the French topé, to toast.

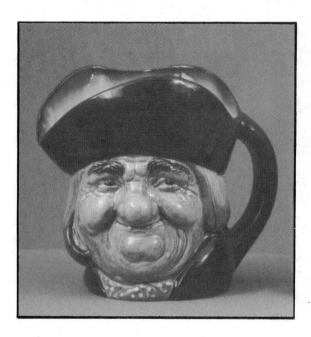

BACKSTAMP A

BACKSTAMP B   BACKSTAMP C

Designer: Charles Noke
Colourway: Green hat, brown coat,
              blue scarf with white spots
Handle: Plain

Backstamps: A. **Doulton**
               B. **Doulton / Toby Philpotts**
                   Incised name on jug "Toby Philpots",
                   but on the backstamp "Toby Philpotts"
               C. **Doulton / Toby Philpots"**
                   Incised name on jug "Toby Philpots",
                   but on the backstamp the corrected
                   spelling of "Toby Philpots"

Doulton Number	Size	Backstamp	Height	Intro.	Discon.	Current Market Value U.K. £	U.S. $	Can. $
D5736	Large	A Doulton	6 1/4"	1937	1951	75.00	150.00	195.00
D5736	Large	B Philpotts	6 1/4"	1937	1951	75.00	150.00	195.00
D5736	Large	C Philpots	6 1/4"	1952	1969	75.00	150.00	195.00
D5737	Small	A Doulton	3 1/4"	1937	1951	40.00	70.00	110.00
D5737	Small	B Philpotts	3 1/4"	1937	1951	40.00	70.00	110.00
D5737	Small	C Philpots	3 1/4"	1952	1969	40.00	70.00	110.00
D6043	Miniature	A Doulton	2 1/4"	1939	1951	40.00	50.00	85.00
D6043	Miniature	B Philpotts	2 1/4"	1939	1951	40.00	50.00	85.00
D6043	Miniature	C Philpots	2 1/4"	1952	1969	40.00	50.00	85.00

TONY WELLER

In Charles Dickens' "The Pickwick Papers", (1837), Tony is a stage-coachman who inherits a pub from his wife. He is the father of Sam Weller, who works for him at the inn.

SHEFFIELD &
ROTHERHAM
BACKSTAMP B

BACKSTAMP D

Designer: Leslie Harradine / Harry Fenton
Handle: Plain
Colourway: Grey hat, maroon coat, white bow with yellow spots

Backstamps: A. Doulton
  B. Doulton / Darley & Son "Souvenir From Darley & Son Sheffield & Rotherham"
    Commissioned by Darley & Son, Sheffield and Rotherham
  C: Doulton / Bentalls "Souvenir From Bentalls Jubilee Year 1935"
    Commissioned by Bentalls to commemorate the silver jubilee in 1935 of King George V.
  D. Doulton / Bentalls "Souvenir from Bentalls - 1936"

Doulton Number	Size	Backstamp	Height	Intro.	Discon.	Current Market Value U.K. £	U.S. $	Can. $
D5531	Ext. Large	Doulton	8 1/2"	1936	1942	150.00	200.00	250.00
D5531	Large	Doulton	6 1/2"	1936	1960	80.00	150.00	195.00
D5530	Small	Doulton	3 1/4"	1936	1960	45.00	70.00	90.00
D5530	Small	Doulton/Darley	3 1/4"	1936	1936	350.00	650.00	700.00
D5530	Small	Doulton/Bentalls	3 1/4"	1935	1935	350.00	650.00	700.00
D5530	Small	Doulton/Bentalls	3 1/4"	1936	1936	350.00	650.00	700.00
D6044	Miniature	Doulton	2 1/4"	1939	1960	40.00	55.00	85.00

Miscellaneous "Tony Weller" Items

TONY WELLER TEAPOT

Doulton Number	Item	Height	Intro.	Discon.	Current Market Value U.K. £	U.S. $	Can. $
D5888	Musical Jug	6 1/2"	1937	1939	250.00	800.00	850.00
D6013	Sugar bowl	2 1/2"	1939	1960	375.00	675.00	675.00
D6016	Teapot	7"	1939	1960	1,000.00	1,500.00	1,750.00
D6051	Bust	4"	1939	1960	65.00	100.00	120.00
HN1616	Bookend	4"	1934	1939	1,000.00	2,000.00	2,000.00
M60	Napkin Ring	3 1/2"	1935	1939	200.00	500.00	500.00

TOUCHSTONE

In Shakespeares comedy, "As You Like It", Touchstone is jester to the exiled Duke of Frederick's court who accompanies Rosalind and Celia into the Forest of Arden.

Designer: Charles Noke
Handle: Head of a clown
Colourway: Maroon, green and light brown

Backstamp: Doulton

Doulton Number	Size	Backstamp	Height	Intro.	Discon.	Current Market Value U.K. £	U.S. $	Can. $
D5613	Large	Doulton	7"	1936	1960	125.00	250.00	275.00

TOWN CRIER

With his familiar "Oyez! Oyez! Oyez!" the crier would gain the attention of passersby and read his proclamation of news, serving as the only vehicle for passing official information in his time.

STYLE ONE: HANDLE: BELL ON SCROLL

Designer: David Biggs
Handle: Bell on scroll
Colourway: Black hat trimmed with gold,
scarlet coat trimmed with gold

Backstamp: Doulton

Doulton Number	Size	Backstamp	Height	Intro.	Discon.	Current Market Value U.K. £	U.S. $	Can. $
D6530	Large	Doulton	7"	1960	1973	135.00	250.00	275.00
D6537	Small	Doulton	3 1/4"	1960	1973	100.00	125.00	150.00
D6544	Miniature	Doulton	2 1/2"	1960	1973	100.00	160.00	200.00

TOWN CRIER

STYLE TWO: *HANDLE: SCROLL WRAPPED AROUND BELL*

Royal Doulton®
TOWN CRIER
D 6895
Modelled by

Stanley James Taylor

© 1991 ROYAL DOULTON

Designer: Stanley J. Taylor	**Backstamp:** Doulton
Handle: Scroll wrapped around bell	
Colourway: Black, maroon and white	

Doulton Number	Size	Backstamp	Height	Intro.	Discon.	Current Market Value U.K. £	U.S. $	Can. $
D6895	Large	Doulton	7"	1991	Current	63.00	165.00	270.00

THE TRAPPER

CANADIAN CENTENNIAL SERIES 1867-1967
ONE OF THREE

An integral part of Canadian history, the early trappers, or voyageurs, were largely responsible for the early exploration of the country. In search of animal pelts for export to the European market, these rugged men spent the winter travelling by canoe, snowshoe, and foot through the wild Canadian north. Trapping is still practised to a smaller extent today, mostly by Canada's native peoples.

The miniature version of The Trapper character jug was put into production briefly in 1983, however before any quantity was produced, the decision was made to withdraw the character. Several dozen have appeared on the market. The Royal Doulton International Collectors Club was not involved.

The Trapper is one of three jugs which received a special backstamp in 1967. The other two, the Lumberjack and the North American Indian complete the three jug Canadian Centennial Series.

The Trapper
D 6612
COPR 1966
DOULTON & CO LIMITED
Rd No 924808
Rd No 49144
Rd No 10600
Rd No 52/66

BACKSTAMP A

CANADIAN CENTENNIAL SERIES
1867 - 1967

The Trapper
D6609
COPR 1966
DOULTON & CO LIMITED
Rd No 924808
Rd No 10600
Rd No 52/66

BACKSTAMP B

Designer:	Max Henk / David Biggs	
Handle:	A horn and a pair of snowshoes	
Colourway:	Dark green and white hat, brown and green clothing	

Backstamps: A. Doulton
B. Doulton / Canadian Centennial
Series 1867-1967

Doulton Number	Size	Backstamp	Height	Intro.	Discon.	Current Market Value U.K. £	U.S. $	Can. $
D6609	Large	Doulton	7 1/4"	1967	1983	70.00	110.00	155.00
D6609	Large	Doul/Cent	7 1/4"	1967	1967	100.00	350.00	300.00
D6612	Small	Doulton	3 3/4"	1967	1983	50.00	60.00	95.00
D —	Miniature	Doulton	2 1/2"	1983	1983	950.00	2,000.00	2,000.00

UGLY DUCHESS

ALICE IN WONDERLAND
ONE OF SIX

The ugly Duchess lives in Wonderland and plays croquet with the Queen. Alice found the game a curious one, with live hedgehogs for balls, flamingos for mallets, and playing cards soldiers who doubled over to serve as the arches.

Designer: Max Henk
Handle: A flamingo
Colourway: Green, purple and pink

Backstamp: Doulton

Doulton Number	Size	Backstamp	Height	Intro.	Discon.	Current Market Value U.K. £	U.S. $	Can. $
D6599	Large	Doulton	6 3/4"	1965	1973	275.00	550.00	700.00
D6603	Small	Doulton	3 1/2"	1965	1973	200.00	350.00	425.00
D6607	Miniature	Doulton	2 1/2"	1965	1973	200.00	325.00	375.00

ULYSSES S. GRANT AND ROBERT E. LEE

THE ANTAGONISTS COLLECTION (TWO FACED JUG)
ONE OF FOUR

Ulysses Samuel Grant (1822-1885). Was an Ohio native, who was made Lieutenant General by President Lincoln and put in command of the Union army in the American Civil War. His successes led to his election as president in 1868.

Robert E. Lee (1807-1870) was the general in command of the Confederate army during the American Civil War. He was ruthlessly pursued by General Grant, who forced him to retreat from his defence of Richmond, Virginia in 1865. Lee's troops were surrounded at the great battle of Appotomax, where he and the Confederate army surrendered and lost the war.

Issued in 1983 in a limited edition of 9,500 pieces.

Designer:	Michael Abberley	**Backstamp:** Doulton
Handle:	Grant: Flag of the Union	
	Lee: Flag of the Confederacy	
Colourway:	Black, grey, brown and red	

Doulton Number	Size	Backstamp	Height	Intro.	Discon.	Current Market Value		
						U.K. £	U.S. $	Can. $
D6698	Large	Doulton	7"	1983	Ltd. Ed. (1986)	145.00	275.00	395.00

UNCLE TOM COBBLEIGH

In the popular 18th century Devonshire song, Tom Cobbleigh and six friends borrow Tom Pearse's old mare to ride to the fair. Unable to support so many, the mare becomes sick and dies and can be found haunting the night-time moors to this day.

"Uncle Tom Cobbleigh"
D.6337
COPR 1951
DOULTON & CO.LIMITED.
Rᵈ Nᵒ 864845
Rᵈ Nᵒ 29158
Rᵈ Nᵒ 6406
Rᵈ Nᵒ 114/51

Designer: Max Henk
Handle: Horseshoe
Colourway: Dark brown hat, green coat, dark grey horseshoe

Backstamp: Doulton

Doulton Number	Size	Backstamp	Height	Intro.	Discon.	Current Market Value U.K. £	U.S. $	Can. $
D6337	Large	Doulton	7"	1952	1960	200.00	475.00	650.00

URIAH HEEP

CHARLES DICKENS COMMEMORATIVE SET
DICKENS TINIES, ONE OF TWELVE

Issued to commemorate the 170th Anniversary of the birth of Charles Dickens. There are twelve jugs in this set, each issued with a certificate of authenticity. A mahogany display shelf completes the set. The set was first sold by Lawleys By Post in the U.K. during 1982 to 1988, and in 1985 onward in North America and Australia.

Uriah Heep
D 6682

Designer: Robert Tabbenor
Handle: Plain
Colourway: Grey and green

Backstamp: Doulton

Doulton Number	Size	Backstamp	Height	Intro.	Discon.	Current Market Value		
						U.K. £	U.S. $	Can. $
D6682	Tiny	Doulton	1 1/2"	1982	1989	30.00	45.00	60.00
		Display for 12 Tinies				65.00	45.00	50.00

VETERAN MOTORIST

In a tradition celebrating the 1896 act of parliament no longer requiring automobiles to be led by a man waving a cautionary flag, a commemorative drive is held each year. Motorists, all in vintage cars, drive from London's Hyde Park south to the coastal town of Brighton to mark the day.

Veteran Motorist
D.6637
© DOULTON & CO. LIMITED.1972
REGISTRATION APPLIED FOR.

Designer: David Biggs
Handle: A horn
Colourway: Yellow hat, green coat, white scarf

Backstamp: Doulton

Doulton Number	Size	Backstamp	Height	Intro.	Discon.	Current Market Value U.K. £	U.S. $	Can. $
D6633	Large	Doulton	7 1/2"	1973	1983	80.00	125.00	155.00
D6637	Small	Doulton	3 1/4"	1973	1983	45.00	75.00	95.00
D6641	Miniature	Doulton	2 1/2"	1973	1983	45.00	65.00	80.00

VICAR OF BRAY

In a popular song of the 18th century, this very adaptable parson boasted that he was able to accommodate himself to the religious views of Charles, James, William, Anne and George, and that "whosoever King may reign, he would always be the Vicar of Bray."

Prior to 1940 these jugs had a distinctive yellow rim.

"Vicar of Bray."
R⁰Nº807475.

Designer:	Charles Noke / Harry Fenton	
Handle:	Plain	
Colourway:	Brown hat, green coat	

Backstamp: Doulton

Doulton Number	Size	Backstamp	Height	Intro.	Discon.	Current Market Value		
						U.K. £	U.S. $	Can. $
D5615	Large	Doulton	6 3/4"	1936	1960	120.00	225.00	300.00

VICE-ADMIRAL LORD NELSON

Character Jug of the Year for 1993. Issued to commemorate The Battle of Trafalgar, October 21, 1805

Royal Doulton®

CHARACTER JUG OF THE YEAR

VICE-ADMIRAL LORD NELSON

D 6932

October 21st 1805

Battle of Trafalgar edition

"England expects that every man will do his duty"

Modelled by

Stanley James Taylor

This special edition will only
be available during the year

1993

© 1992 ROYAL DOULTON

Designer: Stanley Taylor
Handle: The Victory
Colourway: Black, gold and cream

Backstamp: Doulton / Character Jug of the Year

Doulton Number	Size	Backstamp	Height	Intro.	Discon.	Current Market Value		
						U.K. £	U.S. $	Can. $
D6932	Large	Doulton	8"	1993	1993	79.95	225.00	295.00

VIKING

Also known as Norsemen, the Vikings were Scandinavians living between the 8th and 10th centuries who sailed in pirating raids throughout Europe, discovering and settling much of it. Some historians believe they made it as far as North America before any other Europeans.

The Viking large size character jug is reported to carry the Stoke-on-Trent backstamp.

Designer: Max Henk	**Backstamp:** Doulton
Handle: The prow of a viking long ship	
Colourway: Black, green and brown	

Doulton Number	Size	Backstamp	Height	Intro.	Discon.	Current Market Value U.K. £	U.S. $	Can. $
D6496	Large	Doulton	7 1/4"	1959	1975	125.00	225.00	275.00
D6502	Small	Doulton	4"	1959	1975	80.00	115.00	145.00
D6526	Miniature	Doulton	2 1/2"	1960	1975	100.00	135.00	175.00

THE VILLAGE BLACKSMITH

PROTOTYPE

Designer: Max Henk
Handle: Tree above anvil, wheel and horseshoe
Colourway: Blue, brown, black and green

Backstamp: None shown

Doulton Number	Size	Backstamp	Height	Intro.	Discon.	Current Market Value U.K. £	U.S. $	Can. $
D6549	Large	None	7 1/2"	1961	1961	Unique Sold at Auction, London, May 1993 for £6,000.00		

VISCOUNT MONTGOMERY OF ALAMEIN

HEROIC LEADERS
ONE OF THREE

This new design was specially commissioned by Lawleys By Post and produced in a limited edition of 9,500 pieces. It was sold in a set of three: Montgomery, Mountbatten and Churchill.

Royal Doulton®
VISCOUNT MONTGOMERY OF ALAMEIN
1887-1976
D 6850
Modelled by
Stanley James Taylor
© 1989 ROYAL DOULTON
A LIMITED EDITION OF 9500
THIS IS NO. 1609

Designer: Stanley J. Taylor
Handle: Imperial Army flag
Colourway: Black beret, khaki uniform, red flag

Backstamp: Doulton

Doulton Number	Size	Backstamp	Height	Intro.	Discon.	Current Market Value		
						U.K. £	U.S. $	Can. $
D6850	Small	Doulton	3 1/4"	1990	Ltd. Ed.	75.00	115.00	135.00

W. C. FIELDS

THE CELEBRITY COLLECTION
ONE OF FIVE

Born Claude William Dukenfield (1880-1946), W.C. Fields began his entertainment career at the age of eleven as a juggler. Much later he appeared in the "Ziegfeld Follies" and then in 1925 began his work in film. With his rasping voice and bulbous nose, he became a very successful satiric comedian.

The following quote appears on the base of the jug.

"I was in love with a beautiful blonde once. She drove me to drink - 'tis the one thing I'm indebted to her for."

BACKSTAMP B

Designer:	David Biggs	**Backstamps:**	**A.**	**Doutlon**
Handle:	A walking cane		**B.**	**Doulton / American Express**
Colourway:	Black, grey and yellow			"Premier Edition for American Express" Introduced in the U.S.A. as a promotional jug for American Express. Approximately 1,500 jugs bore the special backstamp.

Doulton Number	Size	Backstamp	Height	Intro.	Discon.	Current Market Value		
						U.K. £	U.S. $	Can. $
D6674	Large	Doulton	7"	1983	1986	75.00	125.00	155.00
D6674	Large	Doulton/Amex	7 1/2"	1983	Sp. Ed.	85.00	150.00	175.00

W. G. GRACE

William Gilbert Grace's (1848-1915) exceptional skill as a cricket batsman provided the game with its greatest single development in modern sports history. Debuting in professional cricket at the age of sixteen, Grace rose quickly to the status of England's best batsman, earning the title "The Champion." Throughout his long career, he set many early land-mark records, retiring at the age of sixty after forty-four seasons.

Commissioned by Lawleys By Post. Issued in 1989 in a limited edition of 9,500 pieces.

Designer: Stanley J. Taylor
Handle: Cricket bat and ball
Colourway: Yellow and orange striped cap, black beard

Backstamp: Doulton

Doulton Number	Size	Backstamp	Height	Intro.	Discon.	Current Market Value		
						U.K. £	U.S. $	Can. $
D6845	Small	Doulton	3 1/4"	1989	Ltd. Ed.	45.00	110.00	135.00

THE WALRUS AND CARPENTER

ALICE IN WONDERLAND
ONE OF SIX

On a beach in Wonderland, the walrus and carpenter invite a number of oysters for evening conversation, with the poem "The time has come the Walrus said". He promptly ate them.

Designer: Max Henk
Handle: A walrus
Colourway: Black, green and red

The Walrus & Carpenter
D 6600
COPR 1964
DOULTON & CO LIMITED
Rd No 917233
Rd No 46579
Rd No 10002
Rd No 591/64

Backstamp: Doulton

Doulton Number	Size	Backstamp	Height	Intro.	Discon.	Current Market Value U.K. £	U.S. $	Can. $
D6600	Large	Doulton	7 1/4"	1965	1980	80.00	150.00	180.00
D6604	Small	Doulton	3 1/4"	1965	1980	50.00	75.00	100.00
D6608	Miniature	Doulton	2 1/2"	1965	1980	45.00	70.00	95.00

WILD BILL HICKOCK

THE WILD WEST COLLECTION
ONE OF SIX

James Butler Hickock (1837-1876), after serving as a Union scout in the American Civil War, became a marshall and then sheriff of western frontier towns. An excellent gunman, he earned his nickname from his trigger-happy method of carrying out the law at the many shootouts that erupted from poker games.

He toured briefly with Buffalo Bill's Wild West Show, (1872-1873), and was later murdered at Deadwood.

Royal Doulton

THE WILD WEST
Collection
WILD BILL HICKOCK
D6736
Modelled by

© ROYAL DOULTON IUR 1984

Designer: Michael Abberley
Handle: An upturned whiskey bottle flowing into a glass
Colourway: Black, brown and white

Backstamp: Doulton

Doulton Number	Size	Backstamp	Height	Intro.	Discon.	Current Market Value U.K. £	U.S. $	Can. $
D6736	Mid	Doulton	5 1/2"	1985	1989	50.00	100.00	120.00

WILLIAM SHAKESPEARE

THE SHAKESPEAREAN COLLECTION
ONE OF SIX

Shakespeare (1564-1616) was born in Stratford-upon-Avon. There exists very little information about his early life in Stratford beyond records of his marriage and the births of his children. He apparently moved to London in 1585 and by 1592 had emerged as a promising actor and playwright. He was a part of the theatre company, the "King's Men of James I" throughout his London career, and in 1599 became the new owner of the Globe theatre. Immensely successful in his life as playwright, director, poet and actor, Shakespeare was said to be quite wealthy by the time he returned to Stratford in 1613.

STYLE ONE: HANDLE: INK WELL WITH THE APPEARANCE OF THE GLOBE THEATRE

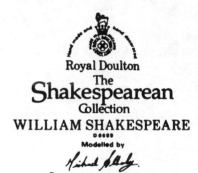

Royal Doulton
The
Shakespearean
Collection
WILLIAM SHAKESPEARE
Modelled by

© ROYAL DOULTON TABLEWARE LIMITED 1983

Designer: Michael Abberley
Handle: A feather quill with an inkwell of the appearance of the Globe Theatre
Colourway: White, grey and yellow

Backstamp: Doulton

Doulton Number	Size	Backstamp	Height	Intro.	Discon.	Current Market Value U.K. £	U.S. $	Can. $
D6689	Large	Doulton	7 3/4"	1983	1991	60.00	130.00	145.00

WILLIAM SHAKESPEARE

STYLE TWO: *HANDLE: CHARACTERS FROM DIFFERENT PLAYS*

Issued in a limited edition of 2,500.

Royal Doulton®
WILLIAM SHAKESPEARE
D 6933
Modelled by

William K. Harper

© 1992 ROYAL DOULTON
LIMITED EDITION OF 2,500
THIS IS No. 2 4

Designer:	William K. Harper
Handle:	Two handles, characters from different plays
Colourway:	Brown

Backstamp: Doulton

Doulton Number	Size	Backstamp	Height	Intro.	Discon.	Current Market Value U.K. £	U.S. $	Can. $
D6933	Large	Doulton	7"	1992	Ltd. Ed. (1993)	250.00	625.00	750.00

WINSTON CHURCHILL

STYLE ONE   HANDLE: UNION JACK AND BULLDOG

Character Jug of the Year for 1992.

Royal Doulton®
CHARACTER JUG OF THE YEAR
WINSTON CHURCHILL
D 6907
Modelled by

Stanley James Taylor

This special edition will only
be available during the year
1992
© 1991 ROYAL DOULTON

Designer: Stanley J. Taylor	**Backstamp:** Doulton / Character Jug of the Year - 1992
Handle: Union Jack and bulldog	
Colourway: Black, brown and white	

Doulton Number	Size	Backstamp	Height	Intro.	Discon.	Current Market Value		
						U.K. £	U.S. $	Can. $
D6907	Large	Doulton	7"	1992	1992	75.00	165.00	210.00

WINSTON CHURCHILL

STYLE TWO   *HANDLE: NEWS CHRONICLE VICTORY ISSUE*

Royal Doulton
WINSTON CHURCHILL
D 6934
Modelled by

Stanley James Taylor

Ⓒ 1991 ROYAL DOULTON

Designer: Stanley J. Taylor
Handle: "News Chronicle" Victory Issue
Colourway: Black, grey, white and cream

Backstamp: Doulton

Doulton Number	Size	Backstamp	Height	Intro.	Discon.	Current Market Value		
						U.K. £	U.S. $	Can. $
D6934	Small	Doulton	4"	1992	Current	35.00	78.00	110.00

THE WITCH

MYSTICAL
ONE OF THREE

Practitioners of magic and sorcery, these powerful women were the source of fear for many. Throughout history, women suspected of practicing witchcraft were persecuted as pagans and devils, often being killed by superstitious Christians in ritualistic ways.

Royal Doulton®
THE WITCH
D 6893
Modelled by

Stanley James Taylor

© 1991 ROYAL DOULTON

Designer: Stanley J. Taylor   **Backstamp: Doulton**
Handle: Part of the witch's hat
Colourway: Black and greys

Doulton Number	Size	Backstamp	Height	Intro.	Current Market Value Discon.	U.K. £	U.S. $	Can. $
D6893	Large	Doulton	7"	1991	1991	120.00	150.00	225.00

THE WIZARD

MYSTICAL
ONE OF THREE

Although defined as a male witch, the term wizard is more often associated with strange and magical powers than with evil. Most legends of wizardry portray them as heros and champions over evil.

Royal Doulton®
THE WIZARD
D 6862
Modelled by

Stanley James Taylor

© 1990 ROYAL DOULTON

Designer: Stanley J. Taylor
Handle: Black cat and a magic wand
Colourway: Blue-grey cap, black coat, red collar

Backstamp: Doulton

Doulton Number	Size	Backstamp	Height	Intro.	Discon.	Current Market Value		
						U.K. £	U.S. $	Can. $
D6862	Large	Doulton	6 3/4"	1990	Current	63.00	155.00	250.00
D6909	Small	Doulton	3 3/4"	1992	Current	28.95	82.50	90.00

WYATT EARP

THE WILD WEST COLLECTION
ONE OF SIX

Wyatt Berry Stapp Earp (1848-1929) like his cohorts, was an expert gunfighter. He worked as a police officer and armed guard and, in 1881 was involved in the famous shootout at O.K. Corral while waging war on the "outlaw element". Later Earp travelled around the West, opening and operating a number of saloons.

Designer:	Stanley J. Taylor	**Backstamp:** Doulton	
Handle:	A gun and sheriff's badge		
Colourway:	Brown coat, light brown hat with red band		

Doulton Number	Size	Backstamp	Height	Intro.	Discon.	Current Market Value U.K. £	U.S. $	Can. $
D6711	Mid	Doulton	5 1/2"	1985	1989	50.00	95.00	110.00

YACHTSMAN

Sailing has a history as old as that of man, and remains constant in its popularity. Small and miniature jugs were piloted but never put into production.

STYLE ONE: *YACHTSMAN WITH LIFE JACKET*

Designer:	David Biggs	**Backstamp:** Doulton
Handle:	A yacht sailing from the front to back	
Colourway:	Blue cap and jersey, yellow lifejacket	

Doulton Number	Size	Backstamp	Height	Intro.	Discon.	Current Market Value U.K. £	U.S. $	Can. $
D6626	Large	Doulton	8"	1971	1980	95.00	120.00	185.00
D --	Small	Doulton	3"	Unknown			Extremely Rare	

YACHTSMAN

STYLE TWO: YACHTSMAN WITH PEAK CAP AND SCARF

Royal Doulton®
YACHTSMAN
D 6820
Modelled by

Stanley James Taylor

© 1988 ROYAL DOULTON

Designer:	Stanley J. Taylor
Handle:	Sailboat with white sails and green trim sailing back to front
Colourway:	Navy blue cap, dark blue jacket, yellow shirt, grey scarf

Backstamps:

A. **Doulton**
For General Release: 1989.

B. **Doulton / Canadian Doulton Show and Sale** Issued to commemorate the first Canadian Doulton Show and Sale at Durham, Ontario July 29th to 31st, 1988. Issued in a special edition of 750 pieces.

Doulton Number	Size	Backstamp	Height	Intro.	Discon.	Current Market Value U.K. £	U.S. $	Can. $
D6820	Large	Doulton	6 1/2"	1989	1991	50.00	115.00	145.00
D6820	Large	Doulton/Durham	6 1/2"	1988	Sp. Ed.	100.00	115.00	145.00

THE YEOMAN OF THE GUARD

THE LONDON COLLECTION
ONE OF TEN

In 1485, Henry VIII organized the Yeoman of the Guard, who formed a bodyguard to the monarch of England. Today the Yeoman, or Beefeaters as they are more commonly known, serve as bodyguards on formal occasions however their duties are purely ceremonial.

Royal Doulton®
THE YEOMAN OF THE GUARD
D 6873
Modelled by

Stanley James Taylor

© 1990 ROYAL DOULTON

BACKSTAMP A

Designer: Stanley J. Taylor
Handle: Raven and tree trunk
Colourway: Black hat, white frills and red jacket

Backstamp: See Backstamps

BACKSTAMP B

BACKSTAMP D

Backstamps: A. Doulton

The jugs bearing backstamps C, D and E were releaseded in the U.S.A. to commemorate the anniversaries of the opening of the four Royal Doulton Rooms in the U.S.A. Special edition of 450 pieces bearing a special backstamp.

B. Doulton/Dillards "**To Commemorate the third anniversary of the opening of the Royal Doulton Room Dillards, New Orleans, Louisiana, U.S.A.**"
Dillards, Louisiana, Georgia, 50 pieces.

C. Doulton/Joseph Horne "**To Commemorate the third anniversary of the opening of the Royal Doulton Room Joseph Horne, Pittsburgh, Pennsylvania, U.S.A.**"
Joseph Horne's, Pittsburgh, Pennsylvania, 75 pieces.

D. Doulton/Strawbridge and Clothier "**To Commemorate the fourth anniversary of the opening of the Royal Doulton Room Strawbridge and Clothier, Philadelphia, Pennsylvania, U.S.A.**"
Strawbridge and Clothier, Philadelphia, Pennsylvania, 75 pieces.

E. Doulton/Higbee "**To Commemorate the fifth anniversary of the opening of the Royal Doulton Room Higbee Cleveland, Ohio, U.S.A.**"
Higbee's, Cleveland, Ohio, 250 pieces.

Doulton Number	Size	Backstamp	Height	Intro.	Discon.	Current Market Value		
						U.K. £	U.S. $	Can. $
D6873	Large	Doulton	7"	1991	Current	63.00	142.50	180.00
D6883	Large	Dillards	7"	1990	Ltd. Ed.	175.00	250.00	275.00
D6882	Large	Horne	7"	1990	Ltd. Ed.	135.00	250.00	275.00
D6885	Large	Strawbridge	7"	1990	Ltd. Ed.	135.00	250.00	275.00
D6884	Large	Higbee	7"	1990	Ltd. Ed.	120.00	250.00	275.00

Sairey Gamp Teapot
D6015

LIQUOR CONTAINERS & JUGS

CAPTAIN COOK

THE INTERNATIONAL COLLECTION
ONE OF FOUR

Commissioned by Pick-Kwik Wines and Spirits in a limited edition of 2,000 pieces.

LIQUOR CONTAINER

THIRD OF A SERIES
THE INTERNATIONAL COLLECTION
Specially Commissioned
from
Royal Doulton®
200ml.   JIM BEAM BOURBON WHISKEY   40% Vol.
PICK-KWIK WINES & SPIRITS
MICKLEOVER, DERBY, ENGLAND
with special permission from
JAMES B. BEAM DISTILLING INTERNATIONAL CO.

Designer: Harry Sales
Modeller: Graham Tongue
Handle: Scroll
Colourway: Black hat, black and yellow uniform
Inscription around Base: "Captain Cook"

Backstamp: Doulton / Pick-Kwik

Doulton Number	Size	Backstamp	Height	Intro.	Discon.	Current Market Value		
						U.K. £	U.S. $	Can. $
D —	Small	Doulton	4 3/4"	1985	Ltd. Ed.	60.00	75.00	95.00

FALSTAFF

The Falstaff, Poacher and Rip Van Winkle character jugs were adapted to liqueur containers for "Bols" Liqueur by Doulton for the bottling firm of W. Walklate Ltd. The small size jugs were commissioned about 1960 by W. Walklate Ltd.

LIQUEUR CONTAINER

Designer: Harry Fenton
Handle: Plain
Colourway: Rose-pink tunic, black hat trimmed with rose-pink plumes, grey beard

Backstamp: Doulton

Doulton Number	Size	Backstamp	Height	Intro.	Discon.	Current Market Value U.K. £	U.S. $	Can. $
D6385	Small	Falstaff	4"	c. 1960	c. 1960	45.00	105.00	130.00

IRISHMAN

Two whiskey flasks depicting a Scotsman and an Irishman set within a wooden tantalus were made in the 1920's for Asprey and Co., New Bond Street, London.

The heads of the flasks are detachable and naturally the Scotsman contains Scottish whiskey and the Irishman, Irish whiskey. Normally traded as a set, see page 460 for the Scotsman. Commissioned by Asprey and Co.

WHISKEY DECANTER

ASPREY & C⁰ LTD
LONDON
R⁴ N⁰ 675852

Designer: Harry Fenton
Colourway: Black hat and coat, green cravat, maroon vest

Backstamp: Doulton

Doulton Number	Size	Backstamp	Height	Intro.	Discon.	Current Market Value		
						U.K. £	U.S. $	Can. $
D6873	Large	Doulton	9 1/2"	1920	1930	750.00	1,500.00	1,750.00

JOHN BULL

THE INTERNATIONAL COLLECTION
ONE OF FOUR

Commissioned by Pick-Kwik Wines and Spirits in a limited edtion of 2,000 pieces.

LIQUOR CONTAINER

SECOND OF A SERIES
THE INTERNATIONAL COLLECTION
Specially Commissioned from
Royal Doulton®
200ml.   JIM BEAM BOURBON WHISKEY   40% Vol.
PICK-KWIK WINES & SPIRITS
MICKLEOVER, DERBY, ENGLAND
with special permission from
JAMES B. BEAM DISTILLING INTERNATIONAL CO.

Designer: Harry Sales
Modeller: Graham Tongue
Handle: Cane with bull dog head
Colourway: Black hat with yellow band, red coat
Inscription around Base: "John Bull"

Backstamp: Doulton / Pick-Kwik

Doulton Number	Size	Backstamp	Height	Intro.	Discon.	Current Market Value U.K. £	U.S. $	Can. $
D ---	Small	Doulton	5"	1985	Ltd. Ed.	60.00	75.00	95.00

MR. MICAWBER

Commissioned by Pick-Kwik Wines and Spirits.

STYLE ONE: LIQUOR CONTAINER

VARIATION No. 1:   **Colourway:** Brown hat, dark blue blazer, maroon cravat
Handle: Dewar's
Inscription on Base: "Dewar's"
Issued: 2,000 pieces

Designer: Harry Sales
Modeller: Graham Tongue
Handle: Dewar's
Colourway: Brown hat, dark blue blazer, maroon cravat
Inscription around Base: "Dewar's"

Backstamp: Doulton / Pick-Kwik

Doulton Number	Size	Backstamp	Height	Intro.	Discon.	Current Market Value		
						U.K. £	U.S. $	Can. $
D —	Small	Var. 1	5"	1983	Ltd. Ed.	60.00	75.00	95.00

VARIATION No. 2:   **Colourway:** Grey hat, green blazer, light blue cravat
   Handle: Pickwick Deluxe
Inscription around Base: "Pickwick Deluxe Whiskey"
   Issued: 2,000 pieces

Doulton Number	Size	Backstamp	Height	Intro.	Discon.	Current Market Value U.K. £	U.S. $	Can. $
D —	Small	Var. 2	5"	1983	Ltd. Ed.	60.00	75.00	95.00

VARIATION No. 3:   **Colourway:** White
   Handle: Pickwick Deluxe
Inscription around Base: "Pickwick Deluxe Whiskey"
   Issued: 100 pieces

Doulton Number	Size	Backstamp	Height	Intro.	Discon.	Current Market Value U.K. £	U.S. $	Can. $
D —	Small	Var. 3	5"	1985	Ltd. Ed.	100.00	150.00	185.00

MR. MICAWBER

Commissioned by Pick-Kwik Wines and Spirits.

STYLE TWO: *CHARACTER JUG*

VARIATION No. 1:   **Colourway:**   Brown hat, blue blazer, maroon cravat
Handle: Dewar's
Inscription around Base: "Dewar's"
Issued: 100 pieces

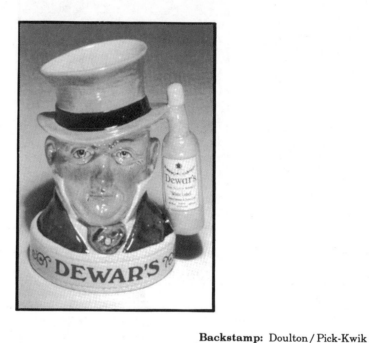

Designer: Harry Sales
Modeller: Graham Tongue
Handle: Dewar's
Colourway: Brown hat, blue blazer, maroon cravat
Inscription around Base: "Dewar's"

Backstamp: Doulton / Pick-Kwik

Doulton Number	Size	Variation	Height	Intro.	Discon.	Current Market Value		
						U.K. £	U.S. $	Can. $
D —	Small	Var. 1	4"	1985	Ltd. Ed.	125.00	200.00	225.00

VARIATION No. 2   VARIATION No. 3   VARIATION No. 4

VARIATION No. 2: Colourway: White
　　　　　　　　　　　Handle: Dewar's
　　Inscription around Base: "Dewar's" in red
　　　　　　　　　　　Issued: 100 pieces

Doulton Number	Size	Variation	Height	Intro.	Discon.	Current Market Value U.K. £	U.S. $	Can. $
D —	Small	Var. 2	4"	1985	Ltd. Ed.	125.00	200.00	225.00

VARIATION No. 3: Colourway: Grey hat, green blazer, light blue cravat
　　　　　　　　　　　Handle: Pickwick Deluxe
　　Inscription around Base: "Pickwick Deluxe Whiskey"
　　　　　　　　　　　Issued: 100 pieces

Doulton Number	Size	Variation	Height	Intro.	Discon.	Current Market Value U.K. £	U.S. $	Can. $
D —	Small	Var. 3	4"	1985	Ltd. Ed.	125.00	200.00	225.00

VARIATION No. 4: Colourway: White
　　　　　　　　　　　Handle: Pickwick Deluxe
　　Inscription around Base: "Pickwick Deluxe Whiskey"
　　　　　　　　　　　Issued: 100 pieces

Doulton Number	Size	Variation	Height	Intro.	Discon.	Current Market Value U.K. £	U.S. $	Can. $
D —	Small	Var. 4	4"	1985	Ltd. Ed.	125.00	200.00	225.00

MR. PICKWICK

Commissioned by Pick-Kwik Wines and Spirits.

CHARACTER JUG

VARIAITON No. 1:   Colourway: Green hat, black coat
Handle: No label / Whiskey
Inscription around Base: "Pick-Kwik Derby Whiskies Wines Ales"
Issued: 2,000 pieces

MR PICKWICK
(FOUNDER & GENERAL CHAIRMAN
OF THE PICKWICK CLUB)
THE MOST FAMOUS OF
CHARLES DICKENS' CHARACTERS FROM
"PICKWICK PAPERS"
FIRST PUBLISHED IN 1846

Designer: Harry Sales
Modeller: Graham Tongue
Handle: Pick-Kwik
Colourway: Green hat, black coat
Inscription around Base: "Pick-Kwik Derby Whiskies Wines Ales"

Backstamp: Doulton / Pick-Kwik

Name	Size	Variation	Height	Intro.	Discon.	Current Market Value		
						U.K. £	U.S. $	Can. $
D ---	Small	Var. 1	4"	1982	Ltd. Ed.	65.00	110.00	135.00

VARIATION No. 4   VARIATION No. 6   VARIATION No. 2

VARIATION No. 2:   Colourway: Brown hat, dark brown coat
                               Handle: Jim Beam
                Inscription around Base: "Pick-Kwik Derby Sells Jim Beam Whiskey"
                               Issued: 2,000 pieces

Name	Size	Variation	Height	Intro.	Discon.	Current Market Value		
						U.K. £	U.S. $	Can. $
D —	Small	Var. 2	4"	1984	Ltd. Ed.	65.00	110.00	125.00

VARIATION No. 3:   Colourway: Beige hat, brown coat
                               Handle: Jim Beam
                Inscription around Base: "Beam Whiskey"
                               Issued: 1,000 pieces

Name	Size	Variation	Height	Intro.	Discon.	Current Market Value		
						U.K. £	U.S. $	Can. $
D —	Small	Var. 3	5 1/4"	1984	Ltd. Ed.	65.00	110.00	125.00

VARIATION No. 4:   Colourway: Beige hat, brown coat
                               Handle: Beam's Black Label
                Inscription around Base: "Beam Whiskey"
                               Issued: 1,000 pieces

Name	Size	Variation	Height	Intro.	Discon.	Current Market Value		
						U.K. £	U.S. $	Can. $
D —	Small	Var. 4	5 1/4"	1984	Ltd. Ed.	65.00	110.00	125.00

VARIATION No. 5:   **Colourway:** White
                           Handle: No label/"Whiskey"
     Inscription around Base: "Pick Kwik Derby"
                        Issued: 100 pieces

Name	Size	Variation	Height	Intro.	Discon.	Current Market Value		
						U.K. £	U.S. $	Can. $
D —	Small	Var. 5	5 1/4"	1985	Ltd. Ed.	100.00	150.00	185.00

VARIATION No. 6:   **Colourway:** White with red transfers
                           Handle: Jim Beam
     Inscription around Base: "Pick Kwik Derby Sells Jim Beam Whiskey"
                        Issued: 100 pieces

Name	Size	Variation	Height	Intro.	Discon.	Current Market Value		
						U.K. £	U.S. $	Can. $
D —	Small	Var. 6	5 1/4"	1985	Ltd. Ed.	100.00	150.00	185.00

THE PICKWICK COLLECTION

THE PICKWICK COLLECTION

MR. PICKWICK / SAM WELLER

Commissioned by Pick-Kwik Wines and Spirits in a limited edition of 2,000 pieces. This is a two-faced liquor container.

LIQUOR CONTAINER

 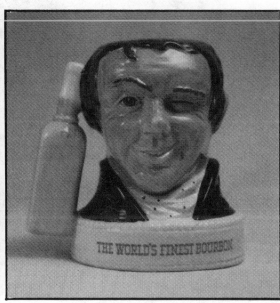

Designer: Harry Sales
Modeller: Graham Tongue
Handle: Jim Beam, Plain bottle
Colourway: Black coat, pink bow-tie, grey coat, yellow cravat
Inscription on Base: "Beam Whiskey" / "The World's Finest Bourbon"

Backstamp: Doulton / Pick-Kwik

Name	Size	Backstamp	Height	Intro.	Discon.	Current Market Value		
						U.K. £	U.S. $	Can. $
D —	Doulton	Small	5"	1985	Ltd. Ed.	60.00	90.00	125.00

OLD MR. TURVERYDROP

Commissioned by Pick-Kwik Wines and Spirits in a limited edition of 2,000 pieces.

LIQUOR CONTAINER

THE PICKWICK COLLECTION
Specially Commissioned from
Royal Doulton®
200ml.   **JIM BEAM BOURBON WHISKEY**   40% Vol.
PICK-KWIK WINES & SPIRITS
MICKLEOVER, DERBY, ENGLAND
with special permission from
JAMES B. BEAM DISTILLING INTERNATIONAL CO.

Designer: Harry Sales
Modeller: Graham Tongue
Handle: Jim Beam
Colourway: Yellow hat, black coat
Inscription on Base: "Beam Whiskey"

Backstamp: Doulton / Pick-Kwik

Name	Size	Backstamp	Height	Intro.	Discon.	Current Market Value		
						U.K. £	U.S. $	Can. $
D —	Small	Doulton	5"	1985	1985	60.00	90.00	95.00

THE POACHER

The Falstaff, Poacher and Rip Van Winkle character jugs were adapted to liqueur containers for "Bols" Liqueurs by Doulton for the bottling firm W. Walklate Ltd. The small size jugs were commissioned about 1962 by W. Walklate Ltd.

LIQUEUR CONTAINER

Designer: Max Henk
Handle: A Salmon
Colourway: Green coat, red scarf, light brown hat

Backstamp: Doulton

Doulton Number	Size	Backstamp	Height	Intro.	Discon.	Current Market Value		
						U.K. £	U.S. $	Can. $
D6464	Small	Doulton	4"	c. 1960	c. 1960	45.00	100.00	100.00

RIP VAN WINKLE

The Falstaff, Poacher and Rip Van Winkle character jugs were adapted to liqueur containers for "Bols" Liqueurs by Doulton for the bottling firm W. Walklate Ltd. The small size jugs were commissioned about 1960 by W. Walklate Ltd.

LIQUEUR CONTAINER

Designer: Geoff Blower
Handle: A man resting against a tree
Colourway: Grey-blue cap, brown robes, figure resting against tree dressed in blue

Backstamp: Doulton

Doulton Number	Size	Backstamp	Height	Intro.	Discon.	Current Market Value		
						U.K. £	U.S. $	Can. $
D6463	Small	Doulton	4"	c. 1960	c. 1960	45.00	100.00	100.00

SAMURAI WARRIOR

THE INTERNATIONAL COLLECTION
ONE OF FOUR

Commissioned by Pick-Kwik Wines and Spirits in a limited edtion of 2,000 pieces.

LIQUOR CONTAINER

FOURTH OF A SERIES
THE INTERNATIONAL COLLECTION
Specially Commissioned
from
Royal Doulton®

200ml.   JIM BEAM BOURBON WHISKEY   40% Vol.
PICK-KWIK WINES & SPIRITS
MICKLEOVER, DERBY, ENGLAND
with special permission from
JAMES B. BEAM DISTILLING INTERNATIONAL CO.

Designer: Harry Sales
Modeller: Graham Tongue
Handle: Sword
Colourway: Black hair, white face
Inscription on Base: "Samurai Warrior"

Backstamp: Doulton / Pick-Kwik

Name	Size	Backstamp	Height	Intro.	Discon.	Current Market Value		
						U.K. £	U.S. $	Can. $
D —	Small	Doulton	5"	1986	1986	60.00	100.00	95.00

SCOTSMAN

Two whiskey flasks depicting a Scotsman and an Irishman set within a wooden tantalus. These were made in the 1920's for Asprey and Co., New Bond Street, London.

The heads of the flasks are detachable and naturally the Scotsman contains Scottish whiskey and the Irishman, Irish whiskey. Normally traded as a set, see page 446 for the Irishman. Commissioned by Asprey and Co.

WHISKEY DECANTERS

ASPREY & Cº LTD
LONDON
Rᵈ Nº 675852

Designer: Harry Fenton
Colourway: Red tam, black coat

Backstamp: Doulton

Doulton Number	Size	Backstamp	Height	Intro.	Discon.	Current Market Value U.K. £	U.S. $	Can. $
D6873	Large	Doulton	9 1/2"	1920	1930	750.00	1,500.00	1,750.00

SGT. BUZ FUZ

Commissioned by Pick-Kwik Wines and Spirits.

CHARACTER JUG

VARIAITON No. 1:   **Colourway:** **White hair, black coat**
                    Handle: **Dewar's**
  Inscription around Base: **"Pick-Kwik Derby Sells Dewar's Whiskey"**
              Issued: **2,000 pieces**

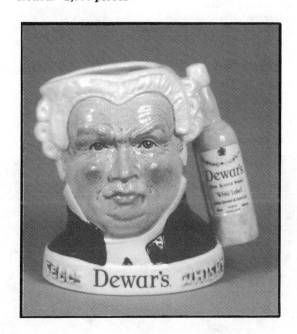

Designer: Harry Sales   **Backstamp:** Doulton / Pick-Kwik
Modeller: Graham Tongue
Handle: Dewar's
Colourway: White hair, black coat
Inscription around Base: "Pick-Kwik Derby Sells Dewar's Whiskey"

Doulton Number	Size	Variation	Height	Intro.	Discon.	Current Market Value U.K. £	U.S. $	Can. $
D —	Small	Var. 1	4"	1982	Ltd. Ed.	65.00	120.00	125.00

VARIATION No. 2: Colourway: White with red transfers
Handle: Dewar's
Inscription around Base: "Pick-Kwik Derby Sells Dewar's Whiskey"
Issued: 100 pieces

Doulton Number	Size	Variation	Height	Intro.	Discon.	Current Market Value U.K. £	U.S. $	Can. $
D —	Small	Var. 2	4"	1985	Ltd. Ed.	75.00	150.00	175.00

VARIATION No. 3: Colourway: White
Handle: Plain bottle
Inscription around Base: "Pick-Kwik Derby Sells Whiskey"
Issued: 100 pieces

Doulton Number	Size	Backstamp	Height	Intro.	Discon.	Current Market Value U.K. £	U.S. $	Can. $
D —	Small	Doulton	4"	1985	Ltd. Ed.	100.00	150.00	185.00

THE INTERNATIONAL COLLECTION

TOWN CRIER OF EATANSWILL

Commissioned by Pick-Kwik Wines and Spirits and issued in a limited edition of 2,000 pieces.

LIQUOR CONTAINER

Designer:	Harry Sales	
Modeller:	Graham Tongue	
Handle:	Jim Beam	
Colourway:	Black hat and maroon coat with yellow trim	

Inscription around Base: "Beam Whiskey"

Backstamp: Doulton / Pick-Kwik

Doulton Number	Size	Backstamp	Height	Intro.	Discon.	Current Market Value U.K. £	U.S. $	Can. $
D —	Small	Doulton	5"	1986	Ltd. Ed.	60.00	90.00	110.00

UNCLE SAM

THE INTERNATIONAL COLLECTION
ONE OF FOUR

Commissioned by Pick-Kwik Wines and Spirits and issued in a limited edition of 2,000 pieces.

STYLE ONE: HANDLE: JIM BEAM BOTTLE

VARIATION No. 1: Inscription around Base: "Uncle Sam"

Specially Commissioned
from
Royal Doulton

200ml. JIM BEAM BOURBON WHISKEY 40% Vol.
PICK-KWIK WINES & SPIRITS
MICKLEOVER, DERBY, ENGLAND
with special permission from
JAMES B. BEAM DISTILLING INTERNATIONAL CO.

Designer: Harry Sales
Modeller: Graham Tongue
Handle: Jim Beam Bottle
Colourway: Red, white and blue
Inscription around Base: "Uncle Sam"

Backstamp: Doulton / Pick-Kwik

Doulton Number	Size	Backstamp	Height	Intro.	Discon.	Current Market Value		
						U.K. £	U.S. $	Can. $
D —	Small	Var. 1	5"	1984	Ltd. Ed.	60.00	90.00	115.00

VARIATION No. 2: Inscription around Base: "Beam Whiskey"

Doulton Number	Size	Backstamp	Height	Intro.	Discon.	Current Market Value		
						U.K. £	U.S. $	Can. $
D —	Small	Var. 2	5"	1984	Ltd. Ed.	60.00	90.00	115.00

UNCLE SAM

Commissioned by Pick-Kwik Wines and Spirits and issued as promotional items in a limited edition of 500 pieces.

STYLE TWO: *HANDLE: EAGLE*

Designer: Harry Sales   **Backstamp:** Doulton / Pick-Kwik
Modeller: Graham Tongue
Handle: Eagle
Colourway: Red, white and blue
Inscription around Base: "In God We Trust"

Doulton Number	Size	Backstamp	Height	Intro.	Discon.	Current Market Value		
						U.K. £	U.S. $	Can. $
D —	Small	Doulton	5"	1986	Ltd. Ed.	110.00	175.00	215.00

WILLIAM GRANT

Issued to commemorate the centenary of the founding of the Glenfiddich distillery. This jug contains 750 ml of 25 year old Grants whiskey.

The uniform is that of a Major of the 6th Volunteer Battalion of the Gordon Highlanders. The Glengarry cap features the symbol of a stag's head. This symbol also appears on all of the company's bottles of whiskey.

STYLE ONE: HANDLE: FOUR OAK CASKS

LIQUOR CONTAINER

William Grant

Founder of William Grant & Sons Ltd
An independent family company for five generations
Specially Commissioned from
Royal Doulton ®
Hand Modelled and Hand Painted
Designed and Modelled by
Grant's 25 Year Old Very Rare Scotch Whisky
One of 500, specially filled in 1986, celebrating the 100 years
since William Grant laid the foundation stone of his
Highland Distillery.

Blended and Bottled by
William Grant & Sons Ltd
The Glenfiddich Distillery, Banffshire, Scotland
Product of Scotland

750ml 43% vol.

BACKSTAMP A

William Grant

Founder of William Grant & Sons Ltd
An independent family company for five generations
Specially Commissioned from
Royal Doulton ®
Hand Modelled and Hand Painted
Designed and Modelled by
Grant's 25 Year Old Very Rare Scotch Whisky
Specially filled in 1987, celebrating the 100 years since
the first whisky flowed from the stills of William Grant's
Highland Distillery.

Blended and Bottled by
William Grant & Sons Ltd
The Glenfiddich Distillery, Banffshire, Scotland
Product of Scotland

750ml 43% vol.

BACKSTAMP B

Designer: Graham Tongue
Handle: Four oak casks
Colourway: Scarlet

Backstamps: **A. Doulton / William Grant 100th Anniversary**
Issued in 1986 in a limited edition of 500 pieces to commemorate
the 100th Anniversary of the laying of the foundation stone.
B. Doulton / William Grant 100 Years
Issued in 1987 in a limited edition of 2,500 pieces to celebrate the
100 years since whiskey first flowed from the stills.

Doulton Number	Size	Backstamp	Height	Intro.	Discon.	Current Market Value		
						U.K. £	U.S. $	Can. $
D —	Large	Doul/100th Ann.	7"	1986	Ltd. Ed.	300.00	450.00	550.00
D —	Large	Doulton/100 yrs.	7"	1987	Ltd. Ed.	200.00	250.00	325.00

WILLIAM GRANT

Commissioned by Grants Glenfiddich Distillery. Issued in 1988 in a limited edition of 5,000 pieces.

STYLE TWO: *HANDLE: FIELD OFFICERS' SWORD*

LIQUOR CONTAINER

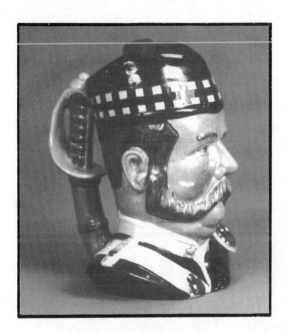

William Grant
Founder of William Grant & Sons Ltd
An independent family company for five generations
Specially Commissioned from
Royal Doulton®
Hand Modelled and Hand Painted
Designed and Modelled by *G.G.Tongue*
William Grant's 25 Year Old
Very Rare Blended Scotch Whisky
One of a limited edition of 5000
William Grant Character Jugs specially styled
with a Field Officer's sword handle
Blended and Bottled by
William Grant & Sons Ltd
The Glenfiddich Distillery. Banffshire Scotland
Product of Scotland
750ml 43% vol.

Designer: Graham Tongue	**Backstamp:** Doulton / William Grant
Handle: Field Officers Sword	
Colourway: Scarlet	

Doulton Number	Size	Backstamp	Height	Intro.	Discon.	Current Market Value		
						U.K. £	U.S. $	Can. $
D —	Large	Doulton/Grant	7"	1988	Ltd. Ed.	200.00	300.00	375.00

Tony Weller Teapot
D6016

LOVING CUPS AND JUGS

ADMIRAL LORD NELSON

This cup was issued in a limited edition of 600 pieces.

Designer: Charles Noke / Harry Fenton
Handles: Block and tackles
Main Colours: Brown, blue, yellow and green
Inscription around base: "England Expects" / "It was in Trafalgar Bay"

Backstamp: Doulton

Doulton Number	Type	Backstamp	Height	Intro.	Discon.	Current Market Value		
						U.K.£	U.S.$	Can.$
—	Cup	Doulton	10 1/2"	1935	Ltd. Ed.	600.00	1,200.00	1,250.00

THE APOTHECARY

Issued in a limited edition of 600.

Designer: Charles Noke / Harry Fenton
Handles: Distorted faces
Main Colours: Green, red yellow

Backstamp: Doulton

Doulton Number	Type	Backstamp	Height	Intro.	Discon.	Current Market Value U.K.£	U.S.$	Can.$
----	Cup	Doulton	6"	1934	Ltd. Ed.	425.00	900.00	1,000.00

CAPTAIN COOK

Issued in a limited edition of 350 pieces.

Designer: Charles Noke / Harry Fenton
Handles: Coconut palms with the flags of
      St. George and the Union Jack
Main Colours: Green, blue, yellow and red

Backstamp: Doulton

Doulton Number	Type	Backstamp	Height	Intro.	Discon.	Current Market Value		
						U.K.£	U.S.$	Can.$
---	Cup	Doulton	9 1/2"	1933	Ltd. Ed.	1,200.00	2,500.00	2,500.00

CAPTAIN PHILLIP

Issued in a limited edition of 350 pieces.

Designer: Charles Noke / Harry Fenton

Handle: Eucalyptus tree trunk

Main Colours: Yellow, blue, red and green

Spout: Face of Captain Phillip

Inscription around base: "Colony New South Wales founded January 1788 Sydney"

Backstamp: Doulton

Doulton Number	Type	Backstamp	Height	Intro.	Discon.	Current Market Value U.K.£	U.S.$	Can.$
—	Jug	Doulton	9 1/4"	1938	Ltd. Ed.	1,600.00	2,750.00	3,000.00

CHARLES DICKENS

Issued in a limited edition of 1000.

Designer: Charles Noke / Harry Fenton
Handle: Open book
Spout: Face of Charles Dickens
Main Colours: Brown, green and red

Backstamp: Doulton

Doulton Number	Type	Backstamp	Height	Intro.	Discon.	Current Market Value		
						U.K.£	U.S.$	Can.$
—	Jug	Doulton	10 1/2"	1936	Ltd. Ed.	550.00	1,200.00	1,300.00

DICKENS DREAM

Issued in a unlimited edition, but probably 1,000 pieces.

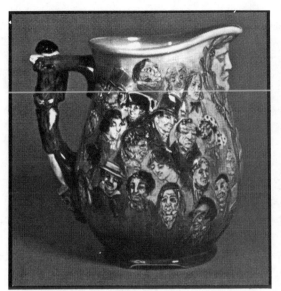 

Designer: Charles Noke
Handle: Poor Jo
Main Colours: Brown, green and red

Backstamp: Doulton

Doulton Number	Type	Backstamp	Height	Intro.	Discon.	Current Market Value		
						U.K.£	U.S.$	Can.$
----	Jug	Doulton	10 1/2"	1933		525.00	1,000.00	1,000.00

GEORGE WASHINGTON

PROTOTYPE

The handle of this prototype differs from the production model in that the stars are moulded in relief set atop a striped background.

Photograph
Not Available
At Press Time

Designer: Charles Noke / Harry Fenton   **Backstamp:** Doulton
Handle: Stars and Stripes
Main Colours: Brown, blue, red and cream
Spout: Face of George Washington
Inscription around base: Declaration of Independence

Doulton Number	Type	Backstamp	Height	Intro.	Discon.	Current Market Value		
						U.K.£	U.S.$	Can.$
—	Jug	Doulton	10 1/4"	1932			Extremely Rare	

GEORGE WASHINGTON

Issued in a limited edition of 1,000 pieces.

Designer: Charles Noke / Harry Fenton
Handle: The Stars and Stripes
Main Colours: Brown, blue, red and cream
Spout: Face of George Washington
Inscription around base: Declaration of Independence

Backstamp: Doulton

Doulton Number	Type	Backstamp	Height	Intro.	Discon.	Current Market Value		
						U.K.£	U.S.$	Can.$
—	Jug	Doulton	10 1/4"	1932	Ltd. Ed.	2,000.00	10,000.00	5,000.00

GUY FAWKES

Issued in a limited edition of 600 pieces.

Designer: Harry Fenton
Handle: Flaming Torch
Main Colours: Green, brown and red

Backstamp: Doulton

Doulton Number	Type	Backstamp	Height	Intro.	Discon.	Current Market Value U.K.£	U.S.$	Can.$
----	Jug	Doulton	7 1/2"	1934	Ltd. Ed.	475.00	750.00	900.00

I.T. WIGG, BROOM-MAN

Believed to be a trial piece only. There are no production pieces known to exist.

Designer: Unknown
Handle: Unknown
Main Colours: Unknown

Backstamp: Unknown

Doulton Number	Type	Backstamp	Height	Intro.	Discon.	Current Market Value U.K.£	U.S.$	Can.$
----	Jug						Unique	

Note: We have no information of photographs for this jug. We would appreciate anyone with further particulars contacting the Charlton Press.

JACKDAW OF RHEIMS

This jug is believed to be a trial piece only. No evidence exists that this jug actually went into production.

Designer: Unknown
Handle: Candle, candlestick and candle-snuffer
Main Colours: Brown, red and green

Backstamp: Doulton

Doulton Number	Type	Backstamp	Height	Intro.	Discon.	U.K.£	Current Market Value U.S.$	Can.$
—	Jug	Doulton	11"	c. 1934			Extremely Rare Only One Known	

JAN VAN RIEBEECK

Issued in limited edition of 300 pieces.

Designer: Charles Noke / Harry Fenton
Handles: Van Riebeeck figures
Main Colours: Yellow, green, blue and red

Backstamp: Doulton

Doulton Number	Type	Backstamp	Height	Intro.	Discon.	Current Market Value		
						U.K.£	U.S.$	Can.$
---	Cup	Doulton	10 1/4"	1935	Ltd. Ed.	1,800.00	3,500.00	3,750.00

JOHN PEEL

Issued in a limited edition of 500 pieces.

Designer: Unknown
Handles: Fox heads on riding whips
Main Colours: Green, red and brown

Backstamp: Doulton

Doulton Number	Type	Backstamp	Height	Intro.	Discon.	Current Market Value		
						U.K.£	U.S.$	Can.$
—	Cup	Doulton	9"	1933	Ltd. Ed.	600.00	1,500.00	1,500.00

KING EDWARD VIII CORONATION

STYLE ONE: ENGLISH EDITION, LARGE SIZE

Issued in limited edition of 2,000 pieces of which 1080 were sold.

Designer: Charles Noke / Harry Fenton
Handle: Names of Commonwealth countries
Main Colours: Green, yellow and red

Backstamps: Doulton

Doulton Number	Type	Backstamp	Height	Intro.	Discon.	Current Market Value		
						U.K.£	U.S.$	Can.$
---	Cup	Doulton	10"	1937	Ltd. Ed.	425.00	1,100.00	1,000.00

KING EDWARD VIII CORONATION

STYLE TWO: ENGLISH EDITION, SMALL SIZE

This small cup was issued in a limited edition of 1,000 pieces of which 454 were sold as the coronation never took place.

Designer: Charles Noke
Handle: Names of Commonwealth countries
Main Colours: Green, red and yellow

Backstamps: Doulton

Doulton Number	Type	Backstamp	Height	Intro.	Discon.	Current Market Value U.K.£	U.S.$	Can.$
—	Cup	Doulton	6 1/2"	1937	Ltd. Ed.	375.00	750.00	750.00

KING EDWARD VIII CORONATION

STYLE THREE: *WELSH EDITION, SMALL SIZE*

Issued in limited edition of 2,000 pieces and made especially for the Welsh market. The portrait of Edward, Prince of Wales, differs from that on the previous cup. The words: "I am still the same man" appear on the jug. These were taken from a speech Edward made while on his first visit to Wales as sovereign.

Photograph Not Available At Press Time

Designer: Charles Noke

Handle: Names of Commonwealth countries

Main Colours: Green, red and brown

Backstamps: Doulton

Doulton Number	Type	Backstamp	Height	Intro.	Discon.	Current Market Value		
						U.K.£	U.S.$	Can.$
—	Cup	Doulton	6 1/2"	1937	Ltd. Ed.	650.00	1,250.00	1,300.00

KING GEORGE V AND
QUEEN MARY SILVER JUBILEE

Issued in a limited edition of 1000 pieces.

Designer: Charles Noke / Harry Fenton
Handles: Names of Commonwealth
         countries and provinces
Main Colours: Green and brown

Backstamp: Doulton

Doulton Number	Type	Backstamp	Height	Intro.	Discon.	Current Market Value		
						U.K.£	U.S.$	Can.$
----	Cup	Doulton	10"	1935	Ltd Ed.	450.00	1,100.00	1,000.00

KING GEORGE VI AND
QUEEN ELIZABETH CORONATION

STYLE ONE: *LARGE DESIGN: UNCROWNED CONJOINED PORTRAITS*
WITHOUT FLEUR-DE-LIS

Designer: Charles Noke / Harry Fenton

Backstamp: Doulton

Handles: Plain

Main Colours: Yellow, red and green

Doulton Number	Type	Backstamp	Height	Intro.	Discon.	Current Market Value		
						U.K.£	U.S.$	Can.$
----	Cup	Doulton	10 1/2"	1937	Unknown	Price Not Established		

KING GEORGE VI AND
QUEEN ELIZABETH CORONATION

STYLE TWO: *LARGE DESIGN: CROWNED CONJOINED PORTRAITS*
WITH FLEUR-DE-LIS

Issued in limited edition of 2000 pieces.

Designer: Charles Noke / Harry Fenton
Handles: Plain
Main Colours: Yellow, red and green

Backstamp: Doulton

Doulton Number	Type	Backstamp	Height	Intro.	Discon.	U.K.£	U.S.$	Can.$
						Current Market Value		
—	Cup	Doulton	10 1/2"	1937	Ltd. Ed.	425.00	1,200.00	900.00

KING GEORGE VI AND
QUEEN ELIZABETH CORONATION

STYLE THREE: *SMALL DESIGN*

Issued in a limited edition of 2000 pieces.

Designer: Charles Noke / Harry Fenton
Handles: Plain
Main Colours: Yellow, green, blue and red

Backstamp: Doulton

Doulton Number	Type	Backstamp	Height	Intro.	Discon.	Current Market Value U.K.£	U.S.$	Can.$
----	Cup	Doulton	61/2"	1937	Ltd. Ed.	325.00	750.00	750.00

MASTER OF FOXHOUNDS

Issued in a limited edition of 500 pieces.

 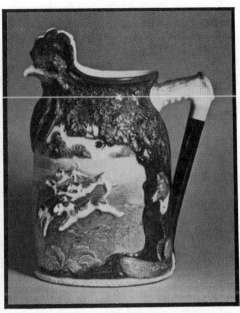

Designer: Charles Noke
Handle: Whip
Main Colours: Green, red and brown
Spout: Rooster's head

Backstamp: Doulton

Doulton Number	Type	Backstamp	Height	Intro.	Discon.	Current Market Value U.K.£	U.S.$	Can.$
—	Presentation Jug	Doulton	13"	1930	Ltd. Ed.	550.00	1,250.00	1,250.00

PIED PIPER

Issued in limited edition of 600 pieces.

Designer: Charles Noke / Harry Fenton
Handle: Tree
Main Colours: Yellow, brown and green
Spout: Window

Backstamp: Doulton

Doulton Number	Type	Backstamp	Height	Intro.	Discon.	Current Market Value		
						U.K.£	U.S.$	Can.$
——	Jug	Doulton	10"	1934	Ltd. Ed.	550.00	1,150.00	1,150.00

POTTERY IN THE PAST

Issued exclusively for the members of the Royal Doulton International Collectors Club.

Designer: Graham Tongue
Handles: Plain
Main Colours: Brown and green

Backstamp: Doulton

Doulton Number	Type	Backstamp	Height	Intro.	Discon.	Current Market Value		
						U.K.£	U.S.$	Can.$
D6696	Cup	Doulton/RDICC	6"	1983	1983	125.00	200.00	225.00

QUEEN ELIZABETH II CORONATION

LOVING CUP

Elizabeth became Queen of England Februray 6, 1952. This commemorative cup features depictions of both Queen Elizabeth II and Elizabeth I. The handles are plain. Issued in limited edition of 1000 pieces.

Designer: Cecil J. Noke / Harry Fenton
Handles: Plain
Main Colour: Brown

Backstamp: Doulton

Doulton Number	Type	Backstamp	Height	Intro.	Discon.	Current Market Value		
						U.K.£	U.S.$	Can.$
—	Cup	Doulton	10 1/2"	1953	Ltd. Ed.	350.00	800.00	700.00

QUEEN ELIZABETH II CORONATION

JUG

This small jug features a portrait of Queen Elizabeth II flanked by the Union Jack and Royal Standard with 'Elizabeth R' underneath. A scene of Windsor Castle is on the other side. This piece was not issued in a limited edition.

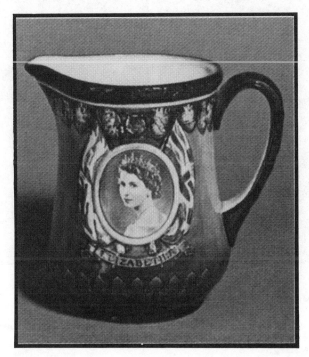

Designer: Unknown
Handles: Plain
Main Colour: Brown

Backstamp: Doulton

Doulton Number	Type	Backstamp	Height	Intro.	Discon.	Current Market Value		
						U.K.£	U.S.$	Can.$
——	Jug	Doulton	6 1/4"	1953	1953	65.00	150.00	125.00

QUEEN ELIZABETH II SILVER JUBILEE

Issued in limited edition of 250 pieces.

Designer: Reg Johnson
Handles: Lion heads
Main Colours: Red, brown and green

Backstamp: Doulton

Doulton Number	Type	Backstamp	Height	Intro.	Discon.	Current Market Value		
						U.K.£	U.S.$	Can.$
—	Cup	Doulton	10 1/2"	1977	Ltd. Ed.	750.00	2,500.00	2,500.00

REGENCY COACH

Issued in limited edition of 500 pieces.

Designer: Charles Noke
Handle: Tree branch
Main Colours: Green and brown
Spout: A parchment and inn sign

Backstamp: Doulton

Doulton Number	Type	Backstamp	Height	Intro.	Discon.	Current Market Value		
						U.K.£	U.S.$	Can.$
—	Jug	Doulton	10"	1931	Ltd. Ed.	550.00	1,100.00	1,100.00

ROBIN HOOD

Issued in a limited edition of 600 pieces.

Designer: Charles Noke / Harry Fenton
Handles: Plain, incised names of "The Merry Men"
Main Colours: Green, red and brown

Backstamp: Doulton

Doulton Number	Type	Backstamp	Height	Intro.	Discon.	Current Market Value		
						U.K.£	U.S.$	Can.$
----	Cup	Doulton	8 1/2"	1938	Ltd. Ed.	550.00	850.00	1,000.00

ROGER SOLEMEL, COBBLER

TRIAL PIECE

Believed to be a trial piece only. There are no production pieces known to exist.

Designer: Geoff Blower
Handle: Unknown
Main Colours: Unknown

Backstamp: Unknown

Doulton Number	Type	Backstamp	Height	Intro.	Discon.	Current Market Value		
						U.K.£	U.S.$	Can.$
----	Jug	Doulton	10 1/2"		Unknown		Unique	

SIR FRANCIS DRAKE

Issued in limited edition of 500 pieces.

Designer: Charles Noke / Harry Fenton   **Backstamp:** Doulton
Handle: Rope and lantern
Main Colours: Brown, red, green and blue

Doulton Number	Type	Backstamp	Height	Intro.	Discon.	Current Market Value		
						U.K.£	U.S.$	Can.$
----	Jug	Doulton	10 1/4"	1933	Ltd. Ed.	550.00	1,000.00	1,100.00

THE THREE MUSKETEERS

Issued in a limited edition of 600 pieces.

Designer: Charles Noke / Harry Fenton
Handles: Trophies of war and the accoutrements of pleasure
Main Colours: Yellow, green brown and red

Backstamp: Doulton

Doulton Number	Type	Backstamp	Height	Intro.	Discon.	Current Market Value		
						U.K.£	U.S.$	Can.$
---	Cup	Doulton	10"	1936	Ltd. Ed.	550.00	1,100.00	1,000.00

TOWER OF LONDON

Issued in a limited edition of 500 pieces.

 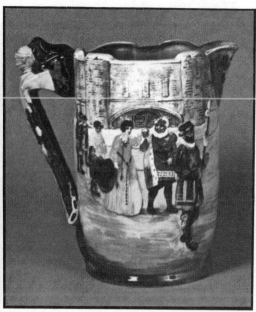

Designer: Charles Noke / Harry Fenton
Handle: Axes, pikes, chains and armour
Spout: Shield bearing the lions of England
Main Colours: Red, green, grey and brown

Backstamp: Doutlon

Doulton Number	Type	Backstamp	Height	Intro.	Discon.	Current Market Value		
						U.K.£	U.S.$	Can.$
----	Jug	Doulton	10"	1933	Ltd. Ed.	600.00	1,250.00	1,250.00

TREASURE ISLAND

Issued in a limited edition of 600 pieces.

Designer: Charles Noke / Harry Fenton
Handle: Palm tree
Spout: Palm leaves
Main Colours: Yellow, green and brown

Backstamp: Doulton

Doulton Number	Type	Backstamp	Height	Intro.	Discon.	Current Market Value		
						U.K.£	**U.S.$**	**Can.$**
----	Jug	Doulton	7 1/2"	1934	Ltd. Ed.	450.00	950.00	1,000.00

THE VILLAGE BLACKSMITH

Issued in limited edition of 600 pieces.

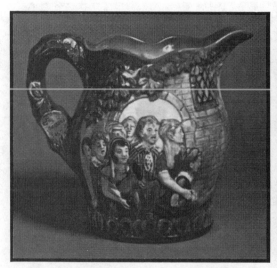 

Designer: Charles Noke
Handle: Branch with milestone at base of handle;
    Milestone incised "Longfellow" on one side
    and "Long-fellow 1842" on the other
Spout: Leaves
Main Colours: Brown, green and red

Backstamp: Doulton

Doulton Number	Type	Backstamp	Height	Intro.	Discon.	Current Market Value		
						U.K.£	U.S.$	Can.$
—	Jug	Doulton	7 3/4"	1936	Ltd. Ed.	450.00	900.00	1,000.00

THE WANDERING MINSTREL

Issued in limited edition of 600 pieces.

Designer: Charles Noke / Harry Fenton
Handles: Trees
Main Colours: Green, brown and yellow

Backstamp: Doulton

Doulton Number	Type	Backstamp	Height	Intro.	Discon.	Current Market Value U.K.£	U.S.$	Can.$
---	Cup	Doulton	5 1/2"	1934	Ltd. Ed.	425.00	900.00	1,000.00

WILLIAM SHAKESPEARE

Issued in a limited edition of 1000 pieces.

Designer: Charles Noke   **Backstamp:** Doulton
Handle: Masks of tragedy and comedy; swords
Spout: Face of Shakespeare
Main Colours: Green, brown and red

Doulton Number	Type	Backstamp	Height	Intro.	Discon.	Current Market Value		
						U.K.£	U.S.$	Can.$
—	Jug	Doulton	10 1/2"	1933	Ltd. Ed.	425.00	1,100.00	1,250.00

WILLIAM WORDSWORTH

Issued in an unlimited edition, but few known to exist.

Designer: Charles Noke
Handles: Tied vines
Main Colours: Green, yellow and red

Backstamp: Doulton

Doulton Number	Type	Backstamp	Height	Intro.	Discon.	Current Market Value		
						U.K.£	U.S.$	Can.$
----	Cup	Doulton	6 1/2"	1933	Unknown	800.00	2,000.00	2,000.00

INDEX

TOBY JUGS

CHARACTER JUGS

LIQUOR CONTAINTERS

LOVING CUPS AND JUGS

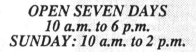

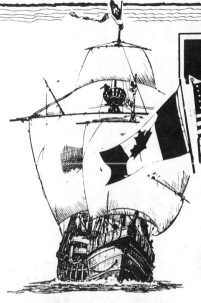

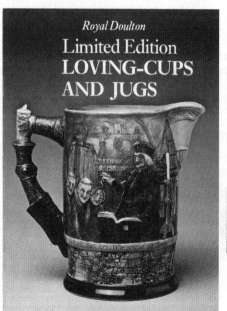

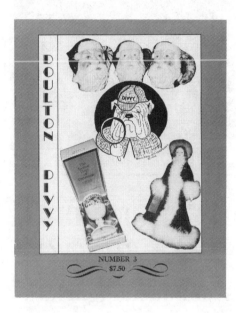